MODERN COMEDIES
for
TEEN-AGERS

Modern Comedies
for
Teen-Agers

A collection of royalty-free one-act plays
for all occasions

by

PAUL S. McCOY

" "

Publishers **PLAYS, INC.** *Boston*

CONTENTS

MODERN COMEDIES
for
TEEN-AGERS

You Don't Belong to Me

Characters

WAYNE GORDON, *a high school senior*
ETHEL GORDON, *his busy mother*
SHELBY GORDON, *his father*
PATSY GORDON, *his vivacious ten-year-old sister*
DIANA HUGHES, *Wayne's former girl friend*
JENNIE WINFIELD, *the big surprise*
MR. MITCHELL, *an advertising representative*

TIME: *A Saturday afternoon in early summer.*
SETTING: *The living room of the Gordon residence.*
AT RISE: SHELBY GORDON *is seated in chair, downstage right, reading a newspaper.* PATSY GORDON *enters brightly from left carrying a cardboard carton which contains several bottles of perfume. Attached to the top of one bottle is an atomizer.*

PATSY (*Moves to table left*): Jeepers, Father! You're just the character I wanted to see. (*Places carton on table.*)

But I thought you were playing golf this afternoon.

SHELBY (*Dryly, as he continues to read paper*): So did I, Patsy. But your mother changed my plans.

PATSY (*At table*): Father, do you realize this is the middle of June?

SHELBY: I believe I've heard a rumor to that effect.

PATSY: Which means that Christmas is only six months away. Doesn't that make you gasp?

SHELBY (*Pays little attention to* PATSY): I still seem to be breathing in a normal manner.

PATSY: But Father, it's time to think about buying Christmas gifts. (*From carton she removes the bottle of perfume with atomizer attached.*) It would be simply horrible if you came up to Christmas Eve without presents for your dear family and friends. (*She presses atomizer; sprays perfume into air.*)

SHELBY (*Still engrossed in paper*): Yes, indeed. Yes, indeed.

PATSY (*Continues to spray perfume across room toward* SHELBY): So it's time you made your gift selections.

SHELBY (*As he reads*): I'm sure you're right, Patsy— (*Suddenly, he breaks off, begins to sniff the air, and puts down his newspaper.*) What on earth is that odor?

PATSY (*Proudly*): It's my perfume, Father. (*Continues to press atomizer*) I'm selling it.

SHELBY: Patsy Gordon, stop spraying that stuff around this room!

PATSY (*Brightly*): Does it do something to you?

SHELBY: It certainly does!

PATSY: This perfume is called "Madness."

SHELBY: "Madness"? That's exactly the reaction I'm getting from it.

PATSY: I'm to sell twenty-four bottles, and then I get a prize—a genuine imitation diamond ring.

SHELBY: Do you mean you're going to peddle that perfume? (*He coughs, then fans the air to disperse the scent.*)

PATSY: Of course I am. Unless you want to buy all twenty-four bottles. (*Indicates carton, then places bottle with atomizer back in carton.*)

SHELBY (*Dryly*): I haven't that many enemies.

PATSY (*Drops into chair*): Father, you've just got to make a purchase. I couldn't get Mother interested, and of course Wayne won't buy any, now that his life is ruined.

SHELBY (*With interest*): I don't believe I've been informed that my son's life is ruined. Although I suppose I'd be the last to hear the tragic news.

PATSY: Haven't you noticed that Wayne is in a deplorable condition?

SHELBY (*Nods*): For two weeks he's been wandering around like a sick calf. (*Sighs*) I suppose it's because I wouldn't buy him a red convertible.

PATSY: The real reason is Diana.

SHELBY: Diana Hughes?

PATSY (*Nods*): Wayne and Diana had a terrible quarrel. She won't even talk to him, and honestly, Father, I can't blame her. Wayne tries to boss everybody. (WAYNE GORDON *gloomily enters from right.*) Well, look who's here—little sunshine, in person!

WAYNE (*Grimly, as he moves to center*): Shut up!

SHELBY (*To* WAYNE): Wayne, don't talk to your sister like that. Where have you been? (*He rises.*)

WAYNE: Upstairs in my room.

SHELBY: Your mother wants us to work on the rose bed this afternoon.

WAYNE: Please don't mention "roses" in my presence.

PATSY: I know why. It's because Diana Hughes has been selected Queen of the Rose Festival.

WAYNE (*Angrily*): I told you to keep still!

SHELBY (*To* WAYNE): What's this about you and Diana breaking up?

WAYNE (*With sarcasm*): I suppose my *darling* little sister has been shooting off her mouth.

SHELBY (*Sharply*): That's enough, Wayne! (*Pause*) Now, I want to know what happened.

WAYNE (*Sighs*): Diana just wouldn't listen to me, that's all. I didn't want her to be Queen of the Rose Festival—

SHELBY: Why not?

WAYNE: Good grief, Father, don't you understand? Diana's too popular. A fellow likes to have a girl to himself—at least a part of the time. But Diana's into everything. So I demanded that she cut out a lot of that crazy stuff.

SHELBY (*Significantly*): In other words, you wanted to monopolize her time—you wanted to be the boss.

WAYNE: Well, I guess a fellow has a right to tell a girl what to do.

PATSY (*Dryly*): Ha! Ha!

SHELBY (*To* WAYNE): He also has a right to pick up a hot poker—but I wouldn't advise it. (*Firmly*) Young man, you'd better change your tactics—and fast. Women just don't go for that stubborn and domineering attitude.

PATSY (*Wildly claps her hands*): Bravo! Bravo!

WAYNE (*Savagely, to* PATSY): Cut it out!

SHELBY (*To* WAYNE): You'd better ask Diana to forgive you—and you'd better mean it.

WAYNE: I tried to apologize, but it didn't work. I wrote her a letter. I really got down in the dust. I told her what a nice person she was and that I'd been a louse—

PATSY: How true! How true! (WAYNE *glares at* PATSY.)

SHELBY: What did she say?

WAYNE: She didn't even answer the letter. That was two weeks ago. I haven't seen her or heard from her since.

SHELBY: Why don't you drop around to her house?

WAYNE (*Dramatically*): How can I? I don't have a red convertible.

SHELBY (*Sputters*): You don't have a—(*Groans*) Give me strength!

ETHEL (*Entering from left*): Shelby, I asked you to weed the rose bed—

PATSY (*Rises*): Careful, Mother! Don't use that terrible word "rose."

ETHEL (*Moves to center*): What's the matter with everybody! (*Peers at* WAYNE) Are you all right, Wayne?

WAYNE: I'll never be all right again. (*Turns on his heel and moves downstage*)

ETHEL: Shelby, have you been criticizing the children?

SHELBY (*Flatly*): Do you mind if I just go out and work in the rose bed? (*Moves upstage and exits at center door.* PATSY *steps behind table.*)

ETHEL (*A bit helplessly*): I can't understand any of you.

PATSY (*Drawing atomizer from carton on table*): Mother, what you need is a bottle of "Madness." (*Begins to spray the air*)

ETHEL: Patsy, stop that!

WAYNE (*Indicating carton*): Mother, make her throw that box of trash away.

PATSY: This isn't trash, Mr. Bighead.

ETHEL: That's enough out of both of you!

PATSY: I haven't done anything.

ETHEL (*Indicates magazine she is carrying*): One of you cut half a page out of this magazine. That's where my story ended, and now I don't know whether the girl married the lion tamer or the pineapple grower.

PATSY: Let me take a look. (*Moves to* ETHEL; *inspects page which has been cut*) Goodness, I'm not so stupid as to do a thing like that. (*Turns from* ETHEL; *moves back to table*) But I know who did.

ETHEL: You do?

PATSY: Your son is the guilty party.

WAYNE: Now see here—

PATSY (*Grins*): Wayne entered a contest. I saw him cut the entry blank out of that magazine.

WAYNE (*Hotly*): You didn't see anything!

PATSY: I see *everything,* smarty. I was trying to sell you a bottle of perfume, and you were working on your entry. But you wouldn't pay any attention to me, even when I sprayed you with "Madness."

WAYNE (*With complete disgust*): At times you make me absolutely ill! (*Moves up to* ETHEL) Mother, I'm going to my room, and I do not wish to be disturbed. I have enough on my mind without listening to the babbling of a silly child! (*He gives* PATSY *a dangerous glare, then quickly exits right.*)

ETHEL: Goodness, your brother is in a frightful mood.

PATSY: Old stormy weather—that's Wayne.

ETHEL (*Moves to chair right*): What sort of contest did Wayne enter? (*Sits*)

PATSY: It was "The Girl of My Dreams" contest.

ETHEL: The girl of my dreams?

PATSY (*Nods*): The Higbee Candy Company is offering prizes to men who write the best statements about the girl of their dreams. Wayne had a box of Higbee chocolates he was going to give to Diana, but after they quarreled, he gave me the candy instead.

ETHEL: Wouldn't it be exciting if Wayne won a prize?

PATSY: He won't—so don't stir up your blood pressure. Anyway, the ad didn't even state what the winner would receive. It's to be a surprise award.

ETHEL: A surprise award? That sounds interesting.

PATSY: I wish somebody would surprise me—by buying twenty-four bottles of "Madness" perfume. (*Again sprays perfume*)

ETHEL: Patsy, get those bottles out of here! You're smelling up the house.

PATSY: But that's the idea. When people come in, I want them to swoon from "Madness."

ETHEL: They'll swoon, all right. (*Firmly*) Now, take that box out to the back porch.

PATSY: But, Mother—

ETHEL: You heard me.

PATSY (*Slowly picking up carton*): Gee whiz! The way I'm pushed around! (*The doorbell rings.*) The doorbell! Maybe somebody wants to buy a bottle of—

ETHEL (*Breaks in*): More likely it's an investigator from the Board of Health. The neighbors have probably been complaining about your perfume. (*Hurriedly*) Now, get it out of here.

PATSY (*Moves gloomily to left*): I don't know how come I had to be a member of this family. (*Doorbell rings again.* PATSY *exits left with carton as* ETHEL *moves quickly upstage. She opens center door revealing* JENNIE WINFIELD, *who carries a traveling bag. In speech, manner and dress she creates the role of a crude and dizzy female.*)

JENNIE (*In a loud, rasping voice*): Hello, honey! (*She steps into room.*) Nice day, huh?

ETHEL (*Annoyed*): Young lady, whatever you're selling, I'm not in the market.

JENNIE: Oh, I'm not selling anything, dearie. I'm looking for a guy by the name of Wayne Gordon. Is this where he hangs out?

ETHEL (*With dignity*): Wayne Gordon is my son.

JENNIE: Then this is the place. (*She closes door behind her.*)

ETHEL (*Irritated*): Young lady, who are you and what do you want?

JENNIE (*In a breezy, informal tone*): Jennie's my name— Jennie Winfield. (*She moves down right, gazing around the room.*) Nice little dump you got here. (*She places her traveling bag on floor.*)

ETHEL (*Moving toward* JENNIE): Miss Winfield, will you kindly explain—

JENNIE (*Breaking in*): Just call me Jennie. We might as well start out on a chummy basis.

ETHEL: Chummy basis?

JENNIE: What's your name, honey?

ETHEL: I am Mrs. Ethel Gordon. But I certainly don't—

JENNIE (*Smiles*): Ethel? Now that's a good, solid name.

ETHEL (*Thoroughly disgusted*): See here, what do you want?

JENNIE: I told you. I'm here to see your son. (*At that moment* SHELBY *enters at center. He takes a step downstage, then pauses abruptly as he sees* JENNIE.)

SHELBY (*With a start*): Oh—!

JENNIE: Hello, handsome! (SHELBY *is shocked. He moves downstage.*) Are you Wayne Gordon?

ETHEL (*Coldly*): That is my husband—Shelby Gordon.

JENNIE: Your husband? (*Laughs loudly*) Dearie, I thought he was your *son!* (ETHEL *glares.*)

SHELBY (*Completely at sea*): What's going on?

ETHEL (*Indicating* JENNIE): This is Jennie Winfield. She insists upon seeing Wayne.

SHELBY (*Turns to* JENNIE): What do you want with our son?

JENNIE: Wayne entered the Higbee Candy Contest. He wrote a statement about the girl of his dreams, and believe it or not, his entry won first prize.

SHELBY (*Startled*): It—did?

ETHEL (*With a gasp*): First prize? My goodness!

SHELBY (*With sudden enthusiasm*): Say, that's all right.

ETHEL: Shelby, can you imagine? Our son—a prize winner. (*Excited*) He'll be written up in the newspapers—the mayor will give him the key to the city— (*At that moment* WAYNE *enters right.* ETHEL *gives a happy cry.*) Wayne! Wayne, darling—you did it!

WAYNE (*Puzzled*): Huh?

ETHEL: You won!

WAYNE: I—*what?*

SHELBY: My boy, you won first prize in the Higbee Candy Contest!

WAYNE (*Almost speechless*): I—I did?

ETHEL (*Indicates* JENNIE): Wayne, this is Jennie Winfield. She just brought us the glad tidings.

WAYNE (*Turns to* JENNIE): You mean my entry was judged the best?

JENNIE: It sure was, junior. You get the award. (WAYNE *grins broadly*.)

ETHEL (*Flutters*): I'm simply overwhelmed.

WAYNE (*Enthusiastically*): Gee, Miss Winfield, what is the award?

ETHEL: I hope it's an electric refrigerator—or an automatic washer—

SHELBY: If I were in Wayne's position, I'd rather have cash.

WAYNE (*Impatiently*): All right, Miss Winfield, what *did* I win?

JENNIE (*After a slight pause*): Well frankly, junior, I don't know.

WAYNE (*Startled*): You don't know?

SHELBY (*Equally startled*): What's that?

ETHEL (*At the same time*): Then why did you make the trip if—

JENNIE (*Throws up her hands*): Hold it, folks—hold it! (*The others gaze at* JENNIE *in puzzled silence.*) You see, I'm the messenger for the Higbee Candy Company. They call me the Higbee Dream Girl. (*Giggles*) Isn't that cute?

SHELBY (*Dryly*): It's amazing.

JENNIE: I was sent here with the official announcement for

Wayne Gordon. (*Brightly*) It's all done up in one of those oversized envelopes, all decorated in gold trim and little red hearts—

WAYNE (*Breaks in impatiently*): All right—all right. Let's see it. (JENNIE *doesn't move.*)

ETHEL: Well, don't just stand there, Miss Winfield. Show us the announcement.

JENNIE (*Begins to giggle*): I—I can't.

SHELBY: You can't?

WAYNE: But why not?

JENNIE: You'll scream when I tell you. I forgot to bring it with me! (*She giggles wildly.*)

WAYNE (*Aghast*): What!

ETHEL: Forgot to bring it with you?

JENNIE (*Nods*): When the president of the company told me I'd been selected to make the presentation, I got all excited and rushed out of the office like it was quitting time. (*Giggles*) I left the announcement lying on the president's desk. I didn't even miss it until I got off the train a few minutes ago. (*With a shriek.*) Isn't that the limit?

SHELBY (*Sputters*): It certainly is!

WAYNE: At least you can *tell* us what the award is.

JENNIE: No, I can't. I'm only the messenger. I'm not in the habit of looking into sealed envelopes.

SHELBY: It could be a check.

ETHEL: Maybe it's a bond or a gift certificate.

WAYNE: But what do we do now?

JENNIE: As soon as the president discovers I left the announcement on his desk, he'll mail it out here.

WAYNE: He'd better!

ETHEL (*To* JENNIE): How long will that take?

JENNIE (*Easily*): Oh, two or three days. Maybe more, if he happens to be on vacation or something. (*Smiles*) Hope it's not going to put you folks out too much.

WAYNE: I suppose we'll just have to wait.

ETHEL: But surely we can find out before— (*Suddenly turns to* JENNIE) Miss Winfield, what do you mean— you hope it won't put us out too much?

JENNIE: Well, of course I'll have to wait too. (*Sits in chair right*)

SHELBY (*With a violent start*): What's that?

WAYNE (*Aghast*): You'll have to wait too?

JENNIE (*Nods brightly*): Sure. I'm hired to make a personal presentation of the award, so I have to stay right here until the envelope arrives.

ETHEL (*Horrified*): But Miss Winfield, you—you can't do that! (*Sinks into chair at left*)

SHELBY (*Bellows*): Of course not. It's impossible!

WAYNE (*Loudly*): All I want is the award!

JENNIE (*Stoutly*): Junior, there isn't going to be any award until I make it in person—so, I'm staying.

SHELBY (*About to choke*): Now, see here—

JENNIE (*To* SHELBY): Calm down, buster. If you want your son to get the first prize in the contest, you have to entertain me until the official document arrives by United States mail.

ETHEL: Why, I—I never heard of such a thing!

WAYNE: Why can't the company just notify me by phone or telegram?

JENNIE (*Coolly*): Junior, I'm the Higbee Dream Girl. You're to be notified by me—and only me. That's part of the plan. (*Smiles broadly*) You know, I'm sort of glad I forgot the announcement. (*Gazes around the room*) Think I'll enjoy relaxing around here for a time. Even an attractive girl like me gets kind of tired of city life.

ETHEL (*Unnerved*): Shelby, what—what are we going to do?

SHELBY (*In complete confusion*): I—I don't know—

JENNIE: Well, I'm not going to sit glued to this chair for the next week, waiting to hear from the company. (*Rises, turns to* ETHEL) Honey, you'd better show me up to my room. (*Picks up her bag*)

ETHEL (*Rises in panic*): Shelby, did you hear that? She talks as though she plans to—to move in and settle down.

SHELBY: Now see here, Miss Winfield—

JENNIE (*Stoutly*): I'm not leaving this house until I make the personal presentation.

WAYNE (*Desperately*): You have to leave. (*With sudden determination*) I—I won't accept the award.

JENNIE: Oh, yes, you will. You entered the contest, Junior. You won first prize. You promised to abide by all the rules. I've been appointed the Higbee Dream Girl, which means I'm supposed to give you the prize. (*Emphatically*) And that's what I'm going to do, if I have to stick around here the rest of my life.

ETHEL (*Begins to sway*): I—I think I'm going to faint—

JENNIE (*Brightly*): Go right ahead, dearie. I'll look after your house and family.

ETHEL (*Straightens up angrily*): You'll do no such thing!

JENNIE: Then I demand to be taken to my room. I want to unpack.

ETHEL: But you—you simply can't—

JENNIE: Then I'll sit out on your front porch and yell and scream—

SHELBY: Oh, take her upstairs, Ethel! Anything to get that female out of my sight!

WAYNE (*Shouts*): Mine too!

ETHEL (*Completely unnerved*): I—I've never been so upset in my life! (*Crosses to* JENNIE) I—I'm certain there's something in the Constitution about this.

JENNIE (*Smiles at* ETHEL): Let's get moving, honey. I've had a hard day, and I need my beauty nap.

ETHEL: But I—I—

SHELBY (*Thunders violently*): Get her out of here, Ethel!

ETHEL (*To* JENNIE): Oh, come along. (*She exits right.*)

JENNIE (*Turns to* WAYNE *and* SHELBY, *smiles broadly*): I'll be seeing you both—you cute little beavers! (*She exits right as* WAYNE *staggers downstage and collapses into chair at right.*)

SHELBY: This is an outrage! What right has she to move in here? I'll file a suit! I'll take it to the Supreme Court— (*At that moment* PATSY *enters from left.*)

PATSY (*To* SHELBY): What'll you take to the Supreme Court, Father? (SHELBY *and* WAYNE *gaze at* PATSY *in stony silence.*) My goodness, what's the matter with you two?

SHELBY (*Grimly*): Your brother won first prize in the Higbee Candy Contest!

PATSY: He did? That's wonderful! (*Turns to* WAYNE) Wayne, what did you get?

SHELBY (*Loudly*): Nothing yet—except the messenger!

PATSY: The messenger?

WAYNE: A girl by the name of Jennie Winfield just arrived. She was hired to make the presentation.

SHELBY: But she forgot to bring along the official notice.

WAYNE (*With a wail*): And now she won't leave until the award arrives by mail, and she can give it to me in person!

PATSY (*Stunned*): You mean she's going to stay until the prize comes?

WAYNE (*Loudly and savagely*): Yes! (*Suddenly* PATSY *breaks into laughter.*) You shut up!

PATSY (*Almost in hysterics*): Oh, this is marvelous!

SHELBY (*Menacingly, to* PATSY): Stop it!

PATSY: Where is she? What does she look like?

SHELBY: She's upstairs—

WAYNE (*Groans*): Unpacking— (PATSY *again breaks into loud laughter.*)

SHELBY (*Grimly*): She's getting out of here if I have to use the National Guard and the U. S. Marines! (PATSY, *still laughing wildly, drops into chair.*)

WAYNE: Make that idiot stop screeching!

ETHEL (*Entering from right*): Shelby, what are we going to do? The girl won't listen to reason. She says she likes our house. And she flatly refuses to leave until the company forwards the award.

WAYNE: Then I don't want the award—no matter what it is!

ETHEL (*Hotly*): Wayne Gordon, why did you have to win a prize that's delivered by special messenger?

PATSY (*With a loud giggle*): I have it! While Jennie's waiting around, she can wash and cook and—

WAYNE: You keep out of this!

ETHEL: Shelby, you've got to do something.

SHELBY (*Nods grimly*): I'm phoning the sponsors. If they don't get that woman out of here, I'll sue them. (*To* WAYNE) Where's the home office of this candy company?

WAYNE: I—I don't remember—

SHELBY (*Sputters*): You don't remember?

PATSY: The address was probably on the box of Higbee chocolates. Wayne gave me the candy after he and Diana—

SHELBY (*Cuts in*): Where's the box?

PATSY (*Deep in thought*): I'm not sure, but I think I threw it in the trash burner in the alley—

SHELBY: Then you're coming with me. We have to find that box! (*Moves grimly to left*)

PATSY (*Rises, follows* SHELBY): Gee, Father, suppose we don't find the sponsor's address? And suppose the sponsor has lost *ours?* Maybe we'll have Jennie on our hands forever! (WAYNE *groans loudly.* SHELBY *stormily exits left, followed by* PATSY.)

ETHEL: What are people going to say when they hear about this? It's going to be difficult to explain.

WAYNE (*Savagely*): Don't tell them anything!

ETHEL: If Jennie stays on and on, how shall we introduce her to our friends?

WAYNE (*Groans*): Don't even mention it!

ETHEL (*Thoughtfully*): Should I say, "This is Jennie Winfield, our son's Dream Girl"?

WAYNE: Mother!

ETHEL: Or maybe I could say, "She brought a prize to Wayne, but she forgot to bring it." (*Shakes her head sadly*) No, that sounds impossible.

WAYNE: It *all* sounds impossible to me!

ETHEL: Or maybe I could say, "Jennie's expecting a letter from the Higbee Candy Company, so she's staying with us until it arrives." But that doesn't make sense either.

WAYNE (*Buries his face in his hands*): Mother—please— (*The doorbell rings.*)

ETHEL: Oh, dear! This is no time for company. (*Starts upstage, then suddenly turns to* WAYNE) Wayne, you didn't enter *another* contest, did you?

WAYNE (*Wildly*): I did not. (ETHEL *opens door at center revealing* DIANA HUGHES.)

ETHEL (*Greatly surprised*): Why—why—Diana Hughes! (WAYNE *jumps to his feet.*)

DIANA (*Smiles brightly*): Hello, Mrs. Gordon. (*She steps into room.*) Hello, Wayne.

WAYNE (*Stares wildly at* DIANA): Not—not *you!*

ETHEL (*In confusion*): I—I won't ask you to—to sit down, because I—I suppose you're in a hurry.

DIANA (*Smiles*): Oh, I'm in no hurry. (*Moves to chair at left of table and sits down.* WAYNE *and* ETHEL *gaze nervously at* DIANA. *At last* DIANA *speaks to* ETHEL.) I happened to be in this neighborhood, and I had a sudden urge to drop in.

ETHEL (*Weakly*): That's nice—

DIANA (*To* ETHEL, *who stands at center*): Mrs. Gordon, I'm going to be very frank. I—I guess you knew that Wayne and I had—had broken up. I suppose you were upset about it, too. (WAYNE *moves downstage to extreme right, his back to* DIANA *and* ETHEL.)

ETHEL: At the moment, I'm upset about a lot of things.

DIANA: Mrs. Gordon, I felt that you should hear my side

of the story. You see, Wayne decided I wasn't his type.

WAYNE (*Swings around quickly*): That's not so, Diana! I tried to—

DIANA (*Coolly stops him*): Please, Wayne. (*Turns to* ETHEL) It seems that Wayne wants a girl who isn't popular or clever.

ETHEL (*Dryly*): Well, I certainly know where he can find one.

DIANA: Wayne doesn't approve of a girl who is selected Queen of the Rose Festival.

WAYNE: Diana, listen to me—

DIANA (*Cuts him off*): I know exactly the kind of girl you would idolize, Wayne—a girl who is both crude and stupid. I hope she shows up in your life.

ETHEL (*Blurts out*): My goodness, she already has!

WAYNE: Mother!

DIANA (*Suddenly interested*): What's that, Mrs. Gordon?

ETHEL (*Hastily*): I mean—Wayne won first prize in a contest.

DIANA: How nice.

SHELBY (*Entering from left, followed by* PATSY): Somebody burned that candy box— (*Breaks off abruptly as he see* DIANA) Oh!

PATSY (*Equally startled*): Diana!

DIANA (*Pleasantly*): How are you both?

PATSY (*Dryly*): We've seen better days.

DIANA: I understand Wayne has won first award in a contest. I'm sure all of you are breathless.

SHELBY: We're not only breathless—we're stunned.

DIANA: Wayne, you must show me your prize. Or has it arrived yet?

PATSY: You ought to see what's arrived!

WAYNE: Diana, I—I've got to talk to you—alone.

DIANA (*As she rises*): I'm afraid there's nothing more that either of us can say, but I wish you the best of everything in the years ahead, Wayne. And someday may the girl of your dreams walk into your life.

PATSY (*With a giggle*): She already has!

WAYNE (*Wildly*): Patsy!

PATSY: A girl showed up and announced that she— (*At that moment* JENNIE *enters at right. She has discarded her hat and earrings. Her make-up is softer, more attractive, and she wears a smartly simple frock.* PATSY *breaks off with a gasp.*) My goodness!

JENNIE (*Quietly, with a little smile*): Hello. (*All in the room turn toward* JENNIE. WAYNE, SHELBY *and* ETHEL *are amazed at the transformation.*)

PATSY (*At last*): You're not Jennie, are you?

JENNIE (*Smiles*): Yes, I am.

ETHEL: Shelby, either that girl has done something to herself, or I'm losing my mind.

DIANA: Come on in, Jennie. (JENNIE *moves to center.*)

WAYNE (*As he points to* JENNIE): Diana, do—do you know her?

SHELBY: Jennie, you didn't look like that when you arrived.

DIANA: Of course she didn't. I dressed Jennie up for the part.

WAYNE: What!

ETHEL: You—dressed her up—for the part?

DIANA (*Nods*): Just a little scheme of mine.

SHELBY (*To* DIANA): What are you trying to tell us?

WAYNE: You mean Jennie isn't employed by the Higbee Candy Company?

JENNIE (*In a tone of quiet refinement*): Of course not, Wayne. It was just an act.

DIANA: Jennie is a close friend of mine. Her home is in Chicago, but she's my house guest this week.

WAYNE (*To* DIANA): I—I don't understand. How did you know that I—I entered a contest?

DIANA (*Coolly*): You made a fatal error two weeks ago, Wayne. (*Pause*) You didn't mail your contest entry to the Higbee Candy Company. Instead you addressed the envelope to me.

WAYNE (*Aghast*): To you?

DIANA: Of course I opened the envelope. Then I read your entry. (*Significantly*) According to your statement, *I* certainly didn't fit the pattern of the girl of your dreams.

JENNIE (*To* WAYNE): Diana was still angry and upset when I arrived yesterday.

DIANA: I certainly was.

JENNIE: She read me your entry, then tore it up. (*Smiles mischievously*) Then I consented to play the role of the messenger of good news.

DIANA (*Coldly*): I hope we've given you some uncomfortable moments, Wayne Gordon. You deserve them.

JENNIE: The entire family has had some uncomfortable moments, Diana.

ETHEL (*Wrings her hands*): Oh, dear—oh, dear!

DIANA: Wayne Gordon, if you thought you could run my life—if you thought I'd ask your permission every time I went out of the house—

WAYNE: But Diana—

DIANA: Well, that's the type of person you described in your contest entry.

WAYNE: But I told you I was all wrong. I said I was sorry. I asked your forgiveness—

DIANA: You did not! Get your bag and hat, Jennie. We're going home. (JENNIE *quickly exits at right as* DIANA *starts up center.*)

WAYNE (*Takes a step after* DIANA): Diana—wait— (*The doorbell rings and* DIANA *pauses.*)

DIANA (*Turning to* WAYNE): More company? Another girl of your dreams, no doubt.

ETHEL (*Grimly, as she moves up to center door*): It had better not be!

SHELBY: Wayne Gordon, I ought to give *you* away as an award. And heaven help the winner! (ETHEL *opens door at center revealing* MR. MITCHELL, *brief case in hand.*)

MITCHELL (*Briskly, as he removes his hat*): Good afternoon, madam. Is this the Gordon residence?

ETHEL: Y-yes—

MITCHELL (*Enthusiastically, as he steps into room*): Greetings to one and all! (*Glances about the room as he moves downstage*) My, what a large and happy family.

PATSY (*Dryly*): Ha! Ha!

MITCHELL: I'm looking for an individual by the name of Wayne Gordon.

SHELBY (*Grimly, as he points to* WAYNE): There he is. He's my son. And if you're from the F.B.I., you're welcome to him.

MITCHELL (*Steps briskly to* WAYNE): So you're Wayne Gordon. (*Firmly shakes* WAYNE's *hand*) Glad to know you, young man. (*Steps quickly to table left where he places his brief case and begins to open it*) Wayne, my boy, I've some exciting news for you today.

ETHEL: We've had enough news around here to last a lifetime.

SHELBY (*Stepping forward*): See here, who are you?

MITCHELL (*Who has now opened brief case*): Mitchell is my name. I'm a field representative for the Higbee Candy Company.

SHELBY: The Higbee Candy— (*Sputters*) Mr. Mitchell, kindly do not mention that name in this house.

MITCHELL: Ah, but you don't understand. (*Removes a sheet of paper from brief case*) Your son has won the first prize in our national contest.

WAYNE (*Shocked*): What!

SHELBY: First prize?

ETHEL (*To* MITCHELL): You can't fool us. You're just putting on an act.

WAYNE: But Mr. Mitchell, I couldn't have won.

MITCHELL: Didn't you enter our contest?

WAYNE: Yes—in a way. But—

MITCHELL: Of course you did. And you're the winner.

ETHEL (*Loudly*): I won't have it! I suppose *you* forgot to bring the award, too, Mr. Mitchell. Well, I won't have you moving in on us for the rest of your life.

MITCHELL (*Annoyed*): Madam, please control yourself. (*Glances at paper in his hand, then turns to* WAYNE) Yes, Wayne, your entry was selected as the best in the country.

DIANA (*Suddenly, to* MITCHELL): But that's impossible. Wayne's entry was destroyed.

MITCHELL: Young lady, kindly do not interrupt. I should

know what I'm talking about. (*Turns to* WAYNE) This is indeed a clever entry, my boy. (*To* SHELBY) You see, Mr. Gordon, each contestant wrote a statement describing the girl of his dreams. And your son constructed his entry in the form of a letter. He pretended he was writing to an imaginary girl by the name of Diana.

ETHEL: Diana?

WAYNE (*Suddenly*): You mean my entry was a letter to—to Diana?

MITCHELL (*Chuckles*): Don't tell me you've forgotten! (*To* ETHEL *and* SHELBY) It was a wonderful letter. Your son developed the idea that he and his girl friend had had a quarrel. In the letter he admitted he'd been stubborn and unreasonable—and he asked this imaginary Diana to forgive him. Then he listed all of her good points.

SHELBY (*Trying to figure it out*): Now wait a minute. You say my son wrote a letter of apology to Diana and—

WAYNE (*As the truth dawns*): That's right, Father. I—I did write the letter. (*Quickly steps to* MITCHELL.) Mr. Mitchell, may I show that—that entry to a friend of mine?

MITCHELL (*Hands letter to* WAYNE): Of course—of course.

WAYNE (*Extends letter to* DIANA): I'd like to have you read my—my entry. (DIANA *takes letter. As she swiftly scans it, she begins to smile.*)

MITCHELL (*Jovially*): I'll bet the young lady didn't know you could write a letter like that!

DIANA (*At last looks up*): No, I—I certainly didn't. (*With an understanding smile*) It's a wonderful entry, Wayne. It—it changes everything. (*Steps to* MITCHELL; *hands him the letter*) It deserved to win, Mr. Mitchell. It's just the kind of a letter a girl would be thrilled to receive.

MITCHELL (*Thoroughly enjoying the situation*): And now about the award. The company promised it would be a surprise, you know. The idea was to give the winner something he really wanted. So we've been checking up on you, Wayne. We find you've been looking at every red convertible in this town. (*Beams*) So the first thing in the morning you'll find a shiny new red convertible in front of your door.

WAYNE (*Eyes shining*): Mr. Mitchell!

ETHEL (*With a little shriek of delight*): You mean he gets a car instead of—of—

DIANA (*To hush up* ETHEL): Mrs. Gordon—please—

SHELBY: Can you beat that!

PATSY (*Begins to giggle*): First he writes an entry. Then he writes a letter. Then he—

WAYNE (*Quickly*): Patsy!

SHELBY (*Warningly*): That's enough out of you, young lady!

MITCHELL (*As he steps to table, replaces letter and closes brief case*): I must hurry along. I'm stopping overnight at a hotel downtown. (*Grins at* WAYNE) But I'll be back in the morning with a news photographer. We'll want to take some shots of you and the new car. (*Picks up hat and brief case*) Goodbye—goodbye, everybody. (*Hurries upstage to center door, then turns*) See you in the morning! (*Quickly exits at center*)

ETHEL (*After a slight pause*): I simply can't understand it.

SHELBY: Don't you see, Ethel? Wayne must have switched envelopes. Diana's letter went to the Higbee Company—

DIANA (*Smiles*): And the candy entry was mailed to me.

SHELBY (*Beams*): I've always said that Wayne was the smartest boy in this town!

JENNIE (*Enters from right with traveling bag and hat.*): I'm ready, Diana.

DIANA: Let's stay a while, Jennie. I'm not angry any more.

JENNIE (*Puzzled*): Not angry at Wayne?

DIANA: Everything's wonderful—perfectly wonderful! (*She smiles at* WAYNE.)

PATSY (*Suddenly steps forward*): Everything is *not* wonderful. Wayne Gordon, the least you could do is buy a bottle of my perfume.

WAYNE: How come?

PATSY: While you were getting ready to mail those letters, I sprayed you with "Madness." That's why you got the envelopes mixed up. My perfume confused you.

WAYNE (*Grins*): Patsy, if this is what happens to a guy who gets sprayed with "Madness," I'll take all twenty-four bottles. (PATSY *gives a little shriek of joy, rushes to* WAYNE, *and throws her arms around him.*)

PATSY: Wayne Gordon, do you realize you're being hugged by a woman who will soon be wearing—a *genuine imitation diamond!* (PATSY *gives* WAYNE *a swift and jubilant kiss on the cheek. The others break into laughter as the curtain quickly falls.*)

THE END

Production Notes

You Don't Belong to Me

Characters: 3 male; 4 female.

Playing Time: 30 minutes.

Costumes: Modern dress. Shelby wears a gardening outfit. When Jennie first enters she wears a large, over-decorative hat, dangling earrings, and a cheap, gaudy dress. For her second entrance she wears a simple summer suit. Patsy is dressed in summer play clothes.

Properties: Cardboard carton containing bottles of perfume, one bottle with atomizer, newspaper, magazine, suitcase, brief case, sheet of paper.

Setting: The living room of the Gordon residence. There are three entrances: an alcove at right leading to the stairs; a door at center which opens onto the front porch; a door at left leading to the rest of the house. There is a large armchair downstage right, while at left there are two smaller chairs, separated by a table. Other chairs, tables, lamps, bookcases, etc., complete the furnishings.

Lighting: No special effects.

Miss Fix-It

Characters

JANET FOSTER, *a gay and spirited sixteen*
HENRY FOSTER, *her turbulent brother of twelve*
CAROL MASON, *Janet's vivacious friend*
WAYNE KENT, *a young painter and decorator*
BERTHA STONEPEPPER, *who sees all and knows all*
TIMOTHY ASHWELL, *elderly and wealthy*
MATILDA KIRCHNER, *the Fosters' neighbor*

TIME: *A morning in early summer.*
SETTING: *The living room of a summer cottage, in the small resort community of Lakeside.*
AT RISE: HENRY FOSTER *is on his knees under the table, grimly wiping the table legs with a large dustcloth; housecleaning is evidently not among his favorite pastimes. The silence is broken at last by an impatient knock on the door at backstage center.* HENRY *pauses, then crawls out from under table. The knock is repeated.* HENRY, *now on hands and knees, gazes toward door.*

HENRY (*Calls loudly*): Come in . . . come in! (CAROL MASON *enters briskly at center, takes one look at* HENRY *and stops short.*)

CAROL (*Aghast*): Henry! Henry Foster!

HENRY (*Without enthusiasm*): Hi ya, Carol.

CAROL: What on earth are you doing?

HENRY: What does it look like?

CAROL (*Dryly*): It looks as if you were learning to crawl. For goodness' sakes, get on your feet. (HENRY *slowly rises. He tosses the dustcloth on top of table.*) Now, what *are* you doing on all fours?

HENRY (*Significantly*): If you want an explanation, go see my sister. I'm more confused than you are.

CAROL: Where is she?

HENRY: Janet? (*Ironically*) In the backyard burning trash.

CAROL: Henry, what's this all about? Janet wouldn't explain anything over the phone. (*With dignity*) And I'm her best friend.

HENRY (*Sadly*): Which is going to be tough on you.

CAROL: Janet called me this morning and insisted that I take the bus out here to Lakeside. Then I was instructed to walk down Shore Drive until I came to a cottage marked "Crestwood."

HENRY (*Sighs*): This is Crestwood, all right, but even *I* didn't know the ghastly details until Sis and I got out here this morning. Then she told me, and I guess she'll tell you.

CAROL: Who owns this summer cottage? Why is it so important that— (*Suddenly*) Henry, is Janet mixed up in something again?

HENRY (*Unhappily*): The answer—I regret to say—is yes. (JANET FOSTER *energetically enters from left, carrying a broom and an empty water pail.*)

JANET (*Delighted, as she sees* CAROL): Carol, darling— (*Places broom against left wall, then moves enthusiastically toward* CAROL.) You found the place!

CAROL (*A bit grimly*): Janet Foster, will you please tell me—

JANET (*Cuts in brightly*): Just a minute, Carol— (*Turns to* HENRY; *hands him the pail.*) Henry, you'll have to get water from a neighbor. The pipes are disconnected.

HENRY (*Backs away*): But, gee whiz—

JANET (*Slips pail over* HENRY'S *arm*): Run along like a good boy. The kitchen floor needs scrubbing.

HENRY (*Loudly*): If you want to know what I think about this foolishness—

JANET (*Sharply*): Henry!

HENRY (*In defeat*): O. K., O. K. (*Gloomily moves up center.*)

JANET: Just ask any of the neighbors. I'm sure they're all lovely people.

HENRY (*Pauses at center door; turns to* CAROL): Carol, you have my sympathy. (*Exits center, leaving door open.*)

CAROL (*Impatiently*): Janet, will you kindly tell me—

JANET (*Brightly*): Sit down, dear. You look upset.

CAROL (*Marches down left to rocking chair*): Why shouldn't I look upset? (*Starts to sit in rocking chair*) Here I am, without—

JANET (*Suddenly as* CAROL *starts to sit*): Not there! (CAROL, *startled, straightens up.*) I haven't dusted the rocker yet. (*Indicates chair to right of table*) You're safe over here.

CAROL (*Exasperated, as she crosses to chair*): I don't know what you're up to, Janet Foster. But I have an uneasy feeling that I won't approve. (*Sits in chair to right of table*)

JANET (*With enthusiasm*): Oh, but you will. And you're going to help me. (*Triumphantly, after a pause*) Carol, I've taken on a new project.

CAROL (*Groans*): Not again!

JANET: I'm devoting my time to the service of others. (*Moves to rocking chair, picks up dustcloth hanging over back, begins to dust chair*)

CAROL: You mean you've taken up professional house-cleaning?

JANET: No. But I *am* rejuvenating this cottage—it'll mean everything to dear Miss Kirchner.

CAROL: Miss Kirchner?

JANET (*Nods*): Matilda Kirchner. She's the wealthy old lady who lives next door to us.

CAROL: Yes, I know her. Does she own this cottage?

JANET (*Nods*): She bought it last week—furniture and all. She plans to spend her summers out here.

CAROL: And she hired you to clean the place?

JANET (*Amused*): Oh, no, darling! She couldn't find any-one to fix it up, so I decided to do it for her—as a surprise.

CAROL (*Rises*): She doesn't even know you're out here?

JANET: Of course not. She told me where the cottage was located, so I had no trouble finding it. (*Breathlessly*)

And with your help and Henry's, I'll get the place in perfect order for her.

CAROL (*Flatly*): I don't like the idea, and I'll bet Miss Kirchner won't either.

JANET: But Carol, I'm doing a good deed. It's time all of us began to think of others.

CAROL: I *am* thinking of others—Miss Kirchner in particular.

JANET: You're sweet, Carol. (*Tosses dustcloth on table*)

CAROL: How did you get in here without a key anyway?

JANET: I—I cut the kitchen screen. (HENRY *appears at center opening. He carries a pail of water.*)

CAROL (*To* JANET): And what will Matilda Kirchner think of that?

JANET (*Without concern*): Henry can fix the screen— (HENRY, *who has overheard, enters.*)

HENRY (*Sourly*): Sure, Henry can fix the screen. Henry can carry water, Henry can have a breakdown from over-work—

JANET (*Firmly*): Henry, I've had enough.

HENRY (*Loudly*): Well, I had enough even before I came out here.

JANET (*Quickly turning on her charm*): Remember, Henry, we're doing this for dear Miss Kirchner. Why don't you scrub the kitchen floor? Carol can dust.

HENRY: What are you going to do—take up the collection?

JANET (*Ignores* HENRY's *remark*): I must make a decision about the picture. (*Moves swiftly to picture which leans against back wall.*) Now you run along, Henry.

HENRY (*Warningly*): If you get into trouble over this, I

wash my hands—I wash my hands— (JANET *has picked up the picture and is gazing at it.*)

JANET (*Suddenly looks up from picture*): Wash your hands? (*Brightly*) Of course, darling, you can wash your hands—in the bucket of water. (*Turns again to picture. With a hopeless groan,* HENRY *exits left, carrying bucket.*)

CAROL (*To* JANET): Janet, if I weren't your best friend, I'd be tempted to walk out. But now that I'm here, I might as well work. (*Picks up dustcloth from table.*)

JANET (*Studies picture as she moves downstage*): It's quite impossible—

CAROL (*Dusting as she speaks*): It certainly is . . . coming out here without an invitation.

JANET: I'm talking about this picture. It was hanging on the wall when I arrived this morning.

CAROL: In this room?

JANET (*Vaguely indicates left wall downstage from doorway*): Over there.

CAROL: You took it down?

JANET: Of course. Miss Kirchner certainly couldn't live with *this*. (*Turns to* CAROL) It was the only picture in the house. I don't blame the owner for leaving it here. (*Again gazes distastefully at picture.*)

CAROL: Is it that bad?

JANET: Take a look. (CAROL *moves to* JANET, *glances at picture.*)

CAROL (*With a start*): It's horrible! Who is that ghastly old woman?

JANET: I haven't the faintest idea—but she's *not* going back on the wall!

CAROL: Is there a storage closet around here?

JANET: If there is, I'll find it. That's where this thing belongs. (*Moves left*) Carry on, darling. I won't be long— (*Exits left with picture.* CAROL *moves up to cupboard. As she dusts the shelves,* WAYNE KENT *appears in open doorway. He peers through doorway and sees* CAROL.)

WAYNE: Good morning— (*He steps through doorway.*)

CAROL (*Swings around with a start*): Oh!

WAYNE (*Grins*): Did I frighten you?

CAROL: Where I come from, people knock on the door.

WAYNE: The door was open. (*Pause*) Do you own this cottage?

CAROL: No—fortunately. (*Places dustcloth on shelf.*)

WAYNE (*Moves down center, gazes around the room*): Nice little place—

CAROL (*Annoyed, as she moves downstage*): Who are you, anyway?

WAYNE: My name's Kent. Wayne Kent. I was driving by and—

CAROL (*Nods*): I know. You saw the open door and decided this was the house by the side of the road.

WAYNE (*Amused*): Not quite. But I am interested in meeting all the newcomers to Lakeside.

CAROL (*Dryly*): I'm a newcomer, all right.

WAYNE: Actually, so am I. I arrived here only last week, but I plan to be in Lakeside most of the summer—that is, if I can make a few dollars.

CAROL: If you're here to sell something, Mr. Kent, I'm sure we already have one.

WAYNE: But you said you didn't own this place. (*Grins*) Remember?

CAROL (*Slightly upset*): Would you mind telling me your business?

WAYNE: I'm a painter.

CAROL: Oh, we're certainly not in the market for a portrait. I've just been looking at one—and I still have the creeps.

WAYNE (*Laughs*): I'm a *house* painter—you know, a decorator. I plan to return to the university this fall, but I came up here for the summer, hoping I could pick up some work. So if you'd just call the owner of this cottage—

CAROL: Sorry, but the owner of this cottage is in the city today. (*Significantly*) And if I'd known a few hours ago what I know now, that's where I'd be, too.

WAYNE (*Sighs*): Well, this puts me on a dead-end street again. (*Disappointed*) Then I suppose there's no use in my hanging around.

CAROL: I'm afraid not.

WAYNE (*After a pause*): Anyway, it was nice meeting you, Miss—Miss—

CAROL: Mason. Carol Mason.

WAYNE: If you ever need your house painted, just call on me. (*Moves upstage, about to leave, when* JANET *enters from left. She stops short.*)

JANET (*Pleasantly, as she sees* WAYNE): Oh, hello.

WAYNE: Hello to you.

JANET: Are you coming or going?

CAROL (*Speaks up*): He's going.

WAYNE (*To* JANET): I was looking for work, but I've been told the owner of this cottage isn't here.

JANET: N-no—

WAYNE: I'm Wayne Kent.

JANET (*Smiles*): And I'm Janet Foster.

CAROL: Wayne, take my advice, and leave right now, unless you want to spend the rest of the day scrubbing.

JANET: Carol! (*To* WAYNE) Can we help you?

CAROL (*Hurriedly to* JANET): He's a decorator— (*Quickly, to* WAYNE) Goodbye, Wayne. Nice to have met you—

JANET (*To* WAYNE, *paying no attention to* CAROL): A decorator?

WAYNE: I thought the owner might want a paint job done here.

JANET: No, I'm afraid— (*Suddenly*) Wait a minute—can you paint kitchen walls?

WAYNE (*Immediately interested*): I'm probably the best kitchen-wall painter in the state.

JANET (*With increased enthusiasm*): Then you're just the man I'm looking for!

CAROL (*Desperately*): Janet!

JANET (*To* WAYNE): The kitchen walls in this cottage are impossible. I'll give you a job right now.

CAROL: Janet, listen to me— (*To* WAYNE) Wayne, listen to me— (*Loudly and impatiently*) Will somebody listen to me?

JANET (*Turns brighly to* CAROL): Remember, darling, I'm running this place.

WAYNE (*To* JANET): But if you don't own this cottage—

JANET: Matilda Kirchner does. She'll gladly pay for any redecorating I decide to do.

CAROL (*To* JANET): Janet Foster, may I open my mouth?

JANET: No!

WAYNE (*To* JANET): You're certain she wants her kitchen painted?

JANET: Of course. She has plenty of money—and she's been looking all over for somebody.

WAYNE (*With a broad grin*): Then I'm her man!

JANET (*Enthusiastically*): When can you start?

WAYNE: This minute. I've got paint, brushes and ladder in my pickup truck. It's parked outside.

JANET: Wonderful!

WAYNE (*In sincere gratitude*): Miss Foster, this is the break I need. It's my first job in Lakeside. You've really made me happy.

JANET (*Her eyes bright*): That's what I'm trying to do— make everybody happy.

WAYNE: And believe me, you're succeeding! I'll get my ladder. (*Swiftly exits through center doorway*)

CAROL (*Sputters*): Janet Foster—

JANET (*Brightly*): Relax, darling.

CAROL: You have no right to hire him.

JANET: Miss Kirchner will be overjoyed. Don't you see? I'm helping them both. I'm being of service to humanity. You ought to try it, Carol. It would give you a wonderful feeling.

CAROL: The only time I'll have a wonderful feeling is when I get away from here.

JANET: Nonsense! Tell Henry he'll have to move out of the kitchen. . . . And darling, you'd better spread some newspapers on the floor. Mr. Kent might drip some paint.

CAROL (*Marches to left*): If I ever buy a summer cottage, you're going to be the last person to know it.

JANET (*Without concern*): And Carol— (CAROL *turns to* JANET) about the picture—

CAROL: Picture?

JANET: The one that hung in here.

CAROL: I suppose you found a place to store it.

JANET: Not exactly, but we don't need to worry any more.

CAROL: What do you mean?

JANET (*Brightly*): I burned it up.

CAROL (*With a start*): Burned the picture?

JANET (*Nods enthusiastically*): On the trash pile in the back yard. Wasn't that a marvelous idea?

CAROL: Marvelous idea? (*Groans.*) Give me strength! (*She snatches up broom, then exits left.* WAYNE, *in painter's coveralls and hat, enters at center, carrying stepladder.*)

WAYNE: Where's the kitchen?

JANET (*Indicates left exit*): Right in there.

WAYNE (*Pauses*): Oh, we didn't discuss color. I suppose Miss Kirchner wants the kitchen done in white.

JANET (*Thoughtfully*): Y-yes, I'm sure she does. Miss Kirchner is definitely the white-wall type. (WAYNE *exits left. A moment later,* HENRY *marches into room through center doorway.*)

HENRY (*Highly irritated*): Carol pushed me out the back door. She said you'd hired some guy to paint the kitchen walls.

JANET: Won't Miss Kirchner be surprised?

HENRY: She'll probably collapse.

JANET: I'm merely being of service to my fellow man.

HENRY: Well, all I can say is, I'd hate to be your fellow man. (CAROL *enters from left*)

CAROL: You and your good deeds! Some day you're going to get crossed up.

JANET: I have perfect confidence in my judgment.

HENRY: Well, you're the only person in the state who does! (*Exits through doorway left in disgust.* JANET, *openly annoyed, looks after* HENRY. BERTHA STONEPEPPER *appears at center doorway, peers briefly into room, then enters.*)

JANET (*Exasperated, as she turns to* CAROL): Honestly, there are times when I could— (*She breaks off as she sees* BERTHA.)

BERTHA: Good morning.

JANET (*Slightly upset*): Good morning—

BERTHA (*Moves down center*): I'm Miss Stonepepper— Miss Bertha Stonepepper. I was walking by—saw the door open—and here I am.

JANET: Y-yes, here you are—

BERTHA: Always make it a point to call on the new folks in Lakeside. (*Sits in chair to left of table*) Don't believe I caught your name.

JANET: I'm Janet Foster, and this is Carol Mason.

BERTHA: Nice to know you both. (*With a flourish*) Well, sit down. Make yourselves at home. (JANET *is uncomfortable;* CAROL *is indignant.* JANET *sinks into rocking chair.* CAROL *sits in chair to right of table.*) I was sure surprised when I ambled by and saw people living here in Crestwood.

CAROL (*Emphatically*): *I'm* not living here.

BERTHA (*To* JANET): Then *you* rented this cottage—

JANET: Oh, no! It belongs to a Miss Kirchner.

BERTHA (*Startled*): What!

JANET: She bought it just recently. Carol and I came out to clean it up.

CAROL: Which was not my idea.

BERTHA (*Suddenly concerned*): My goodness, I didn't even know the place had been sold! 'Course it's been on the market for years, but Timothy didn't tell me he'd found a buyer.

JANET: Timothy?

BERTHA: Timothy Ashwell. He's the man who owned Crestwood before— (*Breaks off, upset*) But this is horrible—simply horrible.

JANET: But why?

BERTHA: My dear girl, I've lived in Lakeside all my life. I'm expected to know everything that goes on. It's traditional. Why, if the news got out that I didn't know about Timothy selling Crestwood, my reputation would be in danger!

JANET (*Politely*): Really?

BERTHA: Timothy will hear from me about this.

JANET: I think Miss Kirchner bought this place rather unexpectedly.

BERTHA: No doubt—because if she'd made an investigation first, she wouldn't have accepted this place as a gift.

JANET: What do you mean?

BERTHA (*Now enjoying herself*): My dear, Crestwood cottage is supposed to be—haunted.

CAROL (*Jumps in alarm*): Haunted! (*For a moment* JANET *is equally startled.*)

BERTHA: This place has been shut up for years. Timothy didn't even try to rent it. (*Speaks ominously*) I understand it has something to do with a picture.

JANET: Picture? (CAROL's *panic increases.*)

BERTHA: It hangs on the wall someplace in this cottage. (*To* JANET) I suppose you've seen it around?

JANET (*With effort*): I—well, I—

BERTHA (*Nods*): Of course you have. Now I never could get much information from Timothy. But it's rumored that if anybody so much as touches that picture, disaster will strike this cottage.

JANET (*Rises*): Disaster?

BERTHA (*Rises*): So don't you girls touch any picture hangin' on the walls. Something terrible will probably happen to you. (*Smiles*) Well, it's sure nice to have met you both. Tell Miss Kirchner I'll be dropping in on her, soon as she gets moved— (*Moves up center, then turns*) Just between you and me, you couldn't hire me to live in this place. (*Brightens*) Now you girls keep away from that picture, but if tragedy should strike, just run up on the drive and get me. (*Pleasantly expectant*) I'm always happy to be around in time of disaster . . . Goodbye. Have fun! (*Exits center*)

CAROL (*Trembling, after a tense pause*): She said—if anybody touched—that picture—

JANET (*Attempts to throw off her nervousness*): It—it's nonsense.

CAROL (*Accusingly, as she moves toward* JANET): You not only touched that picture, you—you burned it!

JANET: What if I did? Good riddance. When we explain to Miss Kirchner—

CAROL: We—we may not live to explain.

JANET (*Successfully throwing off her fears*): You're being

ridiculous, darling. That story's just silly superstition. This cottage isn't haunted. Nothing's going to happen to us. We're as safe as— (*Suddenly, a loud crash is heard from offstage left.* CAROL, *with a wild scream, leaps toward* JANET. *She clutches* JANET *in uncontrolled panic.*)

JANET (*Breaking away*): Carol, stop it— (HENRY *enters from left.*)

CAROL (*Wails loudly as she sees* HENRY): It—it wasn't my fault. I—I didn't touch it! And I'm too young and beautiful to die!

HENRY (*Looks first at* CAROL, *then turns to* JANET): What's up? The gal's off her rocker.

JANET: Henry what—what was it?

HENRY: That crash? (*Grins*) Nothin' at all—except the stepladder fell down. (*To* CAROL) Is that what you're moaning about?

JANET (*Secretly relieved*): See, Carol? Just a little old stepladder—

HENRY: But it sure was funny at that. For no reason, the ladder just all at once gave way. Nobody was even touchin' it. If Wayne Kent had been standin' on it, he would have cracked his neck.

CAROL (*Again in complete panic*): Then Miss Stonepepper was right! There *is* a curse on this house. If you'd kept your hands off that picture—

JANET: Be quiet! (*To* HENRY) Is Mr. Kent all right? I'd better check— (*Quickly exits left.* CAROL *sinks into chair at left of table. Again she groans.*)

HENRY (*Puzzled and annoyed, as he moves to center*): Carol, what's eatin' you?

CAROL (*Her voice trembles*): Miss Stonepepper was here. She knows everything about Lakeside. She—she said this cottage was haunted.

HENRY (*With a violent start*): Huh?

CAROL: It's because of a picture. She said if we touched it, something horrible would happen.

HENRY: Golly, didn't Sis take a picture off the wall?

CAROL (*Wails*): Y-yes—and it was the only picture in the cottage!

HENRY (*With increasing concern*): Then I'm going to tell her to hang it right back. (*Grimly marches to left*)

CAROL: She can't!

HENRY (*Pauses, turns to* CAROL): Why can't she?

CAROL (*Wildly*): Because she—she burned it up!

HENRY (*Wild-eyed*): She—burned—it—up? (*Rushes to left*)

CAROL: Henry, where are you going?

HENRY: I'm turnin' in my resignation! (*Wildly exits left*)

CAROL: Wait, I'm going with you. (CAROL *rushes upstage. But as she reaches center opening,* TIMOTHY ASHWELL *suddenly appears at doorway.* CAROL *stops short, in panic.*)

TIMOTHY (*Steps through doorway*) Where are you going?

CAROL (*Completely confused*): I—I have to catch a dog-train for Alaska—

TIMOTHY (*Blocks her way*): No, you don't. Who are you?

CAROL: I—I'm Carol Mason. (*Backs away*) And—and I've always been a nice person—quiet, friendly . . .

TIMOTHY: You don't look it, young lady.

CAROL (*Trembles*): I've had a bad day. (*Starts to by-pass* TIMOTHY) If you'll excuse me—

TIMOTHY (*With authority, as he steps in front of* CAROL):
Nobody's leaving this house until I say so. Sit down!
(CAROL *backs down right to chair and sits.*) That's better.

CAROL: S-sir, may—may I ask a question—?

TIMOTHY (*Sharply*): I'll do the asking. Who else is here?

CAROL: You mean—here in Crestwood?

TIMOTHY: Where else would I mean?

CAROL (*With effort*): There's Janet Foster—and her
brother Henry—and Wayne Kent— (*With a weak smile*)
Wayne's painting the kitchen.

TIMOTHY (*Aghast*): Painting the kitchen!

JANET (*Calling urgently from offstage, left*): Carol Mason,
don't you dare leave me— (*She rushes through doorway
left, then breaks off with a gasp as she sees* TIMOTHY.
HENRY *enters through doorway left. He, too, stops short.*)

TIMOTHY (*Coldly, to* JANET): Good morning. (*No one in
the room speaks. Then, after a tense pause—*) Nice little
gathering we seem to have here.

JANET (*Steps forward with considerable courage*): What
do you want?

TIMOTHY: Stay where you are! (JANET *pauses.*) I suppose
you're Janet Foster.

JANET: I—I am.

TIMOTHY (*To* JANET, *as he indicates* HENRY): Is that young
man your brother? And where's the character who's
painting the kitchen?

JANET: He—he's in the kitchen, of course.

HENRY: I guess that's pretty obvious—

TIMOTHY: Quiet! (*Grimly, he moves toward left.* HENRY,
frightened, jumps out of the way. TIMOTHY *reaches door
left, then turns.*) One move—and you're all under arrest.

JANET (*Flares up*): You can't talk to us like that! Who do you think you are?

TIMOTHY (*Draws himself up*): Young lady, I am—Timothy Ashwell. I'm going to have a look at the kitchen. (*Exits.*)

CAROL (*Aghast*): He's the one who sold Crestwood to Miss Kirchner.

HENRY: I'm getting out of here. (*Makes a dash toward center door.*)

JANET (*Shouts to* HENRY): You are not! (HENRY *pauses.*) Don't you dare leave this room. No one is leaving until we know what's going on. (HENRY *backs upstage right.*)

CAROL (*To* JANET, *in rising terror*): It's all a part of the curse—that's what it is. And you're responsible, Janet Foster! You took down that picture and—

JANET (*Cuts in sharply*): That's enough, Carol!

CAROL (*Moans, as she moves to extreme left*): Why did I get mixed up in this? Why did I— (MATILDA KIRCHNER *appears at center doorway, peers into room.*)

JANET (*To* CAROL): Stop it, I say!

MATILDA (*From doorway*): Well! (*With a start those in room turn toward* MATILDA.)

JANET (*Gasps*): *Miss Kirchner!*

CAROL: Thank goodness!

MATILDA (*Sweeps down center*): What's the meaning of this?

HENRY: Janet dragged Carol and me out here to Lakeside to—

MATILDA (*Cuts him off*): I know it. (*To* JANET) Your mother told me this morning, Janet . . . said you'd planned to clean up my cottage as a surprise.

JANET: I—I thought it would make you happy.

MATILDA: Something told me I ought to get out here, so I hired a car and driver and headed for Lakeside.

CAROL (*To* MATILDA): You came just in time.

MATILDA (*To* JANET): I've been looking all over this town for you. Finally, I stopped a woman on the street. Her name was Miss Stonepepper, I believe. She said two girls were at this cottage, acting mighty funny. From that description I knew one of them must have been you, Janet.

JANET (*Stoutly*): I haven't been acting funny. I've been cleaning up this place.

MATILDA (*Dryly*): I can't imagine why.

JANET: But Miss Kirchner, this is Crestwood, your cottage.

MATILDA (*Exasperated*): Janet Foster, what's wrong with you? I don't own Crestwood.

CAROL (*Aghast*): What!

HENRY (*Almost chokes*): You don't own it!

JANET (*To* MATILDA): But you told me—

MATILDA: I told you I'd purchased *Woodcrest*—not Crestwood. Woodcrest is a quarter of a mile on up the drive.

JANET (*Completely upset*): What—what have I done?

HENRY (*Ironically*): Nothing at all—just crossed us up again!

CAROL (*To* MATILDA): Janet has been cleaning this place for hours.

HENRY: She even hired a guy to paint the kitchen.

MATILDA (*With a violent start*): Paint the kitchen!

CAROL (*With a sudden little shriek*): Then this *is* Timothy Ashwell's place!

MATILDA (*Crosses right to* CAROL): Who's Timothy Ash-well? (CAROL's *answer is a loud groan.* MATILDA *turns to* JANET.) What on earth have you done?

HENRY (*Answers*): Just fixed up things so we'll go to jail—that's all. (JANET *begins to weep.* WAYNE *rushes into room from left, angry and excited.*)

WAYNE: Somebody's going to pay for this— (*Breaks off abruptly as he sees* MATILDA) Well, madam, who are you? If you're looking for juvenile delinquents, you've come to the right place.

MATILDA (*Draws herself up*): Young man, I am Matilda Kirchner. (JANET *continues to weep.*) And who are you?

CAROL (*To* MATILDA): He's Wayne Kent—

HENRY (*Sadly*): Hired to paint your kitchen . . . except it isn't your kitchen.

WAYNE (*Grimly to* MATILDA): Janet Foster said a Matilda Kirchner owned this cottage.

MATILDA: There's been a slight misunderstanding.

WAYNE (*His voice rises*): Slight? (*To* JANET, *furiously*) This cottage belongs to Timothy Ashwell. He didn't even *want* the kitchen painted. And he flatly refuses to pay me for my time and paint. And not only that—he's going to have everybody arrested.

HENRY (*Moans*): Can't you see me—on my hands and knees—scrubbin' the prison floors—?

WAYNE (*Angrily, to* HENRY): Keep quiet!

CAROL (*Weeps loudly*): My parents are going to miss me—!

WAYNE (*Shouts at* CAROL): You, too! (*In the midst of the confusion,* BERTHA *rushes into room through center opening.*)

BERTHA (*Loudly*): Where's Timothy?

MATILDA (*Surprised*): Miss Stonepepper!

WAYNE: By now Timothy Ashwell has probably sailed through the kitchen roof. (*Grimly he marches to down-stage left.*) The last time I saw him he was ready to explode.

BERTHA: He can't. I won't permit it.

WAYNE (*Dryly*): Ha! (TIMOTHY *enters, grim and angry.*)

BERTHA (*Breathlessly, as she sees* TIMOTHY): Timothy! Timothy, is it true? Have you sold this cottage?

TIMOTHY (*Coldly*): I have not.

BERTHA (*With overwhelming relief*): Then I'm saved— I'm saved!

CAROL (*Dryly*): I wish I could say the same.

BERTHA (*To* TIMOTHY): If you'd sold this house and I hadn't heard about it first, my reputation would have been ruined. (*Rushes to* TIMOTHY, *grasps his hand, kisses it joyfully.*) Thank you, Timothy—thank you— (*Triumphantly she dashes upstage to opening. Then she turns majestically.*) My record is clean. I can hold up my head again. I can still say—without fear of contradiction —that I haven't missed a single rumor in forty years! (*She exits.*)

TIMOTHY (*Sputtering angrily*): Who's responsible for all this? (*Silently* WAYNE, CAROL *and* HENRY *point to* JANET. TIMOTHY *marches to* JANET.) Did you cut the screen in the kitchen window?

JANET (*Trembles*): I—I—

TIMOTHY: Did you decide to have my kitchen painted? (*His voice rises.*) Did you— (*Breaks off suddenly as he gazes at left wall. In amazement he points toward wall.*) Where—where is it?

MATILDA: Sir, what are you raving about?

TIMOTHY: The picture—the picture that hung on that wall! (CAROL *and* HENRY *gaze at* TIMOTHY *in speechless horror.* JANET *waits in panic.*)

MATILDA (*Sharply, to* TIMOTHY): Don't look at me.

HENRY (*At last—to* JANET): O.K., Sis. Give him the glad tidings. It'll only extend our sentence another ten years. (TIMOTHY *turns to* JANET.)

JANET (*As* TIMOTHY *stands over her*): I—I took the picture down.

TIMOTHY (*Without expression*): And what did you do with it?

JANET: I—I—

TIMOTHY: Well?

JANET: I burned it! (*She breaks into wild weeping.* CAROL *covers her face.* HENRY *turns his back.* MATILDA *sinks into chair at right of table.*)

WAYNE (*Points an accusing finger at* JANET): People like you are a menace!

TIMOTHY (*To* JANET): So you burned the picture— (JANET's *answer is a loud wail. But* TIMOTHY's *grim expression suddenly dissolves. He smiles broadly.*) That's wonderful!

JANET (*At first pays no attention*): I—I was only trying to— (*Suddenly breaks off, looks up.*) What—what did you say?

TIMOTHY: It's wonderful! And so are you. (*The others, amazed, turn to* TIMOTHY.)

CAROL: Am I hearing things?

TIMOTHY (*Expansively*): My friends, this lovely girl is one in a million. (*Chuckles*) That picture was a portrait

of my mother-in-law. (MATILDA *rises in amazement.*)
Horrible thing—and you can take that remark any way
you like. (*Beams*) My—er—dear wife and I used to live
in this cottage before we built our new home. That
portrait always hung there— (*He points to wall left,
then shudders.*) When we moved, my—er—dear wife
insisted that the picture come with us. She wanted to
place it above the mantel. (*He shudders again.*) I said
no. So my—er—dear wife retaliated. She said if I
wouldn't hang the picture above the mantel, then it was
to remain right here on this wall forever. And she
warned me that if I'd so much as put a finger on it,
she'd— (*Pauses*) Well, she could do it, too. She's the—er
—muscular type.

JANET (*Rises in amazement*): So you didn't dare touch the
picture—?

TIMOTHY: You wouldn't either, if you knew my wife.
(*Quickly*) My—er—*dear* wife. Of course I couldn't rent
this cottage. Nobody wanted to live with my mother-in-
law's portrait. (*Turns brightly to* JANET) But now the
picture is gone. What a tragedy—what a happy tragedy.
(*Chuckles*) And I didn't even touch it, did I?

CAROL (*To* TIMOTHY): Then you're *glad* she burned it?

TIMOTHY: I'm overjoyed. Why, folks in Lakeside even got
the idea this place was haunted. But I'll have no trouble
in renting it now (*Turns to* WAYNE)—since you've
finished decorating, young man.

WAYNE (*Amazed*): Then you want me to—

TIMOTHY: Of course! I want you to redecorate the entire
cottage. And I've some other properties across the lake.
I'll keep you busy all summer.

WAYNE (*Breathlessly*): How can I ever thank you!

TIMOTHY: Don't thank me. (*Indicates* JANET) Thank this young lady. (*Turns to* JANET) My dear, I'd consider it an honor if you'd have lunch with me. (*Offers his arm to* JANET)

WAYNE (*Steps swiftly to the other side of* JANET): And with me! (*Offers his arm to* JANET)

TIMOTHY (*Nods*): The three of us, then. (JANET *smiles. She accepts the arm of each. The others in the room are stunned.*)

JANET (*Happily*): Mr. Ashwell, you're tops!

TIMOTHY (*Beams at* JANET): Do you know something, my dear? You're a good-deed girl.

WAYNE (*To* JANET, *with a broad grin*): A real servant of humanity. (*Arm in arm the three move upstage, and quickly exit through center doorway.* MATILDA, *speechless, sinks into chair. Weakly* CAROL *grasps the back of chair in which* MATILDA *is seated.* HENRY, *dazed, takes a step forward. He pauses, begins to weave—then suddenly collapses to the floor. The curtain quickly falls.*)

THE END

Production Notes

Miss Fix-It

Characters: 3 male; 4 female.

Playing Time: 30 minutes.

Costumes: Janet and Carol wear summer dresses; Janet also wears an apron. Henry wears blue jeans and T-shirt. Wayne Kent first appears in khakis and sport shirt; he may wear painter's coveralls and hat when he reappears with stepladder. Bertha Stonepepper wears dated middle-aged summer clothes, with hat, bag, umbrella, and gloves. Matilda Kirchner's outfit is trim and aristocratic; she carries gloves and handbag, also. Timothy Ashwell wears a dignified summer suit.

Properties: Two or three dustcloths, pail, mop and other cleaning equipment; stepladder, cans of paint, brushes, and rags.

Setting: The living room of a summer cottage, in the small resort community of Lakeside. The room has a forgotten and neglected appearance. The few pieces of furniture are out of date and somewhat battered. There are two entrances to the room: a door at backstage center which leads outside, and a door at left which leads to the other rooms of the house. At downstage right are two straight-backed chairs, separated by an old scarred table. At downstage left is an old-fashioned rocking chair, with a dustcloth draped over the back. A cupboard with bare shelves stands to left of center opening. On floor to right of center opening, leaning against back wall, face inward, is a large framed picture. At no time is the picture itself visible to the audience.

Lighting: No special effects.

Instructions for Gary

Characters

KAY BARTON, *a high school junior*
MRS. BARTON, *her mother*
GARY FIELDS, *Kay's current interest*
GEORGE WASHBURN, *a bank president*
JOYCE WASHBURN, *his attractive young niece*

TIME: *An evening in spring.*
SETTING: *The living room of the Barton home.*
AT RISE: *The stage is unoccupied. After a brief pause,*
MRS. BARTON *enters from door left. She carries a flower
bowl containing a bouquet of rose buds. She moves to
coffee table where she places bowl. But after stepping
back to view the effect, she is not satisfied. She picks up
bowl and crosses to table at right of stage. As she places
bowl on table,* KAY BARTON *enters from door right.* KAY
carries a pad and pencil.

MRS. BARTON (*Backs to center, as she views flowers*): These roses *do* look nice.

KAY (*Briskly*): Not there, Mother. On the coffee table.

MRS. BARTON: But Kay, the coffee table is too low. I tried it.

KAY: Please, Mother—

MRS. BARTON: I really can't understand why the location of the flowers is so important. After all, this is a dinner party —not a wedding.

KAY (*Steps to table right*): I'm placing a bud vase here. (*Smiles*) You don't mind, do you, Mother?

MRS. BARTON (*Sighs*): If it makes you happier, I'll shift them back to the coffee table. (MRS. BARTON *moves bowl from table right to coffee table.* KAY *drops pad and pencil on table right.*) But I can't follow your reasoning, Kay.

KAY: You're not supposed to. (*Fondly*) Anyway, you're a sweet mother. (KAY *pushes chair to table.*)

MRS. BARTON (*Deep in thought*): I think everything's ready. The ham, the sweet potatoes, the sauce— (*As* MRS. BARTON *speaks,* KAY *drops into chair at table. She picks up pencil; writes on pad.*) It's so terribly important that we make a good impression on Mr. Washburn. (*Turns to* KAY) This is the first time we've entertained him for a meal and— (*She gazes curiously at* KAY.) Kay, what are you doing?

KAY (*Lightly*): Nothing, really. (*Continues to write*)

MRS. BARTON (*Sharply*): Kay!

KAY (*Looks up*): I'm just writing some instructions for Gary.

MRS. BARTON: I can't imagine why it's necessary to write

Gary Fields. He's at this house almost every day, and he'll be here for dinner in a few minutes.

KAY (*Brightly*): Don't give it another thought, darling. (*Again she writes.*)

MRS. BARTON (*Annoyed*): Kay Barton, listen to me. (*With a little sigh,* KAY *puts down her pencil.*) For some reason you're opposed to this dinner party tonight.

KAY (*With affected innocence*): Why, Mother! How can you say that?

MRS. BARTON: Yes, you are. Yet you know perfectly well what this means to us. George Washburn is president of the bank. Your father has applied for a loan so we can expand our business, and Mr. Washburn hasn't given us his answer.

KAY (*Impatiently*): I know all of that, Mother—

MRS. BARTON: When I learned that Mr. Washburn's niece was arriving for a visit, I felt it was an excellent opportunity to extend an invitation. If we make a favorable impression on Mr. Washburn tonight, we might have a better chance of obtaining the loan. (*Pointedly*) But you didn't like the idea.

KAY (*Vaguely*): I was afraid it might be too much work for you—especially since Father is out of town.

MRS. BARTON: Nonsense! With your father away, Mr. Washburn knows that business matters won't be discussed. I told him that his niece would enjoy meeting you and Gary.

KAY: But it's just that— (*Pause*) I mean, we've never met Mr. Washburn's niece. We really don't know what sort of a person she is.

MRS. BARTON (*Suddenly*): So that explains it!

KAY: Explains what?

MRS. BARTON (*Knowingly*): The reason you didn't want me to invite Gary Fields. You were afraid that Miss Joyce Washburn might be dripping with glamour, and if such were the case, you'd feel safer if Gary were home watching TV.

KAY (*With pretended denial*): Mother, what a stupid idea!

MRS. BARTON: You're right. It's a very stupid idea. (*The doorbell rings.*)

KAY (*Jumps up*): That's Gary! (*Hastily gathers up pad and pencil*)

MRS. BARTON: How do you know?

KAY: I told him to come early. (*Rushes to* MRS. BARTON) Be a darling and entertain him a minute. I want to mend my face. (*Gives* MRS. BARTON *a fleeting kiss; then exits left.* MRS. BARTON *opens center door to admit* GARY FIELDS)

GARY (*Cheerfully*): Good evening, Mrs. Barton.

MRS. BARTON: Come in, Gary. (GARY *enters.*)

GARY: It's good to be back here again.

MRS. BARTON (*Dryly*): That's right, I don't believe you've been around for all of two days.

GARY (*Laughs*): I left myself wide open for that answer!

MRS. BARTON: We're always glad to have you, Gary. (*Indicates davenport*) Sit down. (MRS. BARTON *moves chair downstage from table where she sits.*)

GARY (*Pauses before coffee table*): Say, these are pretty roses. I'll bet your husband sent them to you.

MRS. BARTON: Yes. He's out of town.

GARY (*Seriously*): Mrs. Barton, I'm especially glad you invited me tonight. This might be my big chance.

MRS. BARTON: What do you mean?

GARY: You see, I've applied for a summer job down at the bank.

MRS. BARTON (*Startled*): Gary, I didn't know that!

GARY: I've been keeping it a secret.

MRS. BARTON: Have you told Kay?

GARY: Oh, no! I wanted to surprise her—provided I'm selected for the position. (*Affects a pompous attitude*) Of course, the eminent Mr. Washburn, as president of the bank, will have to pass on my application. (*Grins*) But tonight he'll have a chance to get acquainted with me.

MRS. BARTON (*Smiles*): *And* with me, Gary. I too have a reason for wanting to cultivate Mr. Washburn's friendship.

GARY (*Thoughtfully*): You know, he's a funny old duck.

MRS. BARTON: Don't let *him* hear you say that.

GARY: I mean, Mr. Washburn's a bachelor and—well, I don't think he's sold too much on the younger generation.

MRS. BARTON: Most people seem to be afraid of him, and he *is* domineering and demanding. But my husband says that if George Washburn really likes you, he's your friend for life.

GARY: I've been wondering about this niece of his—

MRS. BARTON: You're not the only one who's been wondering about Joyce Washburn.

GARY: I'll bet she's as prim and proper as a lace doily. That would just suit Mr. Washburn.

MRS. BARTON (*Rises*): You'll excuse me, Gary? I want to take a look in the oven.

GARY (*Grins*): By all means, good lady. Don't burn up *this* meal.

MRS. BARTON (*Indicates door right*): Don't you want to sit on the terrace?

GARY: No, thanks. I'll wait in here.

MRS. BARTON: It may take my daughter hours to drag herself away from the mirror.

GARY (*Laughing*): I understand that's a struggle for every female. (KAY *breezes into room through doorway left. In her hand is a single sheet of paper.*)

KAY (*Gaily*): Gary! So nice you could come. I couldn't have survived the evening without you.

MRS. BARTON: Pay no attention to her, Gary. She tells that to all the boys.

KAY: Mother! (MRS. BARTON *exits left.*)

GARY (*Grins at* KAY): You know something, Kay? I like your mother.

KAY: I hope you have the same feeling for the rest of the family.

GARY (*With a flourish*): I'd do anything for a member of the Barton clan.

KAY: Thank you, Gary. That's just what I wanted you to say.

GARY: Tell me, Kay—do I look all right? (*Turns around for inspection*)

KAY (*Puzzled*): Of course you look all right. Why?

GARY: I mean—do you think Mr. Washburn and—and his niece will approve of me?

KAY (*Pointedly*): What difference does it make?

GARY: It makes a lot of difference. But I can't tell you why —at least not yet.

KAY: Since you brought up the subject of Mr. Washburn's niece . . . after all, Gary, none of us has ever seen her. (*Carefully*) And it's terribly difficult for a boy to know how to—well, to approach a girl for the first time.

GARY: Fortunately, that hasn't been one of my major problems.

KAY: I mean, a boy can't be certain how a girl will react to his attentions. (*Smiles brightly*) It takes one girl to understand another.

GARY (*Suspiciously*): What has this to do with Joyce Washburn?

KAY: Well, I thought you might not know just how to treat her.

GARY: Don't worry. I won't sling the gal across the room.

KAY: But after all, I'm the only one who is really capable of determining how you should behave.

GARY: *You?* (*Amazed*) You're going to determine how I should behave—before Joyce?

KAY: That's right. That is, after I've had a look at the girl.

GARY: Now see here, Kay—

KAY (*Indicating sheet of paper in her hand*): See? I've written a list of instructions for you.

GARY: Wait a minute—

KAY (*Hurriedly*): I just want to help you, Gary. I'm always so happy to do something for you. Now, after I've studied Joyce, I'll give you a signal.

GARY: A signal? But Kay—

KAY: Oh, it's very simple.

GARY: This doesn't sound simple to me.

KAY: Now listen carefully to this— (*Reads*) "After Joyce arrives, I will place a bud vase on the living room table.

The number of rose buds in the vase will serve as a signal for your actions. If the vase contains one rose bud, your manner toward Joyce must be strictly formal. Two buds in the vase will permit you to show an impersonal interest in Joyce. But if three roses are in the vase, you may sweep the girl off her feet." (*Hands the paper to* GARY) Here you are, Gary. Read it over until you've memorized it.

GARY (*Almost speechless, as he takes paper*): Kay Barton, do you expect me to—

KAY: Remember what you said—that you'd do anything for a member of this family. See how easy this will be on me— (*Hurriedly*) I mean on *you,* Gary? Now just remember—one rose bud, and you're strictly formal. Two rose buds, and you show an impersonal interest. Three rose buds, and you sweep her off her feet.

GARY (*With rising indignation*): And *you're* going to make the decision?

KAY: Of course, after I take a look at Joyce.

GARY (*Hotly*): If you want to know what I think about all this— (*Doorbell rings.*)

KAY (*Breathlessly*): They're here, Gary! (*She rushes upstage to center door, then turns to* GARY. *She speaks in a loud whisper.*) Remember, don't make a move until you get my signal. (GARY, *thoroughly upset, moves behind table at right as* KAY *opens center door, admitting* JOYCE WASHBURN, *who is very attractive.*)

JOYCE (*Music in her voice*): Hello— (*With a dazzling smile*) You're Kay Barton, aren't you? (*For a long moment both* KAY *and* GARY *gaze at* JOYCE. *The paper slips from* GARY's *fingers and falls to the top of table.*)

KAY (*With effort*): Y-yes, I—I'm Kay Barton—

JOYCE: I'm Joyce Washburn. (KAY *continues to stare at* JOYCE. *The pause becomes embarrassing*.) Shall—shall I come in?

KAY (*Snaps out of her daze*): Of course! By all means! (JOYCE *steps into the room*.) It—it's perfectly wonderful to have you with us.

JOYCE: Uncle George had to stop by the bank, so he dropped me off here. (JOYCE *pauses, then turns to* GARY, *flashes him a bright smile.* GARY, *almost overcome, grasps the table for support*.)

KAY (*At last hurrying downstage*): Joyce, may I present Gary Fields?

JOYCE (*In a soft, intimate voice*): Hello—Gary.

GARY (*In confusion*): Good morning— That is, good night— (*Swallows*) I mean—good evening—

KAY (*To* JOYCE, *with emphasis*): Gary is my *dear* friend and *close* companion.

JOYCE (*Turns to* KAY): Aren't you fortunate?

KAY: Yes—up to now. (MRS. BARTON *enters from door left*.)

MRS. BARTON (*Heartily, as she moves toward* JOYCE): Welcome, my dear—

KAY: Joyce, this is my mother.

JOYCE: It's wonderful to know you, Mrs. Barton. This invitation certainly pleased Uncle George.

MRS. BARTON (*Beams*): That's the nicest thing you could say. But where is your uncle?

JOYCE: He had to pick up a letter at the bank. He'll be along in a few minutes.

MRS. BARTON: Let me have your coat, dear. (JOYCE *starts to remove coat.*)

GARY (*Suddenly steps forward*): I'll take it—

KAY: Never mind, Gary.

JOYCE (*Hands coat to* MRS. BARTON): You were so thoughtful to invite us for dinner. (*Stretches out her arms dramatically*) You have no idea what this does to me.

KAY (*To herself*): Oh, yes, I'm afraid I do.

JOYCE: I told Uncle I wanted to meet all of his friends. (*Turns to* GARY) Gary, I suppose *you're* a friend of Uncle George's?

KAY (*Quickly*): Gary isn't a friend. Just a passing acquaintance.

MRS. BARTON: You young folks sit down and have a good visit. Kay, I'll call you when I need help. (*Exits left*)

JOYCE: I can tell already I'm going to have a marvelous time tonight. (*Moves to table right where she places her evening bag*) I was afraid Uncle George wouldn't know anyone outside of his own generation. It's so nice to be with people my own age. (*Crosses to davenport where she sits*)

KAY (*Sweetly*): I doubt that Gary and I are your age, Joyce. We're probably years and years younger.

GARY: Oh, I wouldn't say that—

KAY: You needn't say anything, Gary. (*Suddenly*) Why don't you creep out on the terrace and put the hose away? Mother told me to roll it up this afternoon, but I forgot.

GARY: What difference does it make whether that hose is rolled up or not?

KAY: Please, Gary.

JOYCE (*Suddenly rises*): I'll go with you, Gary.

KAY (*Quickly*): Oh, no! You—you might trip out there in the dark. Anyway, the night air is horrible in this part of the country.

GARY: What's so horrible about it? I always thought the night air was—

KAY (*Grimly*): Gary!

GARY (*With a shrug*): O.K.—O.K. I'll see you, Joyce.

JOYCE: Don't be too long. We girls need male companionship, don't we, Kay?

KAY (*Sweetly*): Only at times, Joyce, and this isn't the time. (GARY *exits right.*)

JOYCE (*After a pause*): Gary seems to have such an interesting personality.

KAY: First impressions are always unreliable.

JOYCE: Have you known him long?

KAY: Oh, yes, for weeks and weeks.

JOYCE (*Lightly*): Then you don't have to worry about holding him, do you?

KAY: My dear, there are ways to handle any situation.

JOYCE (*Nods*): Yes, I know.

KAY: Will you excuse me a moment? I want to get a bud vase. (*Moves to left.*)

JOYCE: A bud vase?

KAY: For the table. I think every table needs a bud vase, don't you? (JOYCE *stands in puzzled silence as* KAY *exits left. Then she turns; moves to table right. As she picks up her evening bag, she notices the sheet of note paper dropped on the table by* GARY. *At first she glances without particular interest at the instructions. Then, as she continues to read, she replaces her bag on table and slowly picks up the sheet of paper. She reads a few additional sentences, then hurriedly glances around the room. Satisfied that no one is watching her, she moves downstage as she scans the written page.)*

JOYCE (*Half aloud*): "One rose bud . . . manner strictly formal. Two rose buds . . . impersonal interest. Three rose buds . . . sweep the girl off her feet." (*With a sly grin she crumples the paper in her hand, then moves swiftly up to table. She picks up evening bag, opens it, and stuffs the wadded sheet inside. As she turns with her bag,* KAY *enters from left, carrying a bud vase.*)

KAY (*Brightly*): Have you been in here alone?

JOYCE: Oh, yes.

KAY: Oh, I'm so sorry. I didn't mean to be so long.

JOYCE: I haven't minded, really. In fact, I've thoroughly enjoyed myself. (KAY *crosses to table right where she places vase.*) So that's the bud vase. You know, I've taken quite an interest in vases—just recently.

KAY: How nice!

JOYCE: An old heirloom, I suppose?

KAY: Well, Paul Revere had his lantern—and I have my bud vase.

JOYCE (*Suddenly*): I wonder what has happened to Gary? Do you suppose I should investigate?

KAY: Oh, no. He's probably having some trouble disconnecting the hose. Father hasn't been able to get it off for a month.

JOYCE: But poor Gary. After all, he's dressed for a dinner party.

KAY (*Sure of herself*): Gary always follows my instructions.

JOYCE: Really? Some men resent instructions.

KAY: A clever girl can always manage. (*She moves to coffee table.*)

JOYCE (*Knowingly*): Exactly. A clever girl can always manage, and I'm sure you're very clever.

KAY: Thank you for the compliment. (KAY *removes one rose bud from the bowl of roses on coffee table.*) Glamour is nice, of course, but in this competitive age, it takes brains to succeed.

JOYCE: I'm sure you're right, Kay.

KAY (*Brightly*): But don't worry, Joyce, you're very lovely, and that's something—I suppose. (KAY *crosses to table right and places one rose bud in vase.*)

JOYCE (*With equal brightness*): Yes, it's—something.

KAY (*Stands back; admires single bud in vase*): There! Isn't that attractive?

JOYCE (*Affecting surprise*): Attractive? With just one flower in the vase?

KAY (*Nods*): Nothing is more satisfying than a single rose bud.

JOYCE: But my dear, that vase needs more than one bud.

KAY: Oh, no, it doesn't!

JOYCE: But I've just finished reading an article on flower arrangement. The author says—

KAY: I don't care what she says.

JOYCE: But that one little flower looks so—so formal.

KAY (*Nods*): That's exactly the effect I want to create. (MRS. BARTON *enters from left.*)

MRS. BARTON (*Annoyed*): Kay, why on earth did you ask Gary to disconnect the hose?

KAY: I—I thought you wanted it disconnected.

MRS. BARTON: I can't remember that I spoke about it. Anyway, Gary stepped in the mud. He had to come around to the back porch to clean his shoes.

JOYCE: Why, the poor boy!

MRS. BARTON: He wants you girls to wait for him on the terrace. (*She moves left.*)

JOYCE (*Suddenly*): Mrs. Barton—

MRS. BARTON (*Pauses, turns*): Yes?

JOYCE: Kay and I have had an argument. Perhaps you can help us settle it.

MRS. BARTON: An argument?

JOYCE (*Indicates vase*): Kay insists that only one bud should be in the vase, but I say it's not enough.

KAY (*Forcefully*): But I say it *is* enough, and after all, I'm the one who—

MRS. BARTON (*Cuts Kay off*): Just a minute, Kay. (*Studies vase*) I agree with you, Joyce. The vase needs more than one bud.

KAY: It does not!

MRS. BARTON: Kay—please—

JOYCE (*Suddenly*): Let's add another bud, just to see the effect. (*She steps to coffee table; selects another bud.*)

KAY (*With increasing panic*): I want only one bud in that vase.

MRS. BARTON: Joyce probably has a better sense of flower arrangement than you have, Kay. You were never particularly artistic.

KAY: Maybe I'm not artistic, but I'm determined! (JOYCE *places second rose bud in vase.*)

JOYCE (*As she steps back to admire her efforts*): How do you like that, Mrs. Barton?

MRS. BARTON (*Nods*): Much better.

JOYCE (*Studies buds*): Yes—a rather interesting arrangement. But still rather—impersonal, don't you think?

MRS. BARTON (*Thoughtfully*): Well, maybe you're right.

JOYCE (*Brightly to* MRS. BARTON): Suppose we try a third rose in the vase.

KAY (*Horrified*): No! (JOYCE *steps quickly to coffee table, selects a third bud.*) No, I say!

MRS. BARTON: Kay, what's wrong with you?

KAY: That—that vase won't hold three buds—

JOYCE (*Moves to table right*): Of course it will, Kay. (*Places third bud in vase; smiles*) See?

MRS. BARTON (*Nods*): I like that.

KAY: Mother, you don't realize—

MRS. BARTON (*Cuts in sharply*): I realize you're being rude to your guest.

JOYCE (*Continues to study buds in vase*): Yes, that's perfect. Don't you think the buds have a—sweeping effect?

MRS. BARTON: Yes, I really do.

JOYCE: And what do you think, Kay dear?

KAY (*Almost speechless*): I—I think they're going to wither in the heat— (*Rushes to table; picks up vase*) I'll put them in the refrigerator—

MRS. BARTON (*Sternly*): You'll leave them where they are.

KAY: But, Mother—

MRS. BARTON: Put down that vase, Kay. (*Slowly* KAY *places vase on table.*) If you're so anxious to do something, you can take the salad *out* of the refrigerator.

KAY: I—I can't leave—

MRS. BARTON: You'll do as I say! I've never seen you act

like this. Now hurry along. I'm about to lose my patience.

KAY: And I'm about to lose something a lot more important than patience! (*She rushes to door left where she exits.*)

MRS. BARTON (*Nervously turns to* JOYCE): I—I'm terribly embarrassed, Joyce. I can't understand my daughter. (*Moves down left*)

JOYCE (*With an easy smile*): Oh, I can. (*Follows* MRS. BARTON)

MRS. BARTON: Really?

JOYCE (*Nods*): We mustn't criticize the poor child. You see, she has a slight case of—rose fever. (GARY *enters from right.*)

GARY: Isn't somebody going to join me on the terrace? (*Moves to center*) I assure you that I'm no longer afflicted with muddy feet— (*At that moment he sees for the first time three buds in the vase. He gives a violent start.*)

MRS. BARTON: Gary, what's the matter with you?

GARY (*Quickly attempts to control himself*): Er—nothing —(*Gazes again at roses, then swiftly and silently counts to three on his fingers.*) Nothing at all is the matter. In fact, I've never had it so good!

MRS. BARTON: Don't the two of you want to sit outside?

JOYCE (*Nods*): A lovely idea, Mrs. Barton. What is more charming than a terrace in the moonlight? (*Crosses to* GARY; *gives him a bright smile. She speaks dramatically.*) I am sure the night shall be filled with the scent of roses. (*She exits right. Then* GARY *slowly follows her. For a moment* MRS. BARTON *watches them in silence. Then* KAY *plunges wildly into room through doorway left.*)

KAY (*Desperately, after a swift glance around the room*): Mother—Mother, where is she?

MRS. BARTON: Joyce? Gary took her onto the terrace.

KAY: You—you mean Gary came into this room and—and looked around?

MRS. BARTON: Well, I'm certain he didn't have his eyes shut.

KAY (*Groans*): Oh, Mother!

MRS. BARTON: Kay Barton, you're acting like a perfect idiot. If you're not careful you'll ruin everything. What's come over you?

KAY (*Swiftly crosses to right*): I've got to get to the terrace!

MRS. BARTON: Kay, come back here!

KAY (*Pauses; turns*): But Mother—

MRS. BARTON: Come back here, I say. (*Slowly* KAY *moves back toward center.*) I want to talk to you, young lady.

KAY (*Desperately*): There isn't time! You don't know what may be going on at this very minute. You and Joyce wrecked the signal!

MRS. BARTON: We—what? (*The doorbell rings.*) It's Mr. Washburn! (*Breathlessly*) Let him in, Kay. (MRS. BARTON *smooths her hair and straightens her dress, as* KAY *moves tragically upstage.* KAY *opens center door to admit* GEORGE WASHBURN.)

GEORGE (*In a sharp and brittle tone*): Good evening, young lady.

KAY: Hello, Mr. Washburn.

GEORGE (*Removing his hat, and stepping into the room*): Mrs. Barton, how are you?

MRS. BARTON: It's so good to see you, Mr. Washburn. (*She offers him her hand.*)

GEORGE: Is it? (KAY *moves down right. She pauses in front of door right, gazing at door in gloomy silence.*)

MRS. BARTON: Do let me have your hat— (*Nervously she takes* GEORGE'S *hat, then drops it to the floor. Hurriedly she picks it up.*) Oh, dear! (*Begins to blow dust off the hat.*)

GEORGE (*Flatly*): That's a new hat.

MRS. BARTON (*Confused*): I—I'm so sorry—

GEORGE: Just bought it yesterday. On sale at half price.

MRS. BARTON (*With a forced laugh*): This is the first time I've ever dropped the hat of a bank president— (*She laughs again, but* GEORGE *isn't laughing.*)

GEORGE (*Glances around the room*): Is my niece here?

KAY (*Without turning around*): She certainly is!

MRS. BARTON: She and Gary Fields are on the terrace. Won't you join them, Mr. Washburn?

KAY (*Loudly*): Let's *all* join them!

GEORGE (*Gruffly*): No! I can't stand the night air.

KAY: Somebody ought to pass a law against night air.

MRS. BARTON (*Indicates davenport*): Sit down, Mr. Washburn.

GEORGE (*Sits on davenport.*): These young people—always wanting to sit out of doors in the dark. (*Scoffs*) Silly!

KAY: Silly? It's tragic!

GEORGE: Why don't they stay in the house, where it's warm and light? That's what I always did.

KAY: Yes—and you're a bachelor!

MRS. BARTON (*Shocked*): Kay!

GEORGE: What's that?

Mrs. Barton (*Hurriedly to* Kay, *who still stands with her back to* George): Kay, dear, you entertain Mr. Washburn while I finish getting dinner. Are you comfortable, Mr. Washburn?

George (*Bluntly*): I'm starved.

Mrs. Barton (*Laughs nervously*): How nice! I—I mean, it's always a pleasure to—to feed a starving bank president. (*Hurriedly exits left.* Kay *continues to gaze at door right. For a moment* George *watches her in puzzled silence.*)

George: Young lady, you make me nervous. What are you trying to do—look a hole through that door?

Kay: I wish I could!

George: Sit down—sit down. I don't like young people who fidget.

Kay: You'd fidget too, if—

George: Sit down, I say! I want to talk to you. (*Gloomily* Kay *sits.*)

Kay: At the moment I'm not exactly in the mood for conversation.

George (*Gruffly*): That's the trouble with you young people—you don't have a thought in your head.

Kay (*Stoutly*): You'd be surprised at the thoughts I have in my head.

George: Tell me—what do you think of my niece?

Kay (*Vaguely*): Well, she seems to be in—in good health.

George (*Scowls*): She upsets me.

Kay: That's one point we agree on, Mr. Washburn.

George: Joyce has that knack of unconsciously doing the right thing at the right time.

Kay (*With conviction*): Don't I know it!

GEORGE: It annoys me. She's never had a setback in her life. Everything just comes her way. Why, when she smiles at young men, they all but drop dead.

KAY: I wish some of them would.

GEORGE: Things have changed since I was a boy. And they've changed for the worse. This modern generation refuses to take anything seriously. "Let's have fun! Let's make love!" That's all you hear.

KAY: Mr. Washburn, how can you say that?

GEORGE (*Grimly*): I say whatever I want to say in this town, and nobody dares to disagree with me.

KAY (*Meekly*): Y-yes, Mr. Washburn.

GEORGE: Did you know Gary Fields has applied for a summer job in my bank?

KAY (*With a start*): Mr. Washburn! He—he has?

GEORGE: Didn't he tell you?

KAY: N-no—

GEORGE: Then that's *something* in his favor. I detest people who run around, shooting off their mouths.

KAY: You mean you've hired Gary for the summer?

GEORGE: Not yet. I want to check up on him first. Do you think he's ambitious?

KAY (*Sadly*): At the moment I'd guess he was very ambitious.

GEORGE: Do you think he'd follow instructions?

KAY: I—I'm afraid he would.

GEORGE: What's his attitude toward the opposite sex?

KAY: The opposite sex?

GEORGE (*Raises his voice impatiently*): Girls—women— females—

KAY: You don't have to shout.

GEORGE: Does he try to sweep them off their feet? (KAY *sits up with a gasp.*) I'm looking for a young man who puts his work first. If he goes off on a tangent every time he sees a pretty face, I don't want him. If he can't think of anything but—Did your mother say that he and my niece were on the terrace?

KAY (*With discomfort*): Well—yes—

GEORGE (*Grimly*): If I thought he was trying to make love to my niece, I wouldn't hire him if he were the only unemployed male in this town.

KAY (*With increasing nervousness*): You—you wouldn't?

GEORGE: I would not! (*Suddenly rises.*) Why didn't I think of it before?

KAY: Think of what?

GEORGE: I'm going to check up on that young man.

KAY: Check up on him?

GEORGE (*Nods*): I'll slip out on the terrace and see what he's up to.

KAY (*Jumps up*): Mr. Washburn—

GEORGE: If I should find he's making passes at Joyce— (*Begins to move toward door right*)

KAY (*With a little scream*): No! (*Wildly she dashes across the room; blocks* GEORGE'S *path to door right.*)

GEORGE (*Pauses with a start*): What's the matter with you?

KAY: Mr. Washburn, you—you can't go out on that terrace.

GEORGE: I go wherever I please— (*Takes a step forward*)

KAY (*Desperately*): Mr. Washburn, the—the night air— It isn't good for you—

GEORGE: I know what's good for me without being told. There's nothing I like better than night air. Now, young lady, kindly get out of my way.

KAY (*Backs to door right; throws out her arms against door to block his way*): You're not going through this door!

GEORGE (*Sputters*): Do you realize to whom you are talking?

KAY (*Suddenly breaks out in fury*): I'm talking to a hard-headed, stubborn old ox!

GEORGE (*Almost chokes*): What! (*Trembles with rage*) I'll have you know I've never been called an—an ox in my life. (MRS. BARTON *enters from left. She is frozen in horror at what she hears.*)

KAY: That's because everybody's afraid of you! They're afraid to tell you the truth. You don't like young people because you don't know them. You're just a suspicious old goat!

GEORGE (*Almost speechless*): Old goat!

KAY (*Hotly*): You ought to be ashamed—wanting to spy on Gary Fields!

MRS. BARTON (*In complete panic*): Kay—!

KAY: Why don't you have faith and confidence in people? Why don't you trust them? Why don't you—

MRS. BARTON (*Screams*): Kay! (MRS. BARTON *rushes to* GEORGE.) Mr. Washburn, my—my daughter didn't mean —(KAY *moves from door to downstage right.*)

GEORGE: You need not explain, madam. (*Draws himself up*) Excuse me—(GEORGE *crosses to door right where he exits. For a moment there is a tense pause.*)

MRS. BARTON (*Exploding as* KAY *crosses to davenport*): Oh, how could you! (*Near hysteria*) Kay Barton, do you realize what you've done?

KAY (*Grimly, as she sinks onto davenport*): He wanted to spy on Gary—

MRS. BARTON (*Her voice rises*): Now we'll never get a loan from Mr. Washburn. Kay, what's the matter with you?

KAY (*Incoherently*): I only wanted one rose bud in the vase—but Joyce wanted three—and that was the signal for Gary to sweep her off her feet—

MRS. BARTON (*Her patience gone*): I don't know what you're talking about.

KAY (*Almost in tears*): But I didn't know Gary wanted a job at the bank until Mr. Washburn told me—so I tried to keep him from going out on the terrace—

MRS. BARTON: You're not even talking sense, and I don't blame Mr. Washburn for walking out of this house. Oh, I give up—! (*She crosses to door left where she exits. Immediately* GARY *rushes into room from right.*)

GARY: Kay—

KAY (*Quickly*): Did he see you?

GARY: Who?

KAY: Mr. Washburn.

GARY: I'll say he did! (KAY *groans.*) Hey, what's the matter with you?

KAY (*Her voice breaks*): Oh, nothing at all! I'm having the time of my life.

GARY (*Beams*): So am I! (*Chuckles*) And I thought you were jealous! I was so positive you'd put a single rose bud in the vase. (*Smiles broadly*) To think—you'd give me the signal to sweep Joyce Washburn off her feet! (*In a matter-of-fact tone*) Of course, I didn't.

KAY (*Looks up suddenly*): You—didn't?

GARY: Certainly not. Because you trusted me. That's what

a fellow wants—trust and confidence from a girl. (KAY *rises in amazement*.) Sure, you handed me a free ticket, but, baby, I tore it up.

KAY (*Almost speechless*): Gary!

GARY (*Greatly amused*): Then Mr. Washburn came storming out onto the terrace. I think he had an idea I was making love to his niece.

KAY: And—and you weren't?

GARY: Of course not. I spent the time telling Joyce what a wonderful and trusting girl you were.

KAY (*Weakly*): Oh, my goodness!

GARY: Kay, I have a surprise for you. Last week I applied for a position at the bank, and when Mr. Washburn walked out onto the terrace just now, he gave me the funniest look. Maybe he thought he'd find me sweeping Joyce off her feet. Anyway, he walked up to me and said, "Gary, report for work Monday morning." What do you think of that?

KAY: Gary, I've been an idiot. I—I've been acting just like Mr. Washburn—not trusting people.

GARY (*Paying no attention to* KAY's *remark*): I have to tell your mother about the job. She was in on the secret. (*With a grin, he takes* KAY's *hand and gives it a little pat*.) Just hold everything, honey—(*He quickly moves to door left where he exits. Immediately* JOYCE *enters from right. She carries her evening purse*.)

JOYCE (*With considerable irony*): It's lovely on the terrace —alone. (*She moves to table right where she places her purse*.) Rather a new experience for me. You see, your boy friend left me flat, (*Shrugs*) but it really didn't matter. All he could talk about was you.

KAY (*Moves to other side of table*): What—what happened to your uncle?

JOYCE (*Indifferently*): I don't know. He crossed the terrace and then walked out to the car. (*After a slight pause*) I —I wanted to see you, Kay— (JOYCE *picks up purse from table. Without speaking she opens purse and removes the crumpled sheet of paper. She tosses paper on table.*) You win, darling. (KAY *stands in puzzled silence.*) Congratulations! (MRS. BARTON *enters from left.*)

MRS. BARTON (*In a tired, defeated tone*): Dinner is ready, if anybody wants to stay and eat it.

JOYCE: I should say! Mrs. Barton, I've been defeated, but I still have an appetite.

MRS. BARTON: And your uncle?

JOYCE: He started toward the car, but I suppose he'll be back. (*She exits left. MRS. BARTON closes door left after JOYCE exits. As she does so, KAY picks up crumpled paper from table right and unfolds it.*)

KAY (*With a wild little laugh which approaches a sob*): Instructions to Gary—!

MRS. BARTON (*Quickly moves to KAY*): Kay, stop that! I feel like having hysterics too, now that you've wrecked our chances of getting a loan. (*Sighs*) Gary seems to be the only one who's happy around here. He has a job— and for some strange reason he thinks you're wonderful. Something about the confidence you had in him. (*Flares up*) But if you want to know what I think about you, Kay Barton— (*But she breaks off abruptly as GEORGE slowly enters from right. In his hand is an envelope. MRS. BARTON gasps.*) Mr. Washburn—!

GEORGE (*Without expression*): May I come in? (*Without*

*waiting for an answer, he moves to center. But as he does
so, he detours warily around* KAY.)

KAY: Mr. Washburn, I—

GEORGE: Young lady, will you permit me to speak? (KAY
backs away silently. GEORGE *clears his throat.*) I have here
a letter— (*Indicates envelope in his hand, as he turns to*
MRS. BARTON) a letter addressed to your husband, Mrs.
Barton, (*Slowly*) a letter stating that my bank cannot approve the loan which Mr. Barton requested.

MRS. BARTON (*Sadly*): I—I can't blame you—after what
happened.

GEORGE: I dictated the letter this afternoon. I had made up
my mind that we should not make the loan. I had expected to mail this letter after I'd left here tonight.
(*Pause*) But I hadn't planned on an explosion from your
daughter—

MRS. BARTON (*Desperately*): Mr. Washburn, I was never so
embarrassed in my life—

GEORGE (*Raises his hand*): Please, Mrs. Barton—(*He turns
to* KAY.) Young lady, I wish to say something. (*Slowly*)
Your statements were entirely correct.

KAY (*Startled*): *What?*

GEORGE: You were right. I've been a hard-headed, stubborn
old ox.

MRS. BARTON (*Aghast*): Mr. Washburn!

GEORGE: You're the first person who ever had the nerve
to stand up and tell me the truth about myself. (*Begins
to smile slightly*) You've got spirit—spirit and courage—
and that's what I like. (*Turns to* MRS. BARTON) Mrs.
Barton, my bank is honored to make the Barton family
a loan. (*Slowly and with considerable ceremony,* GEORGE

tears the envelope in half; the pieces fall to the floor. KAY *and* MRS. BARTON *stand in amazed silence.*)

MRS. BARTON (*Almost speechless*): Mr. Washburn, I—I don't know what to say—

GEORGE: Just say that dinner is served. I told you I was starved, my good lady. (*He turns to* KAY; *offers her his arm.*) Allow me, my dear—

KAY (*Smiling up at* GEORGE *as she takes his arm*): With pleasure— (*Together they take several steps to left.* MRS. BARTON *is stunned. Suddenly* KAY *pauses.*) Oh, Mr. Washburn, I forgot something— (*Quickly she moves back to table. She takes the three rose buds from vase. Then she again joins* GEORGE.)

GEORGE (*Indicates roses*): What's the idea—dragging those flowers along?

KAY (*Smiles brightly*): Mr. Washburn, you don't know how happy a girl can be—with three rose buds! (*Arm in arm* KAY *and* GEORGE *move toward door left as the curtain slowly falls.*)

THE END

Production Notes

INSTRUCTIONS FOR GARY

Characters: 2 male; 3 female.

Playing Time: 25 minutes.

Costumes: Modern dress. Everyone is dressed in his best clothes. Mrs. Barton wears an apron over her dress.

Properties: Flower bowl containing a bouquet of rose buds, pad, pencil, sheet of paper, evening bag, bud vase, man's hat, letter.

Setting: The living room of the Barton residence. There are three entrances to the room: the front door at upstage center, a door to the rest of the house at left, and a door leading to the terrace at right. At downstage left are a davenport and coffee table. At right, there are two armchairs, separated by a table. Other furnishings may be added but they are unnecessary for the action of the play.

Lighting: No special effects.

Farewell to Calvin

Characters

WEBB ANDREWS, *Calvin's temporary custodian*
PENNY ANDREWS, *Webb's young sister*
HOWARD ANDREWS, *their father*
GRACE ANDREWS, *their mother*
DIANA LANE, *the girl next door*
JOYCE HASTINGS, *Diana's week-end guest*
MARK MANNING, *Joyce's escort for the party*

TIME: *Early Saturday evening.*
SETTING: *Living room of the Andrews' home.*
AT RISE: *The stage is empty. After a pause* WEBB ANDREWS *hurriedly enters from left. He carries a portable type-writer in a case, and a dozen paper labels removed from food cans. His jacket and necktie are over his arm. Swiftly he moves to table right, where he deposits the typewriter case and food labels. Then he crosses left, throws jacket over divan, steps to mirror and slips tie*

under his collar. At that moment PENNY ANDREWS *enters, munching an apple.*

PENNY: What a place to dress! You're supposed to be upstairs in your own room.

WEBB (*Swings around, scowling*): Penny Andrews, why don't you get lost? (*Turns again to mirror*)

PENNY: I'm as much a member of this household as you are.

WEBB: True—unfortunately.

PENNY: If you ask me, you're cluttering up the living room.

WEBB: Can't you see I'm in a hurry? Now—scram!

PENNY: That's a fine way to speak to your delicate little sister.

WEBB: I have to be next door in fifteen minutes. If I'm late for the dinner party, I'm off Diana's list.

PENNY (*Smartly*): Wouldn't that simply break your great big romantic heart!

WEBB (*Grimly*): Will you kindly pipe down?

PENNY (*Nibbling on apple*): Have you seen Diana's weekend guest? (*Pause*) Webb, I asked you a question.

WEBB (*Impatiently*): Yes, I met Joyce Hastings yesterday.

PENNY (*Moves to divan*): You'll certainly have to be the perfect little gentleman at the Lanes' house tonight. (*Sits awkwardly on divan, leaning back against* WEBB's *sport jacket*) What a beautiful foursome it will be—you and Diana, Mark Manning and Joyce Hastings. When Mrs. Lane sees the love light shining in your sweet little eyes, she can extinguish the candles.

WEBB (*Swings around angrily*): One more word out of you —(*Sees* PENNY's *head resting against his jacket. With a shout he leaps behind divan.*) And keep your head off my coat! (*Grasps* PENNY *by the shoulders, pushing her away from the jacket.*)

PENNY (*Jumps up*): Webb Andrews, you practically struck me!

WEBB (*Groans*): Oh, for Pete's sake! Why don't you go to the basement and feed Calvin?

PENNY (*Shrugs*): Calvin is your responsibility, not mine. (WEBB *turns to the mirror, arranging his tie.*) I'll certainly be thankful when that dog is out of this house.

WEBB: Mr. Mayfield is due back in town tonight. I'll be returning Calvin to him the first thing in the morning.

PENNY: It's silly, taking care of Mr. Mayfield's dog for a whole week.

WEBB (*Emphatically*): Mr. Mayfield happens to be my high school principal. He asked me to look after Calvin. I certainly wouldn't refuse a request from my school principal. (PENNY *moves behind table, drops apple core into wastebasket.*)

PENNY (*Idly picking up one of the can labels from table*): Just the same, I'm glad Mr. Mayfield didn't leave you with a pet alligator or a laughing hyena—(*Glances at label*) Hey, Webb—what's this?

WEBB (*At mirror*): What's what? (*His tie is now knotted.*)

PENNY: A label from a can of dog food. (*Glances at the other labels on table*) Gee, these are *all* dog food labels.

WEBB (*Warningly*): Penny Andrews, you keep away from that table!

PENNY: But why this stuff?

WEBB: I promised Mr. Mayfield I'd do something for him.

PENNY: And you've waited until now—practically the last

minute? (HOWARD ANDREWS *appears at center carrying the evening paper. Neither* PENNY *nor* WEBB *sees him at first.*)

WEBB (*With dignity*): Penny, this does not concern you.

HOWARD (*Steps into room*): *What* doesn't concern your sister, Webb?

WEBB: Oh, hello, Dad. Aren't you and Mother due at the Country Club?

HOWARD: We've plenty of time. (*Walks to divan where he tosses newspaper*)

PENNY (*To* HOWARD): That's the way Webb feels about things—there's plenty of time. (*She turns to table, picks up the labels.*) Father, take a look at this junk—

WEBB (*Swiftly*): Don't you dare refer to them as junk! (HOWARD *takes labels.*)

HOWARD: Labels from cans of dog food? Do they belong to you, Webb?

WEBB: Not—not exactly. When Mr. Mayfield left town, he gave me money to buy a dozen cans of Happy-Bark Dog Food. He asked me to take off the labels and mail them to the company.

HOWARD: Why?

WEBB: Mr. Mayfield will receive a free blanket.

PENNY: A free blanket? Doesn't Mr. Mayfield have enough bedding at home?

WEBB (*To* PENNY): A *dog* blanket, stupid. It's for Calvin.

HOWARD: Webb, just when did Mr. Mayfield discuss this order with you?

WEBB: Why—before he left. A week or so ago, I suppose.

HOWARD: And you've neglected it until now?

WEBB (*Nervously*): Well, not exactly. I bought the cans

of dog food this morning, and stored them in the cupboard over the kitchen sink. You should see the special order form I have to use. It's very complicated. It takes time and concentration.

HOWARD: You've had a week to concentrate.

PENNY: Webb couldn't concentrate if he had a year.

WEBB (*Shouts at* PENNY): Nobody asked you for comments!

HOWARD (*To* WEBB): That's enough, Webb.

WEBB: But don't you see, Dad? This is a difficult form. You can't just dash it off. You should see the questions— size of dog . . . weight of dog . . . color and design of blanket desired . . . breed of dog . . . age of dog . . . sex of dog—

PENNY (*Breaks in*): What you need is Calvin's birth certificate.

WEBB (*Angrily*): Father, if that delinquent doesn't keep out of this—

HOWARD: Penny!

WEBB (*To* HOWARD, *with attempted lightness*): Don't you worry, Dad. I'm taking care of the matter as soon as I return from Diana's party.

HOWARD: As soon as you return? (*Quietly, after a pause*) No, Webb. You're not.

WEBB (*Startled*): Huh?

HOWARD: You're sending that order out *before* you go next door.

WEBB: Before? But Dad, I'm already late—

HOWARD: Young man, you've had days to perform a small service for Mr. Mayfield. You've put it off until now.

Therefore, you will cancel all other activities until that letter is in the mail. (*He tosses labels onto table.*)

WEBB (*Stunned*): But Dad—

HOWARD: That's final, Webb.

WEBB: I know I've sort of let it slip, but there's still time to—

HOWARD: Yes, there's still time—provided you go to work immediately. Your mother and I will mail the letter on the way to the club.

WEBB: Diana is expecting me right now!

HOWARD: Your responsibility to Mr. Mayfield comes first, Webb. He paid you to look after Calvin. He also asked you to order a dog blanket.

WEBB: You—you don't understand!

HOWARD: Also, as I recall, you promised Mr. Mayfield that you'd spend considerable time in training his dog to obey instructions. Am I correct?

WEBB: Well—yes—

HOWARD: To my knowledge Calvin has received no special training.

PENNY: Calvin is as dumb as ever.

HOWARD (*To* WEBB): I'm sure you'll agree that I've offered no comments or suggestions concerning Calvin until tonight. I was determined to keep hands off, but now that I find you've even neglected to fill a simple order— (*He breaks off, shakes his head.*) This is not good, Webb. I suggest that you get busy with the order.

WEBB: What will I tell Diana?

HOWARD: I'm certain you won't be too late. Your mother is furnishing the meat dish. I doubt that it's even out of the oven yet.

WEBB: If I could just wait until I get back—

HOWARD: No arguments, Webb.

WEBB: Y-yes, sir. (*He moves slowly to table and begins to remove lid from typewriter. GRACE ANDREWS enters. She carries a market basket which presumably contains her contribution to the dinner party. Over her arm is a fancy table scarf. She wears an apron.*)

GRACE (*Pauses near divan as she sees WEBB*): Webb, I was afraid you'd already gone.

PENNY: I'll say he hasn't. (*WEBB has removed case from typewriter. He places lid on floor, then sits in chair at side of table.*)

HOWARD: Our son may be detained a few minutes, Grace.

GRACE (*Drops table scarf on divan*): Detained?

WEBB (*To GRACE*): Dad simply refuses to listen. He insists that I—(*He starts to rise.*)

HOWARD: That's enough, Webb. (*With a heavy sigh, WEBB sinks back into chair.*)

GRACE: But my casserole dish is ready for Diana's party. (*She indicates basket.*) I just phoned Mrs. Lane that Webb would bring it.

HOWARD: Penny, you'd better take it over.

PENNY: Sure, Father. At your service, Mother dear.

GRACE (*As PENNY takes basket*): Be careful, Penny. That's spaghetti and meat sauce. Don't spill it.

PENNY (*Sniffs basket*): Smells good. (*Moves upstage toward center opening*)

HOWARD: Penny, you can tell Diana and her guests that Webb may be a little late.

PENNY: I'll tell them he's tied up with a dog blanket. (*She exits.*)

GRACE: Really, Howard, I don't understand—

HOWARD: A week ago Mr. Mayfield asked Webb to order a blanket for Calvin, but he has neglected his duty. So he's staying right here until that order is mailed. It's time he learned the meaning of responsibility.

GRACE: But this is such an important event, Howard. Diana is entertaining for Joyce Hastings, and Mark Manning will be there—

HOWARD: I'm certain Webb won't be too late—unless he continues to be interrupted by motherly protests. (GRACE *hesitates, then goes to* WEBB, *slips her arm around his shoulder.*)

GRACE (*Smiles down at* WEBB): Your father is right, Webb. (*Pats his shoulder encouragingly.*) Now hurry and you probably won't miss more than the first course. (*Crosses to divan*) You never cared for tomato soup anyway— (*Breaks off as she sees the cloth centerpiece which she has dropped on divan.*) Oh, dear—that centerpiece— (*She picks up cloth.*) Mrs. Lane asked to borrow this. I should have sent it along with Penny. Webb, you can take it over when you go.

WEBB (*Gloomily*): That'll probably be about next Christmas. (GRACE, *carrying cloth, exits.* HOWARD *sits on divan. He picks up evening paper, unfolds it.* WEBB *suddenly sits up with a start.*)

HOWARD (*As he glances at headlines*): Tell you what, Webb—(*He looks up.*) You fill in the order blank, and I'll take over from there. I'll address the envelope and— Webb, what's the matter with you?

WEBB (*With difficulty*): That—that order blank—

HOWARD: What about it?

WEBB (*Swallows*): I don't know where it is.

HOWARD: What! (*He jumps up.*) You don't know where it is?

WEBB: I remember when Mr. Mayfield gave me the blank. I brought it home and—and that's the last I remember.

HOWARD: As though you didn't have enough trouble!

WEBB (*Rises*): I must have put it somewhere in my room.

HOWARD: At this rate, Mr. Mayfield won't receive a blanket for Calvin's great-grandson!

WEBB (*Breathlessly*): I'll take a look, Dad— (*He moves rapidly upstage and exits at center.* HOWARD *sinks onto divan.* GRACE *enters from left. She has removed apron.*)

GRACE: Did you let Webb go on?

HOWARD (*Dryly*): He is upstairs searching for a lost form. You have to have a form if you want a blanket.

GRACE: What on earth are you talking about? (DIANA LANE *enters.*)

DIANA (*Cheerfully*): Good evening!

GRACE: Diana dear! (HOWARD *rises as* DIANA *enters.*) This is a surprise. (PENNY *appears at center opening, carrying the market basket, presumably empty.*)

DIANA (*To* GRACE): I couldn't wait to thank you, Mrs. Andrews. I've never seen such a wonderful looking dish of spaghetti and meat sauce.

PENNY (*To* GRACE): Mrs. Lane says it's enough to feed an army. Maybe she'll send a hunk of it back in the morning. (*Puts basket on divan.*)

DIANA (*Laughs*): I doubt it, Penny. We'll all probably make pigs of ourselves. (*To* GRACE) It was thoughtful of you, Mrs. Andrews. I know this meant time and trouble.

GRACE: My dear, I was happy to contribute to the festivities.

DIANA (*Pleasantly*): I guess you helped, Mr. Andrews.

HOWARD: No, I've been occupied with another project.

PENNY: You might say Father has been wrestling with a dog blanket.

DIANA: My goodness, Mr. Andrews, you aren't preparing to take Calvin's place, are you? Webb said he was returning the dog in the morning.

HOWARD: We're mailing a certain letter first. At least, I *hope* we're mailing a letter. I'd better take a look. (*To* DIANA) Have fun tonight—you and your house guest and Mark Manning. (*He walks upstage and exits.*)

DIANA (*To* GRACE, *after a slight pause*): That was a funny remark. He said Joyce and Mark and I should have fun tonight, but he didn't say anything about Webb. You don't suppose he has forgotten his own son?

PENNY (*Flatly*): It's Webb who does the forgetting.

DIANA (*Suddenly*): Where *is* Webb? I thought he'd be over by now. Mark has already arrived.

GRACE (*Uncomfortably*): I'm afraid Webb has had—well, a slight mix-up in his plans.

PENNY: You might say Webb stripped his gears on a pile of dog food labels.

DIANA: What!

GRACE (*Quickly, to* PENNY): Penny, please—(*To* DIANA, *with a weak smile.*) If you'll excuse me, perhaps I can stir him up. (GRACE *exits.*)

DIANA: Penny, is something out of order around here? Is Webb in trouble?

PENNY (*Nods slowly*): He brought it on himself.

DIANA (*Urgently*): Penny, you must tell me.

PENNY (*Sighs*): I suppose you might as well know all the gruesome details—even if Mother *is* trying to hush it up. The truth is that Webb will be late to your dinner party tonight.

DIANA: Late?

PENNY: You know that Mr. Mayfield left his dog with Webb this week.

DIANA: Of course. We know all about Calvin.

PENNY: Here's one thing you don't know: Mr. Mayfield asked Webb to buy twelve cans of Happy-Bark Dog Food. Webb was supposed to send off the labels and receive a free dog blanket.

DIANA: Yes?

PENNY: Webb didn't. He waited until this morning to buy the dog food. Then he ripped off the labels, but he didn't write the order.

DIANA: Even though Mr. Mayfield asked him a week ago?

PENNY: Yes. And was Father mad when he found out! Now he says Webb can't leave the house until he has discharged his obligations to Mr. Mayfield.

DIANA: So that's it! Honestly, I'm surprised at Webb.

PENNY (*Sighs*): Seems that Webb was supposed to teach Calvin to obey instructions, too. That was some more unfinished business.

DIANA (*Firmly*): Penny, I don't blame your father. Webb should be more dependable. Perhaps this will teach him a lesson.

PENNY (*Rises*): He needs more than this, if you ask me. (*Suddenly*) Why don't *you* take a hand?

DIANA: I can't imagine what I could do.

PENNY: Maybe you'll think of something.

DIANA: What is Webb doing upstairs?

PENNY: I wouldn't know, but I'm guessing that Webb still has the labels, and the company still has the dog blanket.

DIANA: I'm glad you told me about this, Penny. (*Half to herself*) I'd like to shake Mr. Webb Andrews—(*Suddenly*) You say he has already removed the labels?

PENNY (*Nods*): Webb put the tins in the cupboard over the kitchen sink, and if you ask me, he'd better get them out of there before somebody uses them by mistake.

DIANA (*Thoughtfully*): Uses them by mistake? That *is* an idea—(DIANA *breaks into a sly smile*.) Yes, it is an idea. (*Suddenly smiles at* PENNY) Thanks, Penny. Thanks for everything.

PENNY: Thanks? But I haven't done anything.

DIANA: Oh, yes, you have! I must get back to my guests. I'll run out the back way, through the kitchen. Don't bother to show me out, Penny. Tell Webb we'll expect him later. (*She exits quickly. Then* WEBB *rushes into room. In his hand is a small printed order blank. Without speaking, he dashes to table, drops into chair and wildly rolls the order form into typewriter.*)

PENNY: What'd you do—swallow a bottle of vitamins?

WEBB: Stop asking questions! (*Awkwardly he begins to type order form, using only one finger.*)

PENNY: Diana was here—

WEBB: Mother told me. (*Enthusiastically*) And I'll be next door in ten seconds. (*He begins to type again.* PENNY *moves to* WEBB, *peers over his shoulder.*)

PENNY (*Points to order form*): Hey, you made an error—

WEBB (*Snaps*): Keep away from me!

PENNY: Look—you printed the number "22" instead of "12". It says "I am enclosing—"

WEBB (*Swiftly breaks in*): All right—give me an eraser.

PENNY (*Coolly*): I don't have one.

WEBB (*Shouts*): Then bring me a pencil with an eraser! There's one in the kitchen—and get moving!

PENNY: All right—all right— (*Takes basket from divan and exits.* WEBB *turns to the typewriter again. Slowly he completes the blank, and tears it from the machine.* PENNY *rushes into the room, looking frightened. Breathlessly*) Webb—Webb!

WEBB (*Impatiently holds out his hand*): Here—give me the pencil.

PENNY: Webb, listen to me!

WEBB: I haven't time!

PENNY: But those cans of dog food!

WEBB: Cans of dog food?

PENNY: Where'd you put them this morning?

WEBB (*Puzzled*): In the cupboard—above the kitchen sink.

PENNY: Webb, they're not there now!

WEBB: Not there? (*He suddenly rises.*) But that's where I stacked them, after I removed the labels.

PENNY: There are no unlabeled cans on that shelf!

WEBB (*Annoyed*): I suppose Calvin marched upstairs from the basement and removed his dog food from the kitchen shelf.

PENNY: Suppose somebody used them by mistake! The cans were without labels. Mother prepared a hot dish for Diana's party, didn't she?

WEBB (*Nods*): Sure. Spaghetti and meat sauce.

PENNY: Exactly—*meat sauce!* Suppose she took down those cans from the shelf and—

WEBB (*Aghast*): Penny, you're crazy! I've never heard of such nonsense!

PENNY: It won't be nonsense if mother's meat sauce isn't meat sauce—but Happy-Bark Dog Food.

WEBB: Penny, stop it! You're out of your head.

PENNY (*Stoutly*): Then you dig up those tins.

WEBB: I sure will. (WEBB *attempts to hide his alarm. He moves rapidly to left.*) They—they're on the shelf. That's where I put them. That's where they *have* to be!

PENNY: And if they're not—? (WEBB *doesn't answer. He rushes through doorway left.* PENNY *stands frozen. The doorbell rings, but* PENNY *is not aware of it. She sinks weakly into chair down right.* MARK MANNING *calls out cheerfully.*)

MARK (*Off*): Hey, anybody home? (*He peers through center opening from right.*) Hi ya, Penny. (PENNY *jumps up.* MARK *moves down center.*)

PENNY (*With effort*): Oh, it—it's you, Mark.

MARK: Didn't you hear the doorbell? (PENNY *shakes her head.*) What's the matter with you? (PENNY *shakes head again.*) I brought along a friend. (*He steps upstage to center, calls into hall.*) Come on in! (JOYCE HASTINGS *appears.*) Penny, I want you to meet Joyce Hastings.

PENNY (*Without enthusiasm*): H-hello—

JOYCE (*Smiles at* PENNY): Hello, Penny.

MARK: We've come for Webb.

JOYCE: He's late. Where is he?

PENNY (*With effort*): In the kitchen, taking a quick inventory.

JOYCE: Inventory?

MARK (*To* PENNY): I want Joyce to meet your parents. They're around?

PENNY (*Feebly*): Upstairs, I think.

MARK: Would you ask them to come down?

JOYCE (*To* PENNY): We haven't much time, Penny. Mrs. Lane is holding up dinner for us.

MARK (*Grins easily*): And I'm hungry as a dog! (PENNY *shudders.* WEBB *enters from left, looking shaken.*)

JOYCE (*Lightly to* WEBB): Well, Webb! It's about time you showed up.

PENNY (*Desperately, to* WEBB): Webb—(WEBB *turns to* PENNY.) Did—did you find—*anything?*

WEBB: No. (PENNY *groans softly.*)

JOYCE (*To* PENNY): Will you call your parents, Penny? This may be the only chance I'll have to see them. (*She sits in chair right.*)

PENNY: Yes—(*She exits slowly.*)

JOYCE (*To* WEBB): Isn't your sister well, Webb? She doesn't seem to act quite normal.

MARK (*To* WEBB): And neither do you, pal.

WEBB: Oh, I'm all right—(*He sinks onto divan.*) We're both fine.

JOYCE (*To* WEBB, *a bit impatiently*): Do you realize that Mrs. Lane is waiting for you?

MARK (*To* WEBB): It isn't like you, Webb, to be late for anything.

JOYCE: Dear Mrs. Lane did come to our rescue. She let Mark and me sample the hot dish your mother sent over.

WEBB (*With a violent start*): She—she let you sample it?

JOYCE (*Nods*): And it *is* delicious.

MARK: Best meat sauce I've tasted since I was a pup.

WEBB: You—you mean you've eaten some of it—both of you?

JOYCE: Of course we have.

WEBB: And you're all right?

JOYCE: Certainly.

MARK (*Grins*): Although I must admit that the meat sauce did something to me. I just can't explain—but I've never tasted anything quite like it.

JOYCE (*Smiles*): Neither have I, for that matter. Somehow it seems to give me a new lift—almost as though I were another person.

MARK (*Nods*): I suddenly feel alive, happy and frisky.

JOYCE: I've never had food affect me like this.

MARK: The feeling seems to grow stronger all the time. (WEBB *sits in stunned silence.*)

JOYCE (*To* WEBB): I simply must ask your mother for the recipe.

MARK (*To* JOYCE): Maybe Webb knows what went into the dish— Do you, Webb?

WEBB (*Attempts to hide his horror*): I—I'm not just certain—

JOYCE (*Peers across at* WEBB): Webb, you *do* look pale.

MARK (*Heartily, to* WEBB): You'll snap out of it after you've eaten a man-sized helping of that spaghetti and meat sauce.

JOYCE (*To* WEBB): You'll feel like another person.

MARK: By the way, Webb—Mrs. Lane asked us to bring back that center cloth for the table. Penny didn't have it when she came over with the basket.

WEBB: I suppose it's in the kitchen—

MARK: Mind if I take a look? (MARK *moves to doorway and exits.*)

JOYCE (*Suddenly rises, speaks in a strange voice*): Oh—oh —! Oh, my goodness—!

WEBB: Joyce, what's the matter?

JOYCE: I don't know, but all at once I feel like somebody else. Or maybe, *something* else!

WEBB (*Gasps*): Oh, no! (HOWARD *enters, followed by* PENNY.)

PENNY (*To* JOYCE): Here's my father. Mother will be down in a minute.

HOWARD: So you are Joyce Hastings—

JOYCE: Indeed I am, Mr.—*Bow wow!* (JOYCE *seems to lose control of her voice.* WEBB *and* PENNY *jump in horror.* HOWARD *is shocked.*)

HOWARD: What—what's that?

JOYCE (*Embarrassed*): Oh, I do beg your pardon. I don't know what got into me. (*Attempts a smile*) I meant to say—*Bow wow!* (HOWARD *stumbles back in fright.*)

JOYCE (*Nervously*): Oh, excuse me!

HOWARD (*With effort*): Young lady, are you ill?

JOYCE: Goodness, no. At least I was all right until I—*bow wow!* (HOWARD *backs behind table at right.* PENNY *dashes behind* WEBB.)

HOWARD (*To* WEBB): Webb, I think this girl needs a doctor.

JOYCE (*Affects great embarrassment*): Of course not, Webb. It's just that I seem to—*bow wow!* (*Immediately* GRACE *enters.* JOYCE *turns to* GRACE.)

GRACE (*Beams*): My dear Joyce Hastings! Penny told me you'd come over. You don't know what a pleasure this is! I've been looking forward to your visit all day.

JOYCE (*Smiles*): I simply had to run over to—*bow wow!*

GRACE (*With a violent start*): *What!*

JOYCE: Oh, dear—I beg your pardon— (GRACE *is stunned.*)

HOWARD (*Warningly*): Grace, stay back!

JOYCE (*Takes a step toward* GRACE): I don't know what's come over me—*bow wow! (With a shriek* GRACE *jumps back.*)

HOWARD: Grace, we need help!

JOYCE (*Again takes a step toward* GRACE): Oh, no, Mrs.— *bow wow!* (GRACE, HOWARD, WEBB *and* PENNY *are in panic. Door at left opens.* MARK *scampers into the room on all fours. Over his back is pinned the fancy center-piece, substituting for a dog blanket. He leaps happily to center.* GRACE *screams.* PENNY *shrieks.* HOWARD *bel-lows.* WEBB *almost collapses.*)

MARK (*Prancing on all fours*): *Bow wow! Bow wow!*

GRACE: Help! Help! (WEBB *takes one wild look, then plunges upstage, and rushes out.*)

HOWARD (*Shouts at* JOYCE): Get your—your companion out of here!

JOYCE: He isn't a companion. He's just another—*bow wow!*

GRACE (*Groans*): Oh—oh—! (*She drops onto divan.*)

HOWARD: I'm calling the police!

GRACE: Get the dog catcher!

JOYCE (*Rushing in front of* HOWARD, *speaks in a frightened but normal tone*): No—no—! (MARK, *still on all fours, romps upstage to center and exits.* JOYCE *grasps* HOWARD *by the arm.*) Mr. Andrews, listen to me! Please—

HOWARD (*Freeing himself*): You're mad—both of you! (*He moves again toward door left.* PENNY *jumps up, blocking his way.*)

PENNY: Father, don't! (GRACE *moans.* JOYCE, *thoroughly frightened, backs upstage and exits unnoticed.*)

HOWARD (*Roars at* PENNY): Out of my way! Climb on the divan! They'll bite you!

PENNY: Father, stop it! They've gone—Mark and Joyce have gone!

HOWARD: Gone? (*Turns*) Grace, are you all right?

GRACE: All right? I don't think I'll ever be all right again.

HOWARD: They've lost their minds!

GRACE: It must have something to do with dog days.

HOWARD: They went off the beam at the same moment.

GRACE: What on earth caused it?

PENNY: Happy-Bark Dog Food! That's what caused it.

HOWARD: What did you say?

GRACE: Happy-Bark Dog Food?

PENNY (*Her voice trembles*): I—I warned him. I tried to tell Webb that—that— (*She drops onto divan, weeping loudly.*)

HOWARD: See here, young lady, what's behind this? (PENNY'S *sobs increase.*)

GRACE: Howard, our daughter is out of her mind, too! It—it's something she caught from the other dogs— (WEBB *enters at center from right, weak and shaken.*)

WEBB: Where—where are they?

GRACE (*Wildly to* HOWARD): Maybe he caught it, too!

(*Goes to* WEBB, *attempts to soothe him.*) Webb, dear, you're not an animal. You're our son. You must cling to that thought.

WEBB: Good grief, I'm all right.

GRACE: Thank goodness! But I'm not certain about Penny. If this is some sort of a virus going around—

PENNY: Nothing's wrong with me, either. After all, we didn't even taste it.

HOWARD: Taste it? Taste what?

PENNY: Mother's spaghetti and meat sauce.

GRACE (*With a start*): My—*what?*

PENNY: Except it wasn't meat sauce. It was Happy-Bark Dog Food.

GRACE: Penny Andrews, what are you talking about?

PENNY: You'd better let Webb explain.

HOWARD (*To* WEBB): What's the meaning of this?

WEBB: I just don't believe it.

GRACE: Webb, you're not talking sense.

HOWARD (*Snaps*): Who *is?*

WEBB (*To* GRACE): Those—those cans of dog food. After I'd removed the labels, I put the tins in the cupboard over the kitchen sink. Then the cans disappeared.

PENNY (*To* GRACE): And you were in the kitchen this morning, making meat sauce. (HOWARD *gives a violent start.* PENNY *rises.*)

WEBB (*To* GRACE): And Joyce and Mark admitted they'd already sampled the sauce.

GRACE (*Horrified*): Why—why—

HOWARD: Grace Andrews, did you put dog food in—

GRACE: Certainly I didn't!

WEBB: Mother, you're certain?

GRACE (*Indignantly*): Don't you think I know the difference between meat sauce and dog rations?

HOWARD: Then what's the meaning of those bloodhound antics around here?

GRACE: If anyone is attempting to suggest that my meat sauce would make people act like that—(*Suddenly* DIANA *appears at center opening.*)

DIANA: Of course not, Mrs. Andrews.

GRACE: Diana! (DIANA *moves down center.*) You—you *are* still Diana? (DIANA *nods.* GRACE *turns to* HOWARD.) Howard, she's normal!

DIANA: I'm horribly ashamed.

GRACE (*To* HOWARD): See, Howard—she can even talk without barking. (JOYCE *and* MARK *appear at center opening.*)

JOYCE: And so can we, Mrs. Andrews. (GRACE *gives a little scream, backs away.*)

GRACE: Howard, they're back—teeth and all!

MARK (*Moves downstage*): Mrs. Andrews, we're perfectly harmless—though you'll probably never believe it. Believe me, we owe both of you an apology.

DIANA: It was my idea, but I didn't plan on you two getting in on it. I wanted to teach Webb a lesson.

PENNY (*To* DIANA): *Your* idea?

WEBB: A lesson?

DIANA (*To* WEBB): I knew you'd neglected that order, Webb, and I knew how your father felt about things. Penny, too. So when I was here earlier, I slipped into the kitchen and removed the cans. Then I persuaded Joyce and Mark to put on a dog act.

JOYCE: Before we could get under way, *you* walked in, Mr. Andrews.

MARK: And then *you*, Mrs. Andrews.

DIANA: I wanted to give Webb a good scare. I hoped he'd be so shocked that he'd never again forget an obligation.

WEBB: Diana!

HOWARD: If it didn't frighten our son, it certainly shook up his parents.

GRACE: You mean this was just for Webb's benefit? (*Phone rings offstage left.*) Oh, dear, the phone—(*She moves left.*)

PENNY (*Calls to* GRACE): If it's the dog catcher, tell him everything's under control. (GRACE *exits.*)

DIANA (*To* HOWARD): I hope you'll forgive us, Mr. Andrews—and you, Webb. (*Smiles*) I'll even help you with the blanket order.

HOWARD (*Hesitates*): Well, I do forgive all of you— (*Emphatically*) That is, if this has taught my son a lesson. Well, Webb? (WEBB *doesn't answer. He suddenly drops onto divan, covers his face.*) Webb, what's the matter?

WEBB (*Looks up sadly*): It's—it's too late.

DIANA: Too late?

WEBB: Calvin won't need a blanket now. Maybe he won't need anything—ever. It—it's farewell to Calvin.

JOYCE: Farewell to Calvin?

PENNY: Webb, is something wrong with that dog? You've been in the basement.

WEBB: I'll say I have. (*Pause*) Calvin isn't down there. He—he escaped.

DIANA: Escaped?

WEBB (*Nods sadly*): The basement window was open. I'd left the stepladder under it.

HOWARD: Son, you didn't!

MARK: Calvin climbed the ladder?

PENNY (*Groans*): With all the canine antics around here, I'll bet poor Calvin could have climbed the Washington Monument.

JOYCE: Where'd he go?

WEBB (*Grimly*): How should I know? Did you expect Calvin to leave me a note?

DIANA (*To* WEBB): What is Mr. Mayfield going to say? (GRACE *enters briskly from left.*)

GRACE: You could never guess who phoned!

PENNY (*Hopefully*): Was it Calvin?

GRACE: It was Mr. Mayfield.

WEBB (*With a start*): Mr. Mayfield?

GRACE: He got in late this afternoon, and what do you think? Not more than five minutes ago he heard something scratching at his front door. (*Triumphantly*) It was Calvin!

WEBB (*Rises*): Calvin?

GRACE (*Enthusiastically*): Calvin had come home. You must have let him out, Webb. Anyway, Mr. Mayfield was simply overjoyed. He said he'd asked you to give Calvin some training, and that you'd certainly done a wonderful job. It seems this is the first time Calvin has ever shown enough intelligence to come home by himself. Mr. Mayfield said you're a responsible and trustworthy young man, Webb—and that he's proud to have you in his school.

HOWARD (*After a pause*): What do you know about that!

DIANA (*With a twinkle in her eye*): Webb Andrews, you're a fortunate young man.

WEBB (*Grins*): If I'm fortunate, it's because of you, Diana Lane. You certainly know how to send a guy into action.

HOWARD (*With a broad smile*): Ladies and gentlemen, considering the outcome of the evening, I wish to announce that I'm withdrawing any further objections.

GRACE (*Suddenly thoughtful*): But there's just one thing—

HOWARD: What's that, Grace?

GRACE: After what I've been through, I doubt that I'll ever again have the courage to cook *spaghetti and meat sauce!* (*The others break into hearty laughter as the curtain quickly falls.*)

THE END

Production Notes

Characters: 3 male; 4 female.

Playing Time: 30 minutes.

Costumes: Modern dress. Webb wears dark slacks and an open-collared white shirt upon entering. Howard wears a business suit. Grace wears an attractive dress and small tea apron on first appearance; she later wears an evening wrap over her dress. Joyce and Diana are dressed in suitable party clothes.

Properties: Jacket and tie, portable typewriter and a dozen tin can labels for Webb; apple, for Penny; newspaper, for Howard; market basket and fancy table scarf, for Grace; order blank, for Webb.

Setting: The living room of the Andrews' home. At center back is an opening which leads into front hall. Offstage right is the front door; offstage left are the stairs leading to basement and floor above. A door at left of stage connects with the rear of the house. At downstage right are a table and chair. The divan is downstage left. Hanging on the left wall downstage from door is a small mirror. Behind table right is a wastebasket. Other furnishings and decorations may be added to give the room a comfortable appearance.

Lighting: No special effects.

No Treat for Gilbert

Characters

CAROL PIPER, *a high school girl*
ROSS HIGGINS, *Carol's date*
MADGE PIPER, *Carol's mother*
GILBERT PIPER, *Carol's father*
PAULINE VERMILLION, *the wife of Gilbert's employer*

TIME: *Early on Halloween evening.*
SETTING: *The Pipers' living room.*
AT RISE: *The stage is unoccupied. After a pause, the sound of hurried footsteps is heard offstage. The center door suddenly opens.* GILBERT PIPER *enters, seeming upset. He slams the door behind him and rushes onstage.*

GILBERT (*Loudly*): Madge! Oh, Madge! (*His voice rises.*) Madge, where are you?
MADGE (*From offstage left*): Is that you, Gilbert?

GILBERT: You know it is. (MADGE PIPER *enters from left. She wears a smart evening frock.*)

MADGE (*As she sees* GILBERT): It's time you were home, Gilbert. You're late tonight.

GILBERT (*Excitedly*): Late? Of course I'm late! I've never been so late in my life, and of all times—

MADGE (*Breaks in soothingly*): Relax, Gilbert.

GILBERT: Relax? Madge Piper, do you know what happened to me?

MADGE: You look as though you'd been chased by the F. B. I.

GILBERT (*Starts to remove his suit coat*): When I left the office and reached the parking lot, what do you think I found?

MADGE: A traffic ticket?

GILBERT (*Fumes*): No, but some hoodlum had let the air out of my two front tires. I'd just like to get my hands on—

MADGE: Never mind, Gilbert. After all, this *is* Halloween.

GILBERT (*Throws his suit coat over back of divan*): It took me an hour to get help—one solid hour! (*Faces* MADGE.) Madge, do you realize that you and I have a dinner engagement at the country club tonight?

MADGE: Of course.

GILBERT: Do you realize we're to be the guests of my boss and his wife?

MADGE: Gilbert, for goodness' sake—

GILBERT: I've already been delayed sixty minutes. I'm not even dressed. (*He begins to loosen his tie.*)

MADGE (*Steps to* GILBERT): Gilbert, that's enough. Our dinner date with Mr. and Mrs. Vermillion isn't until eight o'clock. Now sit down and relax. (*Pushes him towards divan.*)

GILBERT: I haven't time to sit around.

MADGE (*Again pushes* GILBERT *back onto divan*): Yes, you have. Anyway, you don't even need to drive your car to the club. Mrs. Vermillion herself is picking us up.

GILBERT (*Startled*): Mrs. Vermillion?

MADGE (*Nods calmly*): She phoned a few minutes ago. Her husband has a conference. He'll go directly to the club. The three of us will meet him there.

GILBERT: Doesn't Pauline Vermillion think I'm capable of driving my own car?

MADGE: If she could see you now, she'd think you weren't capable of driving a kiddie car.

GILBERT (*Relaxes slightly, but still speaks with emphasis*): Listen, Madge, this is the most important night of my life. If we turn up late, old Jonathan Bradford Vermillion will probably give this promotion to somebody else in the office.

MADGE: Gilbert, you're simply working yourself into a nervous state. You certainly don't look like a rising and aggressive business executive at the moment. You should be thankful that neither J. B. nor Pauline Vermillion is around. (*Pats his shoulder soothingly.*) Now just lie down a few minutes. I'll call you in plenty of time. (*She sits in chair and thumbs through magazine.* GILBERT *stretches out on couch momentarily, then sits up suddenly.*)

GILBERT: Madge—

MADGE (*Glances up*): Yes?

GILBERT: My tuxedo!

MADGE: What about your tuxedo?

GILBERT: Is it back from the cleaners?

MADGE: Of course.

GILBERT: Do you realize it's the only thing I own that's proper for this occasion? I tremble to think what J. B. would say if I showed up at his ritzy club wearing any old suit. He's very proper, you know.

MADGE (*Patiently*): Yes, darling, I realize it. (*Pause*) Ross Higgins came by with your suit this afternoon.

GILBERT: Ross Higgins? Why should *he* be dragging my tuxedo all over town? He's supposed to be taking a workout with the high school football team.

MADGE (*With an amused smile*): Ross wants to make a good impression on you, Gilbert. You know very well he's taking Carol to the Halloween dance tonight.

GILBERT (*With affected dignity*): I did *not* know he was taking our daughter any place. (*Dramatically*) Nobody keeps me posted on events around this house. If Carol started dating the King of Siam, I'd be the last to know.

MADGE (*Calmly*): Turn over and take a nap, Gilbert. (GILBERT *lies back on divan.* CAROL PIPER *breezes noisily into room from left.* CAROL *is a popular and vivacious high school student. Her outfit is modern and informal. She carries a transparent envelope which contains a corsage.*)

CAROL: Happy Halloween!

MADGE (*Smiles at* CAROL): Carol, dear!

CAROL (*Turns to* MADGE): Mother, you forgot your corsage.

MADGE (*Suddenly rises*): Goodness! I left it in the refrigerator, didn't I?

CAROL (*At table*): I'll pin it on you.

GILBERT (*Fumes*): It's probably seven o'clock right now.

MADGE (*To* GILBERT): Gilbert, for goodness' sake! (CAROL *pins corsage on* MADGE's *dress.*)

GILBERT (*With attempted dramatics*): I'm sure it doesn't interest my wife and daughter that this could be the greatest evening in my life.

MADGE: Yes, dear, it does. But we've heard it all before. (*As though quoting an often-repeated statement*) An opening has developed in your office. You are one of several who is being considered for the position. And now your boss, J. B. Vermillion, invites you and me to the country club for dinner. It may mean that you have been selected for the job. If so, the announcement will doubtless be made tonight.

GILBERT: Then why isn't everybody in this house as excited as I am?

MADGE (*Dryly*): If we were, the roof would fall in.

CAROL (*Turns to* GILBERT): I'm excited.

GILBERT: Well, it's about time.

CAROL: I mean, I'm excited because Ross Higgins is taking me to a Halloween dance.

GILBERT (*Groans*): That! Only *that!*

CAROL (*To* GILBERT): It's a costume affair. We go at nine o'clock.

GILBERT (*Points at* CAROL's *outfit*): Don't tell me *that's* the costume.

CAROL: Of course not, I haven't changed yet. (*Suddenly*) Father, you can do something for me. (*She picks up the two masks from the table.*)

GILBERT: All I want to do is put on my suit!

CAROL (*Indicates masks*): You can select the mask I'll wear.

I'm supposed to make a choice. (CAROL *places one of the masks in front of her face.* GILBERT *groans.*) Don't you like it? (*She removes the mask.*)

MADGE (*To* CAROL): At the moment, darling, I can't think of anything that your father *does* like.

CAROL (*To* GILBERT): Maybe you'll approve of this one. (*She places the other mask before her face.*)

GILBERT (*To* CAROL): You look like a misplaced refugee from outer space.

CAROL: Ross is going to wear the mask I don't select. (*She removes the second mask.*)

GILBERT (*Stoutly*): There ought to be a law against those faces.

CAROL: But, Father, this is Halloween. We *are* supposed to wear *something.*

GILBERT: I have to get dressed, too.

MADGE (*To* GILBERT): Your tuxedo is hanging in the downstairs closet. It's still in the cleaners' bag.

GILBERT (*Crosses to left*): If they haven't done a decent job on it—(*He breaks off as the doorbell rings offstage.*) Now, who's that? (MADGE *opens center door.* ROSS HIGGINS *appears at doorway.* ROSS *is a friendly, energetic and muscular young man. At the moment he wears a pirate's outfit.*)

CAROL (*Surprised and pleased*): ROSS!

GILBERT (*Sees* ROSS, *groans*): Oh, no!

MADGE (*Regains her composure*): My goodness, it—it *is* Ross Higgins.

ROSS (*Amused, as he swaggers into the room*): Your money or your life! (*He pretends to cover them with an imaginary gun.*)

CAROL (*To* ROSS, *as she steps forward to greet him*): Honestly, that costume is a sensation.

MADGE: I thought the Halloween dance wasn't until nine o'clock.

ROSS (*Grins easily*): Don't mind me. I'm just early—by a few hours.

GILBERT (*Suddenly*): Well, I'm not early! (*Shouts*) Where's my tuxedo, I say? Somebody bring me my tuxedo! (GILBERT *rushes to center.*)

CAROL (*To* MADGE): Get it for him, Mother, before he blows out the windows. (MADGE *exits.*)

ROSS (*To* GILBERT): You seem a little upset, Mr. Piper.

GILBERT (*With dignity*): I am *not* upset. I'm as calm as Niagara Falls.

CAROL (*To* ROSS): Mother and Father are having dinner with the Vermillions tonight.

ROSS (*Impressed, as he speaks to* GILBERT): J. B. Vermillion, the president of your company? (GILBERT *nods.*)

CAROL (*To* ROSS): Father thinks Mr. Vermillion will offer him a promotion.

ROSS (*To* GILBERT): Congratulations, sir.

CAROL (*To* ROSS): Father hasn't cinched the job yet. J. B. is a demanding man.

GILBERT (*Emphatically*): And so's his wife!

ROSS: I believe I saw something in the paper about Mr. Vermillion. Hasn't he established a fund for underprivileged children?

CAROL: Mr. Vermillion plans to build a clubhouse for the youth of the city. He thinks that a lot of adults are neglecting the younger generation.

GILBERT: It's his pet project. And believe me, you don't joke about it.

CAROL (*To* GILBERT): Father, what's the slogan Mr. Vermillion uses in his drive for funds?

GILBERT: His slogan? (*With reverence.*) It's "Treat Every Child the Way You Would Treat Your Own."

ROSS (*Repeats the slogan*): "Treat Every Child the Way You Would Treat Your Own." (*To* GILBERT.) Not bad advice, is it, Mr. Piper?

CAROL (*Amused*): At the moment Father is not in the mood for anybody's advice.

MADGE (*Enters from left. She carries the garment bag from the cleaners', inside of which is an article of clothing*): Here you are, Gilbert.

GILBERT (*Plunges to* MADGE): Let me have it— (*He snatches bag from* MADGE *and begins to tear off the paper protection.*)

CAROL (*To* ROSS): I really didn't expect you so early. I hope you won't mind waiting until I've changed. (GILBERT *suddenly breaks in with a bellow. The exposed apparel is not* GILBERT'S *suit, but a woman's short coat. As* GILBERT *yells, the others turn swiftly toward him. As* CAROL *swings around*) Father!

MADGE (*Above* GILBERT'S *roar*): Gilbert, what on earth's the matter?

GILBERT (*Enraged, as he holds up the hanger*): Look! *Look!*

ROSS (*With a violent start*): Mr. Piper!

MADGE (*Equally amazed*): Gilbert, that *isn't* your suit! (GILBERT *trembles with rage.*)

CAROL (*Horrified*): A woman's coat!

GILBERT (*Quietly, but menacingly*): Ross Higgins, *you* delivered this from the cleaners!

ROSS (*In panic*): But sir, I—I asked for your suit. They gave me a garment bag, so I took it for granted that it contained—

GILBERT (*Roars*): Oh, you did, did you? You're not supposed to take *anything* for granted!

ROSS (*Backs away slightly*): But, sir—

GILBERT (*Cuts in*): Stop shouting at me!

MADGE (*To* GILBERT): Gilbert, they must have given Ross the wrong bag.

GILBERT: What am I expected to do—wear *this* instead of a suit? Maybe I should pin a flower on my undershirt! I'm ruined—*ruined!*

CAROL (*To* GILBERT): Ross will go after your suit.

ROSS: Of course, sir—

GILBERT (*To* ROSS): You'd *better* go after my suit!

ROSS: Yes, sir. (*Hesitates uneasily*) Of course, if the cleaners shouldn't be open—

GILBERT: Then break down the door—tear in the wall— (*He takes a step toward* ROSS.)

ROSS (*Backs away*): I'll do my best, sir.

MADGE (*Hastily, to* ROSS): You can go out the back way, Ross. It's closer.

GILBERT (*To* ROSS, *as he takes another menacing step forward*): And don't you dare come back until—

ROSS (*Frightened*): Yes, sir! (ROSS *turns, then dashes off left.*)

CAROL (*To* GILBERT): If it were a costume affair, Mother or I could lend you something.

GILBERT (*Dryly*): A stole and a pair of earrings, no doubt!

MADGE (*To* GILBERT): Gilbert, get upstairs. As soon as Ross returns, I'll bring the suit up to you.

CAROL: You still have plenty of time.

GILBERT: I *haven't* plenty of time. (*With trembling fingers he begins to unbutton his shirt.*) J. B. Vermillion was the inventor of punctuality. When somebody comes in to work late, and J. B. starts glaring at his watch, it means a termination slip in the pay envelope—(*To* MADGE, *as he starts to pull off his shirt.*) If we're late for dinner, Madge, you might as well call the relief agency. (GILBERT *jerks off his shirt. He exits left.*)

CAROL (*To* MADGE): Father's at the boiling point.

MADGE: You really can't blame him. If Ross doesn't get his suit—(*She breaks off at sound of doorbell off center.*) That was the doorbell.

CAROL (*Nods*): Probably some youngsters, out for Halloween trick or treat.

MADGE (*Hurriedly*): Then get rid of them, Carol. (*Quickly she crosses to divan, gathers up the woman's coat, together with* GILBERT'S *suit coat, his hat and necktie.*) I haven't any treats, and I don't want another trick tonight. I've already had enough Halloween excitement for a generation. (*Swiftly* CAROL *gathers up the torn garment bag from floor.*)

CAROL (*Moves to* MADGE, *hands her the torn bag*): Here, take this with you.

MADGE (*Almost overloaded*): Open the library door for me. (*The doorbell rings again.* CAROL *rushes to right. She opens door to library.* MADGE *hurriedly follows* CAROL.) And tell those delinquents at the door to keep away from this house or I—I'll make them a present of

Gilbert! (MADGE *exits at right.* CAROL *rushes upstage to center door. As she reaches door, she notices the two Halloween masks on table. Hurriedly she picks up a mask, places it in front of her face. As she throws open the door, she begins to shout before she sees the visitor.*)

CAROL (*With a piercing yell*): Get away from here or I'll — (*She breaks off with a horrified gasp. At doorway stands* PAULINE VERMILLION, *a dignified, elegantly attired woman of sixty. She is majestic, domineering and imposing, but as she sees* CAROL, *her stately attitude collapses. She shrieks violently.* CAROL, *in equal terror, snatches off the mask.*) Mrs. Vermillion!

PAULINE (*Groans, as she steadies herself on doorway*): Oh, oh!

CAROL (*Wildly tosses mask onto table, rushes to* PAULINE): Oh, my goodness!

PAULINE (*Gazes weakly at* CAROL): You're Carol Piper.

CAROL (*Takes* PAULINE *by the arm, carefully pulls her through center doorway*): Of course I am, Mrs. Vermillion.

PAULINE (*Still stunned*): I'm sure I've never come face to face with—with anything quite like that.

CAROL (*Greatly embarrassed*): I *do* apologize, Mrs. Vermillion. (CAROL *closes center door as* PAULINE, *swaying slightly, moves down left.*)

PAULINE: I doubt that I'll ever be quite the same.

CAROL: It's just that I thought you were someone else. It's Halloween, you know.

PAULINE: Indeed, I know it now. (*She sinks weakly into chair, places her party purse on chair beside her.*)

CAROL: I thought you were some of the neighboring children, out for trick or treat.

PAULINE: No doubt you meant well, my dear. (*Pause*) But please, don't ever try that again.

MADGE (*Loudly, as she enters from right*): Carol, I hope you told that stupid character at the door that— (*She breaks off in horror as she sees* PAULINE.) *Oh!*

PAULINE (*Smiles with effort*): Mrs. Piper—

MADGE (*Stunned, as she gazes at* PAULINE): Mrs. Vermillion!

PAULINE: My dear, you needn't act so startled. After all, *I'm* not wearing a Halloween mask.

CAROL (*Attempts to explain to* MADGE): You see, Mother, when I went to the door—

MADGE (*Briefly, to* CAROL): Never mind. (*She continues to gaze in panic at* PAULINE.) Mrs. Vermillion, I didn't expect you to— (*She breaks off.*)

PAULINE: You didn't expect me to arrive so early? (*Pointedly*) I'm sure it would have been *safer,* if I hadn't. (*Smiles slightly*) It seems I was mixed up on the hour. I told you that dinner at the club was set for eight o'clock, but dear J. B. just phoned. He insists our reservations are for seven o'clock.

MADGE (*Horrified*): *Seven* o'clock?

PAULINE (*To* MADGE): I told J. B. I'd call you, but he was opposed to the idea. J. B. said you'd both be ready hours ahead of time, considering the importance of this engagement. Anyway, according to J. B., your husband is always so punctual. That's one of the reasons that J. B. has decided to— (*She breaks off with a significant little laugh.*) But you'll know more about that later this evening, Mrs. Piper.

CAROL (*Openly alarmed, as she takes a step forward and speaks to* PAULINE): Do you mean that Mr. Vermillion is already at the club?

PAULINE (*To* CAROL): He'll be there by the time your parents and I arrive. (*She turns to* MADGE.) J. B. is attending a meeting to raise funds for underprivileged children. Of course your husband has told you all about the campaign. (*Proudly*) I helped dear J. B. compose the slogan, "Treat Every Child the Way You Would Treat Your Own." (*Beams*) Doesn't it simply shake you?

MADGE (*To* PAULINE): I'm certainly shaken at the moment.

PAULINE (*Glances briefly around the room*): Your husband *is* ready, I presume? (*There is a pause. Both* MADGE *and* CAROL *attempt to hide their panic.*)

MADGE (*At last speaks to* PAULINE): Well, he's ready—in a way. (*Weakly.*) That is, loosely speaking.

CAROL (*Suddenly turns to* MADGE, *speaks significantly*): Mother, I'd better watch at the back door. (*She moves left.*)

PAULINE (*Questioningly, to* CAROL): The back door, did you say?

CAROL (*Pauses, turns to* PAULINE *with a nervous smile*): I have to look for somebody who'd better be coming up the alley—and quick! (*She swiftly exits at left.*)

PAULINE (*To* MADGE, *after a startled pause*): Really, Mrs. Piper, isn't your daughter acting a bit—well, a bit odd?

MADGE: Tonight it seems to run in our family.

PAULINE: Shall we be on our way? (*But* MADGE *doesn't*

move. PAULINE *is slightly annoyed.*) Mrs. Piper, didn't you hear me? (*Pause*) Is something the matter?

MADGE (*With effort*): It's just that I don't think Gilbert would want to walk into the club in his present condition.

PAULINE (*A bit coolly*): Really? But I was led to believe that Mr. Piper is the most dependable member of my husband's organization.

MADGE (*Desperately*): He is! But just now he—(*Breaks off*) I mean, I told him that you wouldn't be along until—(*Breaks off again*) That is, when he opened the bag—(*Utterly confused*) Oh, dear!

PAULINE (*Annoyed*): I'm afraid I don't understand you, Mrs. Piper.

MADGE: But he—(*Breaks off, tries again*): It's just that I think you and Mr. Vermillion would feel more comfortable if Gilbert and I drove out to the club a little later.

PAULINE (*Startled*): Later?

MADGE: I'm certain poor Gilbert would feel a lot more comfortable.

PAULINE: Mrs. Piper! Are you suggesting that—

MADGE (*Cuts in breathlessly*): Gilbert and I will be along as soon as certain things show up.

PAULINE: Are you trying to say that Mr. Piper is not yet ready to accompany me to the club?

MADGE: He didn't think you'd be along until later.

PAULINE (*With cool dignity*): Really, Mrs. Piper, that has nothing to do with it. In my husband's organization, every employee is expected to be ready to snap to attention at the drop of a hat.

MADGE: But this is more than just a hat. (*Pleads*) Please, Mrs. Vermillion, it isn't that Gilbert doesn't want to go. He has been talking about it from the moment he got home. (*Emphatically*) You have no idea how he's been talking!

PAULINE (*Slowly and significantly*): Mrs. Piper, I'm afraid my husband isn't going to like this.

MADGE: I don't like it either, and neither does Gilbert.

PAULINE (*Rises, leaving her purse on chair*): Very well. I seem to have but one course of action. I shall drive to the club alone, (*Pointedly*) but I have a feeling that my husband will be most unsympathetic. (*She moves up center.*)

MADGE: We'll be there as soon as we can.

PAULINE (*Pauses at center door, turns to* MADGE): I trust you realize the seriousness of this, Mrs. Piper. A situation such as this usually leaves J. B. cold.

MADGE: Believe me, Mrs. Vermillion, this one has certainly left *Gilbert* cold.

PAULINE: I am sorry, Mrs. Piper, but of course there is nothing more that I can do now. Nothing at all. (PAULINE *exits at center.* MADGE, *stunned, gazes hopelessly at the closed door. Immediately* GILBERT *calls from offstage.*)

GILBERT (*From off left*): Madge! Madge! (MADGE *turns toward door left.*) If that rattle-brained Ross Higgins doesn't show up in the next—(GILBERT *marches into the room from left. He has removed his office suit and shirt. For protection he has awkwardly wrapped himself in a large white sheet.*)

MADGE (*With a violent start*): Gilbert!

GILBERT (*Folds his arms, gazes defiantly at* MADGE): Well?

MADGE: That *sheet!*

GILBERT: All right, so I'm wearing a sheet, and I shall go on wearing it until—

MADGE (*Breaks in urgently*): Gilbert, listen to me! Pauline Vermillion has been here and—

GILBERT (*At first pays no attention*): I don't care if—(*He breaks off in sudden horror.*) Pauline Vermillion!

MADGE (*Breathlessly*): She came by to drive us to the club. There was a mistake about the hour, but J. B. was certain you'd be ready and—

GILBERT (*Almost speechless*): Madge, is this the truth?

MADGE (*About to weep*): I said you weren't able to go yet. I promised we'd come on later. But Pauline Vermillion was terribly unhappy and—

GILBERT: *She's* unhappy? (*With a groan of despair.*) Do you know what this means?

MADGE: Gilbert, I just couldn't explain about the suit. (CAROL *enters hurriedly from left. She carries a large cloth laundry bag.*)

CAROL (*Stops short as she sees* GILBERT): *Father!*

GILBERT: Yes, I'm your father! Do you know what has happened to me because my tuxedo wasn't ready?

CAROL (*Attempts to break in*): Father, please—

GILBERT (*Dramatically, as he marches to right*): I'll probably never be able to afford anything better than what I'm wearing right now! I've already lost that promotion, and I'm no doubt out of a job. Tomorrow, I'll get a termination slip in my pay envelope and—(*Breaks off, then roars.*) What's happened to that young idiot?

CAROL: Ross? I didn't see him. I looked down the alley. (*She turns to* MADGE.) Wouldn't Mrs. Vermillion wait?

MADGE: No. (*Sympathetically, to* GILBERT) Gilbert, I'll try to find Ross. (*She moves swiftly to left.*) We still have a chance.

GILBERT: I won't even have a chance in a free soup line! (MADGE *exits left.*)

CAROL (*To* GILBERT): I *am* sorry.

GILBERT (*In defeat*): You'll be a lot sorrier when you have to wash dishes and scrub floors to take care of your starving father.

CAROL: If Ross shows up, you'll have time to dress.

GILBERT: I'll never dress again! I'm going upstairs to bed, and that's where I'll stay. Yes, you'll get used to me, after you've seen me around the house like this for the next fifty years.

CAROL (*Exasperated, as she steps to* GILBERT): Well, if you're going to be here that long, you might as well get to work. (*Extends the laundry bag*) Take this laundry bag upstairs with you. (GILBERT *takes the bag.*) It was on the back porch.

GILBERT: Why didn't you leave it there?

CAROL: Halloween pranksters would have picked it up.

GILBERT (*Groans*): I wish Halloween pranksters would pick *me* up!

CAROL: Oh, stop it, Father! Things will work out somehow. By the time Ross and I return from the dance, you'll be—

GILBERT (*Suddenly*): Return from the dance? (*Grimly*) Young lady, you're not going to that dance.

CAROL (*Shocked*): But, Father—

GILBERT: From now on, the only place you'll be going is to work. (GILBERT *marches upstage, snatches up one mask from table.*) I'm burning these idiotic masks.

CAROL: Oh, no! (GILBERT *turns from table. The laundry bag hangs over his arm. He carries the mask.*)

GILBERT: You might as well put your fancy costume back in the closet.

MADGE (*Entering swiftly from left*): Ross is here! (*To* GILBERT.) He has your suit, Gilbert.

GILBERT: I don't care if he has the crown jewels!

ROSS (*Entering from left, out of breath. He carries a freshly pressed tuxedo draped over a hanger*): I have it, Mr. Piper. (*He moves to* GILBERT.) But I had quite a time! The manager was just leaving. He thought I was a bandit, but I finally convinced him (*He extends suit to* GILBERT.) there'd been an error.

GILBERT (*Flatly*): You're too late.

ROSS (*Taken back*): Too late?

MADGE (*Attempts to argue*): Now, Gilbert—

GILBERT (*To* ROSS): I wouldn't have that tuxedo now if it were the last one on earth!

ROSS (*Shocked*): Mr. Piper! (*The doorbell rings offstage.*)

GILBERT (*To* ROSS): Get it out of my sight!

CAROL (*Breaks in desperately*): Father, you can't do that!

GILBERT (*To* ROSS): Take it away, I say!

ROSS (*To* GILBERT, *in confusion*): You want me to hide it?

GILBERT: I don't care what you do! Tear it to pieces—cut it to shreds! (GILBERT *takes a menacing step toward* ROSS.)

MADGE (*Swiftly moves to* GILBERT, *grasps his arm*): Gilbert, stop it! (Ross *is thoroughly frightened. In panic he dodges* GILBERT, *then rushes across the stage. Carrying the tuxedo, he exits right. The doorbell rings again, this time more insistently.*)

CAROL: Mother, the doorbell's ringing.

GILBERT (*Emphatically*): Who cares!

MADGE (*To* CAROL): See who it is. (CAROL *moves upstage to center door.* MADGE *and* GILBERT *stand at left of stage.* GILBERT, *draped in the sheet, carries laundry bag and mask.* MADGE *speaks desperately to* GILBERT.) Gilbert, you have to listen to reason. We can still make it out to the club, if you'll— (*At that moment* CAROL *opens center door. In doorway stands* PAULINE.)

CAROL (*With a gasp of amazement*): Mrs. Vermillion! (MADGE *swings around with a violent start.* GILBERT *is thrown into panic. Wildly he slaps the mask in front of his face.*)

PAULINE (*Still in doorway, as she speaks coldly to* CAROL): I believe I left my purse in here. (*She steps into the room.*) As I recall I was seated in that chair—(*She starts to indicate chair down left. Then for the first time she sees* GILBERT. *She breaks off in sudden horror. For a moment* PAULINE *is speechless. Then she points to* GILBERT *with a slightly trembling finger.*) What is *that?*

MADGE (*Weakly*): Where, Mrs. Vermillion?

PAULINE (*Continues to gaze at* GILBERT): That horrible creature standing at your side. (MADGE *slowly turns to* GILBERT. *She makes a weak attempt at surprise.*)

MADGE: Well, I declare—(*Turns to* PAULINE, *smiles unconvincingly.*) It must be the garbage collector.

PAULINE: Nonsense!

CAROL (*Suddenly steps forward, speaks to* PAULINE): You see, Mrs. Vermillion, tonight is Halloween.

PAULINE (*With dignity*): I'm entirely aware of that.

CAROL (*Desperately*): And we're celebrating.

PAULINE: Celebrating Halloween?

CAROL (*Attempts a weak smile*): You know—trick or treat. It's an annual custom.

MADGE (*With an effort to be helpful*): That's right—like New Year's or Ground Hog Day. (*For a moment* PAULINE *makes no answer. At last she turns to* GILBERT. *Then she slowly advances to him.*)

PAULINE (*Pauses, faces* GILBERT): Put down that mask! (GILBERT *continues to hold the mask before his face.* PAULINE *is coldly insistent.*) I said put down that mask!

CAROL (*Desperately, to* PAULINE): I can't see what difference it makes *now*, Mrs. Vermillion.

PAULINE (*Commandingly*): I have spoken! (*Then she turns once more to* GILBERT.) Did you hear me? (*There is another pause.* GILBERT *slowly removes the mask from his face.* PAULINE *studies* GILBERT *in expressionless silence. At last she speaks.*) So it *is* you, Mr. Piper.

GILBERT (*Meekly*): Hello.

PAULINE (*Turns to* MADGE, *indicates* GILBERT): Mrs. Piper, *this* is your husband!

MADGE (*Smiles with supreme effort*): My goodness, it isn't the garbage collector, is it?

PAULINE (*To* MADGE): Why didn't you explain this to me?

MADGE: Explain?

PAULINE (*Nods*): When I was here before.

GILBERT (*Suddenly*): Mrs. Vermillion! (PAULINE *turns to* GILBERT.) Honestly, you'd never have seen me in this condition if—

PAULINE (*Cuts* GILBERT *off*): You need not attempt to excuse yourself, Mr. Piper. I understand completely.

CAROL (*To* PAULINE): You see, Mrs. Vermillion, Father expected to be ready when you came by, but you turned up an hour early, and he couldn't possibly leave until he—

PAULINE (*Breaks in*): I know. (*Pause*) He couldn't leave until he had properly fulfilled his obligation.

MADGE (*Not understanding*): Obligation? That isn't what the man at the store called it.

PAULINE (*Turns to* GILBERT): You took your obligation to heart, didn't you, Mr. Piper?

MADGE (*To* PAULINE): N-no. He took it to the cleaners.

PAULINE (*Continues to face* GILBERT): Mr. Piper, you need not continue to hide the facts. Your appearance is sufficient evidence—the sheet, the mask, the trick-or-treat bag—(*She points to laundry bag over his arm.*)

GILBERT (*Startled and puzzled*): Huh?

PAULINE (*To* GILBERT): Your arrangements are obvious. You had of course planned to go out with the neighborhood children tonight—on their annual Halloween expedition. (*For a moment the others are stunned.*)

MADGE: But Mrs. Vermillion, he—

PAULINE (*Stops* MADGE): Quiet, please. (*Once more she turns to* GILBERT. *Now she begins to smile slightly.*) You know, Mr. Piper, I feel certain that J. B. will approve completely.

GILBERT (*Aghast*): Approve?

PAULINE (*Nods*): As you are aware, J. B.'s consuming interest is in the development of properly supervised recreation for young people. That's why he's raising funds for the new clubhouse. When I tell him that you were willing to forego an important dinner engagement in order to take your place at the head of neighborhood festivities—(*She breaks off, then smiles.*) J. B. is going to be proud of you, Mr. Piper. (MADGE *and* CAROL *are speechless.*)

GILBERT (*At last, to* PAULINE): He is?

MADGE (*With a little gasp*): Oh, my goodness!

CAROL (*Her eyes suddenly bright*): Father!

PAULINE (*To* GILBERT): If J. B. has any doubts as to your qualifications for promotion, this will indeed dispel them. (PAULINE *smiles at* GILBERT *with deep satisfaction.* GILBERT *is dazed.*)

CAROL (*To* PAULINE): Mrs. Vermillion, you mean that everything's all right?

PAULINE (*Turns to* CAROL): Your father has proved that he is a man of sterling character. (*To* GILBERT) Take all the time you need with your Halloween activities, Mr. Piper. Under the circumstances, J. B. and I shall be entirely willing to wait at the club. (*She steps to chair left, picks up her purse. Then she speaks to* MADGE.) I'll see you later, my dear. (*She moves upstage to center door, then turns.* CAROL, MADGE *and* GILBERT *watch her in speechless silence. She speaks to* GILBERT.) Mr. Piper, you are indeed putting into practice that great slogan which J. B. and I created—"Treat Every Child the Way You Would Treat Your Own." (*She smiles broadly.*) Congratulations! (*She exits at center. For a moment the others stand in amazed silence. At last* MADGE *sinks weakly into chair.* CAROL *drops onto divan.* GILBERT *continues to stand down left. Suddenly* ROSS *enters from right. He still carries the tuxedo.*)

Ross (*Humbly, to* Gilbert): Mr. Piper, I want to apologize to you for—

Gilbert (*Suddenly takes a step toward* Ross): Don't you dare apologize! (Ross *startled, jumps back.*)

Carol (*To* Ross, *as she rises*): Ross, you can't imagine what has happened!

Madge: It's simply amazing!

Gilbert (*To* Ross): Young man, this afternoon you made the best error you'll ever make in your life.

Ross (*Startled*): Huh? (Gilbert *steps to* Ross, *takes the suit.*)

Gilbert (*Moves to* Madge, *hands her the suit*): Guard this suit until I get back. (Madge, *seated in chair left, takes suit.*)

Ross (*To* Gilbert): Until you get back? (*At first* Gilbert *makes no answer. He turns from* Madge, *then crosses to* Ross.)

Gilbert (*To* Ross): You're coming with me. (*He takes* Ross *by the arm.*)

Ross (*With a startled jump*): What's that?

Gilbert (*To* Ross): Young man, I'm about to fulfill an important obligation to the youth of this neighborhood. And you'll make a perfect assistant. (*He grins broadly.*) Don't ask questions, but you and I have a Halloween date with (*Breaking off*)—trick or treat! (*With one hand,* Gilbert *places the mask in front of his face. With the other hand he guides* Ross *upstage toward center door.* Carol *and* Madge *smile in genuine happiness and relief.* Gilbert *and a still-confused* Ross *reach door center. The curtain quickly falls.*)

THE END

Production Notes

No Treat for Gilbert

Characters: 2 male; 3 female.

Playing Time: 30 minutes.

Costumes: Gilbert wears a conservative business suit and hat when he first appears. Later, he appears draped in a sheet. Madge wears an evening dress. Carol wears a skirt and sweater, or some other casual dress. Ross wears a pirate's costume. Mrs. Vermillion wears an evening dress and a formal coat. She carries a party purse.

Properties: Corsage in cellophane bag and a laundry bag, for Carol; dry cleaners' bag containing woman's short coat, for Madge; tuxedo on hanger, for Ross.

Setting: The comfortable and attractive living room of the Pipers. There are three entrances to the room—the outside door at center back, a door at left of stage which connects with the rear portion of the house, and a door at right of stage which opens into the library. At downstage right are divan and coffee table. At downstage left is an armchair. A magazine rack stands at side of chair. The living room table is located against wall upstage and to immediate left of center door. On table are two grotesque Halloween masks.

Lighting: No special effects.

Sounds: Doorbell as indicated.

She's Not Talking

Characters

ANNE KERRY
BLANCHE KERRY, *her mother*
PHIL MURRAY
EUGENIA DOBBS
JONATHAN WICK

TIME: *Saturday morning.*

SETTING: *The living room of the Kerry home.*

AT RISE: BLANCHE KERRY *is seated on the sofa, reading a magazine. She shakes her head gloomily, then sets the magazine aside. Then she vigorously rubs her throat, wincing at the resulting pain. The telephone rings. BLANCHE rises, goes to the phone, and picks it up. She opens her mouth, trying desperately to speak, but no sound comes out. She tries again. ANNE KERRY enters, running, carrying a medicine bottle and a teaspoon.*

ANNE: I'll get it, Mother. (BLANCHE *hangs up the phone, and pantomimes to* ANNE, *indicating that the caller has*

hung up.) Did they hang up? (BLANCHE *nods her head.*)
Poor dear! Here, I have your medicine. It's time for another dose. (*She unscrews top of bottle.* BLANCHE *shakes
her head hopelessly.* ANNE *is upset.*) Mother, you simply
have to take this solution if you expect to clear up your
throat by evening. (BLANCHE *again shakes her head.*)
You haven't spoken for two days. It's horrible! (BLANCHE
nods in emphatic assent.) This is the first time you've
had laryngitis since I can remember. Now of all times!
(ANNE *pours a small portion of liquid from bottle into
teaspoon. She extends it to* BLANCHE's *mouth.*) Here you
are. (*Grudgingly* BLANCHE *opens her mouth. She swallows the liquid.* ANNE *steps back slightly, surveys her
mother hopefully.*) Now do you feel better? (BLANCHE
shakes her head.) Mother, can't you say anything at
all? (BLANCHE's *only response is a hoarse and muffled
grunt.* ANNE *speaks with increasing concern.*) Mother,
what *are* we going to do? If you can't speak in a natural
tone by tonight—(*Breaks off as the doorbell rings.*
BLANCHE *starts to rise, but* ANNE *stops her.*) I'll see who
it is. (*Hurriedly she crosses to table, where she places
bottle and spoon. Then she turns to* BLANCHE.) After all,
Mother, you're in no condition for vocal greetings! (*As*
ANNE *moves to door,* BLANCHE *sinks back onto divan.*
ANNE *opens door. At doorway stands* PHIL.)

PHIL (*Grins pleasantly*): Hello, Anne.

ANNE: Phil! Come in.

PHIL (*Steps into room*): How's your mother?

ANNE (*Sighs*): Just the same, I'm afraid.

PHIL: You mean she *still* can't talk? (ANNE *nods as she
closes door.*)

ANNE: The poor dear sounds like a Diesel engine lost in a snowdrift.

PHIL (*Steps to* BLANCHE, *smiles sympathetically*): This *is* rough, Mrs. Kerry. (BLANCHE *nods emphatically.*) Anything I can do for you? (BLANCHE *sighs, gloomily shakes her head. Then* PHIL *turns to* ANNE.) I suppose you'd rather pass up that dance tonight, Anne?

ANNE (*Nods*): I must, Phil.

PHIL (*With understanding*): Sure—with your mother in this condition and your father out of town for the week end.

ANNE (*Sadly*): That's not the half of it. (*She hesitates.*) Phil, we were going to keep it a secret, but now that mother has lost her voice—(*She breaks off, speaks to* BLANCHE.) Shall I tell him? (BLANCHE *nods.*) Mother was asked to appear on a radio panel next week. It's to be broadcast over our local station.

PHIL: Radio panel?

ANNE (*Nods*): One of those informal discussion affairs. The program is sponsored by Wick's Washing Machines.

PHIL (*Heartily*): Say, that sounds all right. Your mother should be a whiz on a panel show.

ANNE: On the radio without a voice?

PHIL: She'll be all right in a few days. (*To* BLANCHE) Won't you, Mrs. Kerry?

ANNE: Phil, you don't understand. Mother is scheduled for a personal interview tonight.

PHIL: Personal interview?

ANNE (*Nods, as she picks up bottle and spoon from table*): Eugenia Dobbs is coming here tonight for an informal chat with Mother.

PHIL: Eugenia Dobbs? Who's she?

ANNE: Miss Dobbs is an advertising representative who handles the Wick Washing Machine account. She is also to act as moderator on the program.

PHIL: She'll be here this evening?

ANNE (*Unhappily*): Miss Dobbs insists upon first talking with the panel members in their own homes. When she finds Mother speechless, she's sure to select somebody else. (ANNE *exits, leaving door open.*)

PHIL (*Whistles*): Good grief, that *is* a situation! (*To* BLANCHE) But no doubt she'll understand, Mrs. Kerry. (BLANCHE *shakes her head sadly.*) Or perhaps you'll be all right by tonight. (*Again* BLANCHE *shakes her head.*) Have you ever met this Eugenia Dobbs? (ANNE *enters.*)

ANNE: That's what makes it so embarrassing. Miss Dobbs simply won't believe that Mother has a good voice. If I explain to Miss Dobbs about the laryngitis, she'll be afraid to book mother for the program next week.

PHIL (*To* BLANCHE, *as he drops onto divan at her side*): Believe me, I'm sorry, Mrs. Kerry. (*Smiles sympathetically*) But after all, that program isn't too important.

ANNE: It *is* important, Phil. Each woman who appears on the panel is to receive a new Wick's Washing Machine.

PHIL: A new washing machine? (PHIL *turns questioningly to* BLANCHE; BLANCHE *nods emphatically.*)

ANNE: We could really use one around this place. You should see our old machine in the basement. It trembles with age. Jonathan Wick, who's president of the company, will appear on the program. He's to present the washing machines to the panel members.

PHIL (*To* BLANCHE): I don't blame you for being so upset.

(*Grins*) Don't worry, Mrs. Kerry. I'll drop around again tonight. Perhaps Anne and I can convince the dear lady that you'll be in good voice by next week.

ANNE (*Dryly*): You couldn't convince Eugenia Dobbs that the sun rises in the east. Her notification letter to Mother sounded like something from the Magna Charta.

PHIL (*Rises*): I wish I could come up with an idea.

ANNE (*To* PHIL): I wish you could come up with a new washing machine. (*Crosses to* BLANCHE) Mother, you'd better go upstairs for a rest. There's no need to stay down here. (*Sighing,* BLANCHE *rises.* ANNE *takes her arm.*) Here, I'll help you.

PHIL: You'll be all right, Mrs. Kerry.

ANNE (*To* BLANCHE): Of course you will. (BLANCHE, *pauses, turns to* PHIL. *Desperately she attempts to speak, but the effort is in vain.*) You poor, poor dear! (ANNE *and* BLANCHE *exit. The doorbell rings.* PHIL *hesitates, glances around uncertainly. Finally he opens door.* EU- GENIA DOBBS *sweeps into the room.*)

EUGENIA (*Aggressively*): All right, where is she?

PHIL (*Puzzled and confused*): Where is *who?*

EUGENIA: Mrs. Blanche Kerry, of course. (*Pause*) This *is* the Kerry residence?

PHIL: Yes.

EUGENIA (*Faces* PHIL *majestically*): I am Miss Eugenia Dobbs.

PHIL (*Startled*): Eugenia Dobbs?

EUGENIA (*Nods*): I handle the advertising account for the Wick Washing Machine Company.

PHIL (*Uneasily*): Yes, I know.

EUGENIA: I am also to act as moderator on the Wick radio

program next week. In fact, it is *my* project—*my* brain
child—*my* achievement. (*She breaks off, peers at* PHIL.)
Young man, are you a member of this family?

PHIL: No. I'm Phil Murray.

EUGENIA (*Crisply*): The gardener, no doubt.

PHIL: The gardener?

EUGENIA: You may announce me now.

PHIL: *Now?* Miss Dobbs, I'm certain you weren't expected
until tonight.

EUGENIA: I have had to change my plans. Mr. Jonathan
Wick himself, and in person, wishes to discuss the program details with me this evening. Therefore, I must interview the panel members during the day.

PHIL: I'm afraid you can't see Mrs. Kerry just now. You
see, she's—

EUGENIA (*Cuts in*): Kindly do not interrupt me, young
man. In my business we have no interruptions, except for
commercials. Mrs. Kerry is to appear on my radio panel
next week— (*Dramatically*) although I still do not believe that radio is the best medium for exploiting the
Wick product. In my opinion, Jonathan Wick should
sponsor a television hour, but Mr. Wick is most determined and outspoken.

PHIL (*Slyly*): Then you two must make quite a pair.

EUGENIA: I have attempted to bring Mr. Wick to my way
of thinking, but he clings to radio. He's definitely the
clinging type. (*Suddenly*) But enough of this. (*Majestically she sits on divan.*) You may bring in Mrs.
Kerry.

PHIL (*Emphatically*): Miss Dobbs, I'm trying to tell you—
you can't see Mrs. Kerry.

EUGENIA: I do not care to *see* her. This is radio—not television. Only the sound will be important. I wish only to hear Mrs. Kerry speak.

PHIL: That's just it.

EUGENIA (*Raises her hand*): No interruptions, I said. However, since you appear to be a member of the household staff, I shall give you the necessary instructions.

PHIL (*Desperately*): Miss Dobbs, you have to listen—

EUGENIA (*Cuts in*): Don't haggle, or I shall report you to your superiors. Now, before I meet Mrs. Kerry, I will place a blindfold over my eyes. I do not desire to be visually influenced by the sight of this panel member. Rather, I must catch her personality only through the voice.

PHIL (*With sudden interest*): Only through the voice?

EUGENIA (*Nods*): Exactly as if I were a radio listener. (*For a moment* PHIL *doesn't answer, but* EUGENIA's *statement has given him a sudden idea. A slow smile begins to form.*)

PHIL (*Takes a step toward* EUGENIA): Miss Dobbs, I want to get this straight. (*Slowly*) You expect to blindfold yourself before you interview Mrs. Kerry? You don't want to see her?

EUGENIA (*With dignity*): That's what I said. (*With considerable triumph*) You may be interested in knowing that this is my original idea.

PHIL (*Attempts to hide his growing elation*): And *you* may be interested in knowing that I think it's the best idea since Benjamin Franklin flew his kite in a thunderstorm.

EUGENIA (*Condescendingly*): Thank you. (*Pause*) Of course,

the blindfold arrangement for the interview would not
be necessary if I could sell Mr. Wick on a television presentation. But since he demands radio, then I shall give
him the *best* in radio.

PHIL (*Breathlessly excited*): Miss Dobbs, this is great!
(*Quickly corrects himself*) I mean it's a sound plan.
(*Pretends to be a bit disheartened*) However, I am
afraid you can't interview Mrs. Kerry at the moment.

EUGENIA: Why not?

PHIL: She's upstairs resting.

EUGENIA (*Rises impatiently*): In my profession we do not
rest.

PHIL (*Steps to* EUGENIA, *pats her arm with affected sympathy*): But you must remember, Miss Dobbs, that Mrs.
Kerry is only an average housewife. She needs her morning nap.

EUGENIA: I *never* nap.

PHIL (*Pretends to have a sudden idea*): Miss Dobbs, why
don't you call on one of the other panel members first?
When you drop back here later, I'm sure Mrs. Kerry
will be ready for you.

EUGENIA: Are you attempting to confuse my schedule?

PHIL (*Easily*): Not at all. But at the moment Mrs. Kerry
is hardly a fit subject for an interview. A little later I'm
sure we could arrange a more satisfactory meeting.

EUGENIA (*Hesitates*): Very well. I shall return shortly.

PHIL (*Beams*): We shall expect you, Miss Dobbs. We shall
expect you.

EUGENIA (*Moves toward door, turns*): Before you return
to your garden duties, I trust you will prepare Mrs.
Kerry for my arrival.

PHIL (*With a flourish*): My dear lady, I am famous for my preparations. (EUGENIA *exits. Immediately* PHIL *snaps his fingers in happy excitement. His grin is broad and enthusiastic.* ANNE *enters from left.*)

ANNE: I finally got Mother upstairs.

PHIL (*Swiftly moves to* ANNE): Anne!

ANNE (*Startled*): Phil, what's the matter?

PHIL (*Steps to* ANNE, *pulls her to center*): What do you know? Eugenia Dobbs was here.

ANNE (*Shocked*): Eugenia Dobbs? She wasn't expected until tonight.

PHIL: Her plans have been changed. I sent her off for another interview. She'll return shortly.

ANNE: Didn't you tell her about Mother?

PHIL (*Cuts in*): I didn't tell her anything. She did all the talking. Listen, Anne. I've a great idea. If it works, Eugenia Dobbs will believe she's had a pleasant interview with your mother.

ANNE (*Protests*): That's impossible.

PHIL (*Breathlessly*): Maybe not. Now, get this, Anne—Miss Dobbs wants to *hear* your mother, not *see* her. Miss Dobbs is interested only in voices. She doesn't want to be influenced by looks. So before she meets your mother, she's putting on a blindfold.

ANNE: A blindfold?

PHIL (*Nods*): So she can concentrate on your mother's voice, as a radio listener would.

ANNE: You know Mother can't talk.

PHIL (*Grins*): Anne, get set for the special bulletin. (*Pause*) You're going to talk for your mother.

ANNE (*Aghast*): I'm going to *what?*

PHIL: Your mother and Miss Dobbs will be in the same room, but Miss Dobbs will wear a blindfold. When she asks your mother a question, *you* will answer.

ANNE (*Starts to protest*): Now, see here, Phil—

PHIL: It's our only chance.

ANNE: Why, I've never heard of such a thing!

PHIL: Neither has Miss Dobbs, I hope. (*Persuasively*) You said yourself that Miss Dobbs would toss your mother off the panel if the interview fell through. No voice— no washing machine.

ANNE (*Slowly*): Yes, I know.

PHIL: Well?

ANNE (*After a pause*): Phil, do you think I could? Do you suppose I could talk for Mother?

PHIL (*Vigorously*): Of course you could! By next week your mother will be in good voice again. (*Grins*) And dear Miss Dobbs will never know the difference.

ANNE: What will Mother say about all this?

PHIL (*Chuckles*): That's just it. In your mother's silent condition, she can't say anything.

ANNE (*Begins to warm to the idea*): Phil, perhaps it *is* worth a try.

PHIL (*Nods enthusiastically*): Exactly! Don't tell your mother anything. She might balk. When she *does* realize what's going on, she can't make a sound of protest. (*For a moment* ANNE *is silent. Then she breaks into a soft giggle.*)

ANNE: Phil, it does sound shattering! (*Suddenly thoughtful*) What sort of answers would I make to Miss Dobbs' questions?

PHIL: That's up to you. Anything to impress the old girl.

ANNE (*At last makes up her mind*): All right.

PHIL (*Beams*): Great!

ANNE: I'll get Mother. (*She starts toward exit.*) We won't be long.

PHIL (*Calls to* ANNE): Anne!

ANNE (*Turns*): Yes?

PHIL: Don't bring your mother in here until Miss Dobbs arrives. When the blindfold is in place, I'll call you.

ANNE (*Moves to opening, then turns to* PHIL): Phil, do you know something? For the first time in my life, no matter what sort of statements I make, Mother can't argue with me! (*She exits. The doorbell rings.* PHIL *is startled. He hesitates, then moves upstage. He opens door. At doorway stands* JONATHAN WICK.)

JONATHAN (*With dignity*): Good morning, good morning. Is this the Kerry residence?

PHIL: Yes.

JONATHAN (*Steps into the room, closes door behind him*): Then it is my civic duty to introduce myself. (*Impressively*) I am Jonathan Wick.

PHIL (*With a start*): Jonathan Wick?

JONATHAN (*Nods*): President of the Wick Washing Machine Company. You have no doubt heard of my product —and I quote—"The Washer With the Personality"— "The Machine That Cleans Your Daintiest Duds"— "If Washday Makes You Sick, Enjoy a Holiday With Wick."

PHIL (*Amazed*): Jonathan Wick! Yes, I've certainly heard of you, sir.

JONATHAN: I wish to speak with Miss Dobbs. Miss Eugenia Dobbs. I believe she is at present interviewing Mrs.

Kerry. I had an appointment with Miss Dobbs this evening regarding my forthcoming radio program. However, I find I have other commitments tonight, so I shall confer with Miss Dobbs immediately. (*He sits on divan.*)

PHIL (*Uneasily*): Sir, Miss Dobbs isn't here.

JONATHAN: Not here? (*Annoyed*) Young man, why didn't you so inform me?

PHIL: You didn't give me a chance.

JONATHAN: Fiddlesticks! I've been sitting here for hours, utterly speechless. But did you tell me about Miss Dobbs' absence? You did not! (*He rises.*) Where is she?

PHIL: I don't know, sir. Miss Dobbs left a few minutes ago, but she's coming back.

JONATHAN: Then I shall await her arrival. (*He again sits on divan.*)

PHIL (*Suddenly alarmed*): But Miss Dobbs hasn't even interviewed Mrs. Kerry yet.

JONATHAN: Very good. That will give me an opportunity to join the merry little conference.

PHIL: *You?*

JONATHAN: Who has a greater right to be present than I?

PHIL: It's just that we—we'd planned to—(*Confused, he breaks off.*) That is, we didn't exactly expect you or anybody else, without a blindfold.

JONATHAN: Young man, what are you talking about? I declare, you are a most confusing houseman.

PHIL: Houseman?

JONATHAN (*Nods*): That is of course your status. My eyes are always open.

PHIL: That's just what I was afraid of.

JONATHAN: You may go now.

PHIL: But—but—(*After an uneasy pause*) Mr. Wick, wouldn't it be more satisfactory if Miss Dobbs interviewed Mrs. Kerry without—(*He breaks off.*)

JONATHAN (*Questioningly*): Without my presence? Certainly not! I consider this a happy situation. I can confer with Miss Dobbs, as well as attend an informal interview. (*Suddenly*) And by the way, which of my models does Mrs. Kerry currently use?

PHIL (*Puzzled*): Which of your models?

JONATHAN (*Nods*): She of course owns a Wick Washing Machine. (*Pause*) Doesn't she?

PHIL: I don't know, sir.

JONATHAN: You don't know? As an employee of this household, you are most unobserving. Where is the laundry room in this establishment?

PHIL: Laundry room? (JONATHAN *nods*.) I think the washing machine's in the basement.

JONATHAN (*Rises*): Then I shall check on it personally.

PHIL: Check on it?

JONATHAN: I make it a point to inspect the laundry equipment in every home I enter. I've been doing it for twenty years. I keep a chart on such data. (*Gazes around impatiently*) Where is the basement?

PHIL (*Slowly*): You mean you want to go downstairs and take a look at Mrs. Kerry's washing machine?

JONATHAN (*Impatiently*): Young man, don't you follow me?

PHIL: Follow you? (*Begins to grin*) I have a feeling I'm way ahead of you. (*Quickly he crosses to* JONATHAN, *takes him by the arm.*) Mr. Wick, if you're determined to go downstairs, I shall be delighted to show you the way. (*He begins to escort* JONATHAN *toward exit.*)

JONATHAN: At last, young man, you are showing signs of cooperation. You are acting with spirit.

PHIL (*Grins broadly*): You have no idea, Mr. Wick! You have no idea! (PHIL *and* JONATHAN *exit. After a slight pause the doorbell rings. Then the ring is repeated. Still no one appears. At last the door opens.* EUGENIA, *annoyed, peers into the empty room. She enters, closing door behind her. Gazing impatiently around the room, she moves downstage. Then* PHIL *enters breathlessly. He beams enthusiastically.*) Miss Dobbs! What a pleasure to see you again!

EUGENIA (*Stoutly*): I rang the doorbell twice.

PHIL (*Nods*): It must have been most annoying.

EUGENIA: As a gardener, you were transplanting, I presume?

PHIL (*Nods slyly*): Yes. (*Pause*) Transplanting from the living room to the basement.

EUGENIA: Mrs. Kerry is now prepared for my interview?

PHIL (*Beams*): We're all prepared.

EUGENIA (*Opens her purse*): Then I shall put on my blindfold. (*She removes a blindfold or standard eye mask from purse.*)

PHIL (*Steps hurriedly to* EUGENIA): Of course, Miss Dobbs, but in the sunroom, please. (*He grasps her arm, starts to escort her toward door right.*)

EUGENIA (*Startled*): In the sunroom?

PHIL (*Nods, smiling brightly*): It's an old Victorian custom

around here. We never permit visitors to put on blind-
folds in the living room.

EUGENIA: That's odd. Really, I can't understand why.

PHIL (*Hurriedly opens door*): Custom, Miss Dobbs, custom.
(*Urgently* PHIL *pushes* EUGENIA *through doorway. He
closes door. Then he starts across the room. As he does
so,* ANNE *and* BLANCHE *enter left.* ANNE *holds* BLANCHE
firmly by the arm. BLANCHE *is puzzled and confused,
but silent.* PHIL *stops short. He speaks in an animated
but somewhat hushed tone.*) Good! I was about to call
you.

ANNE: We heard the doorbell, so Mother and I came on
down.

PHIL (*Significantly, to* ANNE): Everything's set.

ANNE: Then she's here? (PHIL *nods. He indicates door
right.* ANNE *turns to* BLANCHE *with a bright smile.*)
Phil and I have a surprise for you. Perhaps you'd better
sit down. (ANNE *leads* BLANCHE *to chair.* BLANCHE *gazes
searchingly at* ANNE.) Right here, where you'll be comfortable. (*Slowly* BLANCHE *sits, but she's becoming suspicious. Suddenly* EUGENIA'S *voice is heard.*)

EUGENIA (*Offstage*): Young man! Young man! (ANNE
glances questioningly at PHIL. PHIL *nods.* ANNE *steps
behind chair in which* BLANCHE *is seated.* PHIL *moves
toward door right.*)

PHIL (*Answers* EUGENIA): Yes, Miss Dobbs? (BLANCHE *gives
a violent start. In shocked but silent amazement she starts
to rise.* ANNE *holds* BLANCHE *firmly by the shoulders.*)

EUGENIA (*Offstage, as* PHIL *opens the door*): My eyes are
covered.

PHIL (*Through doorway*): Splendid!

EUGENIA (*Offstage*): Is Mrs. Kerry ready?

PHIL: Indeed she is! Just move straight ahead. (EUGENIA, *wearing a blindfold, moves through doorway. Her arms are outstretched.* BLANCHE *gazes at the scene in horror.* PHIL *steps to* EUGENIA, *grasps her arm.*) My, you *do* look mysterious, Miss Dobbs. (*He leads* EUGENIA *toward divan.*) Careful now! Easy—down this way.

EUGENIA: Is Mrs. Kerry in the room?

PHIL (*Heartily*): She certainly is. Sit here on the divan, Miss Dobbs. (BLANCHE *is near the explosive point. She tries to cry out. Then she again attempts to rise, but* ANNE *holds her gently by the shoulders.* EUGENIA *carefully sits on divan.* PHIL *peers intently at the blindfold, then speaks to* EUGENIA.) You're certain you can't see?

EUGENIA (*With dignity*): Young man, when I cover my eyes, I cover them. When I plunge into a situation, I plunge.

PHIL (*Cheerfully*): This is going to be one of the most fascinating plunges you've ever taken. (PHIL *moves to center. He speaks to* BLANCHE *as he indicates* EUGENIA.) Mrs. Kerry, this is Miss Eugenia Dobbs. (BLANCHE *is horrified. In vain she attempts to speak.*)

EUGENIA (*Dramatically, to* BLANCHE): Mrs. Kerry, this *is* a pleasure! (*For a moment no one speaks.* ANNE *glances nervously at* PHIL, *who gives her an urgent smile of encouragement.*) I said, this is a pleasure, Mrs. Kerry. (ANNE *remains behind* BLANCHE'S *chair. She keeps her hands on* BLANCHE'S *shoulders.*)

ANNE (*At last answers* EUGENIA, *in a pleasant but highly affected tone*): Ah, thank you, Miss Dobbs! (*As* ANNE *speaks,* BLANCHE *almost chokes. Again she wildly, but unsuccessfully, attempts to jump up.*)

EUGENIA (*To* BLANCHE): You know why I am here, Mrs. Kerry?

ANNE (*Gains confidence*): Indeed I do. You desire to hear my voice, but you do not wish to be influenced by my appearance.

EUGENIA: Exactly. I want to catch your character from conversation alone, just as my listening audience will do.

ANNE: I've been looking forward to your visit, my dear.

EUGENIA (*Listens intently*): Mrs. Kerry, you *do* have a lovely voice.

ANNE (*Brightly*): Thank you.

EUGENIA: A voice so young, so fresh.

ANNE (*With affectation*): I may not be young, Miss Dobbs, but I'm certainly fresh. (BLANCHE *sputters silently. At that moment there is an urgent but muffled pounding offstage, as if someone were attempting to attract attention behind a locked door in another portion of the house.*)

JONATHAN (*His voice indistinct, as the pounding continues*): Let me out! Let me out!

EUGENIA (*Sits up with a start*): What was that? (ANNE *is genuinely astonished by the interruption. Puzzled and confused, she turns toward opening left. Swiftly but quietly* PHIL *goes to* ANNE). That sound seems to be coming from the basement. (*In hurried pantomine* PHIL *attempts to explain to* ANNE. *He points toward left opening, then points downward, as though indicating basement. Then he pretends to shake an imaginary doorknob. He strikes the air with his fists as though pound-*

ing on a door. ANNE *appears to understand, but she's obviously upset and confused.* BLANCHE *makes frantic gestures.* EUGENIA *speaks insistently.*) Mrs. Kerry, I asked you, what was that noise? (PHIL *silently but desperately indicates to* ANNE *that she must answer.*)

ANNE (*With effort*): It was nothing.

EUGENIA (*Insistently*): Mrs. Kerry, at the moment my hearing is most acute. I'm certain someone is trying to get out of your basement.

ANNE (*Vaguely*): It often happens.

EUGENIA (*Shocked*): Often?

ANNE: You know how those things are.

EUGENIA (*With dignity*): Indeed I do not. (*Suddenly*) Mrs. Kerry, are you keeping someone a prisoner in your basement?

PHIL (*Suddenly breaks in, to* EUGENIA): Miss Dobbs, perhaps I can explain.

EUGENIA (*To* PHIL): Explain? *You?*

PHIL: Mrs. Kerry's washing machine is one of the old models. When it runs it sometimes puts up a terrible protest. (ANNE *is startled by the explanation.*)

EUGENIA: The commotion I heard certainly didn't sound like a broken-down washing machine.

PHIL (*Brightly*): My dear Miss Dobbs, we *do* have to put up with some strange conditions around here. (*To* ANNE.) Don't we, Mrs. Kerry?

ANNE (*Emphatically*): That's the truth!

PHIL (*Turns to* EUGENIA): So you see, Miss Dobbs—

EUGENIA (*Annoyed, to* PHIL): Young man, will you kindly stop breaking in on the conversation? You should be

back in the garden, or wherever you belong. I'm interviewing Mrs. Kerry.

PHIL (*To* EUGENIA): I apologize, but I felt an explanation
was necessary. (*He glances significantly at* ANNE.)

EUGENIA (*To* PHIL): Very well. Now run along and reset
your petunias. (*As though dismissing* PHIL, *she now
speaks to* BLANCHE.) Mrs. Kerry, during the panel show
next week I shall ask questions which will be of interest
to the mothers in our listening audience. These listeners
will want to know your hopes—your plans—your problems.

ANNE (*With sincerity*): At the moment I certainly *do*
have my problems.

EUGENIA: Tell me of your goals, Mrs. Kerry.

ANNE: My goals? (*She gazes questioningly at* PHIL. *He nods
encouragement.*) Above all else, I wish to give my darling daughter everything she desires. (BLANCHE *is furious.*)

EUGENIA (*Startled*): You do?

ANNE: My daughter is such a splendid young woman—so
attractive, so intelligent. My ambition is to grant every
wish of her heart. (BLANCHE *jumps wildly to her feet.*
PHIL *steps to* BLANCHE. *He shakes his head vigorously
at her, as though pleading that she make no further
move.*)

EUGENIA (*Completely unaware of the action across the
room*): That is a rather startling answer, Mrs. Kerry.

ANNE (*With affected brightness*): I suppose some people
would say I'm a rather startling person.

EUGENIA: I don't believe I've ever heard such a frank statement.

ANNE: I doubt that you ever will again.

EUGENIA: Mrs. Kerry, do you believe that parents should be strict with their children?

ANNE (*Emphatically*): I do not! Children must be given every freedom. Parents should never criticize, never condemn, never question.

EUGENIA (*Amazed*): You *do* have a liberal attitude. (*Smiles*) You know, I rather like your youthful viewpoint.

PHIL: Her viewpoint is youthful, all right.

EUGENIA (*To* PHIL, *in annoyance*): Are you still around?

PHIL: I'm so intrigued, I simply can't tear myself away. (ANNE *almost breaks into a laugh.*)

EUGENIA (*To* BLANCHE): Mrs. Kerry, I feel that your answers will stir up much controversy among our listeners. That, of course, is what Jonathan Wick desires. (*Smiles majestically.*) We must sell his washing machines, you know.

ANNE (*To* EUGENIA): I have always felt it was my duty to stand up for the youth of today.

EUGENIA: That voice of yours, my dear! One would think you were still in your teens. I've never heard such tone quality in a mature individual.

ANNE (*Affects a light laugh*): It isn't often that I let myself go like this.

PHIL: Truer words have never been spoken.

ANNE (*To* EUGENIA): No doubt when I appear on your program next week, I'll sound like any other mother and wife.

EUGENIA: My dear, I honestly hope not. (BLANCHE's *indignation is evident. She attempts to break in on the conversation. Although she continues to open her mouth*

and speak with wild emphasis, no sound is forthcoming.)
Now, Mrs. Kerry, I should like to hear your opinion on
—(BLANCHE *desperately leaps to her feet. She frees her-*
self, then starts to rush toward EUGENIA. ANNE, *standing*
behind BLANCHE'S *chair, makes a wild but unsuccessful*
attempt to grasp her mother. EUGENIA *continues to*
speak.)—on several important topics which I shall bring
up as moderator. We shall open our discussion with—
(ANNE *forgets her role. She shrieks as* BLANCHE *starts*
across the room.)

ANNE: *Stop it!* (EUGENIA *breaks off with a start.* ANNE
rushes to BLANCHE, *grasps her arm.*)

EUGENIA (*Shocked*): Mrs. Kerry, what did you say? (PHIL
is in equal panic, as ANNE *attempts to hold* BLANCHE.
He, too, rushes to BLANCHE. *The swift actions of the*
three result in considerable noise and confusion in the
room. EUGENIA *rises.*) I am certain I hear noises in this
room!

BLANCHE (*To* EUGENIA, *in a rush of words*): I'll say you do!
(BLANCHE *stops short in amazement. She's aghast at her*
accomplishment.)

ANNE (*Horrified*): Mother! (PHIL *groans.*)

BLANCHE (*In complete wonder*): I spoke! (*In wild panto-*
mime ANNE *and* PHIL *attempt to silence* BLANCHE.)

EUGENIA (*Demandingly*): Mrs. Kerry, what's going on?

BLANCHE (*In happy amazement, paying no attention to*
EUGENIA): My goodness, I'm all right! I'm *cured!*

EUGENIA (*Desperately*): Mrs. Kerry! Your voice! It's chang-
ing!

BLANCHE (*With increased joy*): I can say anything! Simply
anything!

EUGENIA: Madam, you're not even listening to me! (*Swiftly she pulls off her blindfold. Now she faces* BLANCHE, ANNE *and* PHIL. ANNE *and* PHIL *are in panic.* EUGENIA *speaks to* BLANCHE.) You are not cooperating. At the start of this interview, I was elated—(*She breaks off suddenly as she sees* ANNE. *She gazes at* ANNE.) Who are you?

BLANCHE (*Still enthused by the return of her voice*): This is my daughter, Anne. (*She beams at* ANNE.) Anne, did you hear Mother speak right out loud? I can talk as well as ever!

ANNE (*Moans*): Oh, Mother! (*She turns from* BLANCHE.)

PHIL (*Equally pained*): Oh, gosh! (*He turns from* BLANCHE.)

EUGENIA (*With rising suspicion*): Something has been going on behind my back. I sense confusion in this room.

BLANCHE (*Happily begins to repeat the alphabet*): A— B—C—D—

EUGENIA (*Wildly*): Mrs. Kerry, stop that!

ANNE (*Suddenly turns to* EUGENIA): Miss Dobbs, you might as well know the truth. (*Pause*) Mother wasn't answering your questions.

EUGENIA (*Stoutly*): Of course she was.

ANNE (*Steps forward*): You heard *my* voice, Miss Dobbs. (EUGENIA *is shocked.*) Mother had laryngitis. She couldn't speak. So I did the talking.

EUGENIA (*Horrified*): *You?* Oh, no!

BLANCHE (*Turns to* ANNE): Anne, I should be terribly angry at you. But Mother's so happy to be able to talk again that she—

EUGENIA (*Breaks in angrily*): Mrs. Kerry, is this the truth?

BLANCHE (*Nods*): Yes. I didn't know anything about it until Anne brought me down here. Then I was simply thunderstruck. That is, until I—

EUGENIA (*Hotly, to* BLANCHE): Mrs. Kerry, do you realize this entire interview has been a horrible fake?

PHIL (*Turns to* BLANCHE): Mrs. Kerry, we were only trying to help you.

ANNE (*To* BLANCHE): We knew Miss Dobbs would never put you on the panel if she thought you couldn't make a sound.

BLANCHE (*To* EUGENIA): I'm all right now, Miss Dobbs. Oh, I was angry at first, but it *is* understandable, isn't it? We *did* need a new washing machine—

EUGENIA (*Cuts in coldly*): You might as well forget that washing machine, Mrs. Kerry. *You're off the panel!*

BLANCHE (*To* EUGENIA): Now, see here—

ANNE (*To* EUGENIA): Miss Dobbs—

EUGENIA (*Dramatically*): Oh, I was never so humiliated in my life! If Jonathan Wick knew what had happened, he'd probably cancel the program.

PHIL: Jonathan Wick? Oh, my goodness! (*Wildly he rushes to left, but before he can reach the exit,* JONATHAN *suddenly steps into room, mussed and dirty.*)

JONATHAN (*Stops, glares at* PHIL): Well!

EUGENIA (*Aghast*): Mr. Wick!

BLANCHE (*Startled*): Wick? Jonathan Wick?

JONATHAN (*Coldly*): Exactly—Jonathan Wick.

PHIL (*Nervously*): I was just on my way to—to check up on you.

EUGENIA (*To* JONATHAN): Mr. Wick, I didn't know you were here!

BLANCHE (*Gazes at* JONATHAN): My good man, you don't exactly look like the president of a—a washing machine company.

JONATHAN (*Steps to* BLANCHE): Madam, are you Mrs. Kerry?

BLANCHE: Yes. (*Suddenly*) And thank goodness, I have a voice to say so!

JONATHAN (*To* BLANCHE): Do you know where I've been?

BLANCHE: Not under the shower. I'm certain of that.

JONATHAN: *Locked* in your basement! (*Before the others can speak.*) And do you know who committed this ghastly crime? (*He points an angry finger at* PHIL.) Your houseman!

BLANCHE: But Phil isn't my houseman. He's only—

JONATHAN (*His voice rises*): I don't care *who* he is. I merely desired to inspect your washing machine. (*Again he points to* PHIL.) This delinquent showed me to your basement stairway. I went down the steps. Then he locked the door.

EUGENIA (*Suddenly, to* JONATHAN): Mr. Wick! So it was you I heard shouting and pounding.

JONATHAN (*Dramatically*): I was a prisoner in a dungeon.

BLANCHE (*Stoutly*): Mr. Wick, our basement is no dungeon! My husband cleaned it last week.

JONATHAN (*Pays no attention to* BLANCHE's *comment*): And do you know how I escaped? *By climbing through a basement window!*

EUGENIA: Mr. Wick!

JONATHAN: When I finally freed myself, I plunged through the back door, and here I am, torn and tattered in mind and body!

BLANCHE (*Amazed, as she turns to* PHIL): Phil, why on earth would you do such a thing?

PHIL (*To* BLANCHE): Mr. Wick wanted to be present at the interview. So I just had to get rid of him.

EUGENIA (*Steps forward, speaks to* JONATHAN): Do you know *why* they wanted to get rid of you, Mr. Wick? Because they knew *you'd* discover the fraud!

JONATHAN (*Startled*): Fraud?

EUGENIA: I was blindfolded, Mr. Wick. I wished to *hear* Mrs. Kerry, not *see* her. Unknown to me, Mrs. Kerry had lost her voice, so her daughter answered my questions.

JONATHAN: Answered your questions?

EUGENIA (*Nods*): I supposed it was Mrs. Kerry speaking. But she couldn't say a word.

BLANCHE (*Stoutly*): I certainly can now!

EUGENIA (*Dramatically*): The wool was deliberately pulled over my eyes!

PHIL: It wasn't wool. It was a blindfold.

EUGENIA (*To* JONATHAN): I was trying so hard to make this a perfect radio program.

JONATHAN (*Cuts in loudly*): Wait a minute—everybody! (*The others cease speaking.*) Let me get this straight. (*To* BLANCHE) You had lost your voice, madam?

BLANCHE (*Nods*): I had, but I can talk now, If you don't believe me—

JONATHAN: I do! (*To* ANNE) And you, young lady?

ANNE: I simply answered for Mother. Miss Dobbs was blindfolded. She didn't know who was talking.

EUGENIA (*To* JONATHAN): Here I sat, Mr. Wick, completely innocent. I'd spent hours attempting to make your radio program smooth and interesting.

JONATHAN (*Faces* EUGENIA): Miss Dobbs, my radio program is cancelled.

EUGENIA (*Horrified*): Cancelled? Mr. Wick!

JONATHAN (*To* EUGENIA): You didn't like the radio idea at the beginning, did you?

EUGENIA: No, but I *have* thrown my heart and soul into it.

JONATHAN: Miss Dobbs, there will be no radio panel and no radio moderator.

EUGENIA (*Crushed*): You mean I'm out of a job?

JONATHAN: Not at all. (*Then he speaks with sudden amusement.*) Your job *now* is to put the Wick Washing Machine program on television.

EUGENIA: Television? (*The others are equally startled.*)

JONATHAN: You've given me the idea for a wonderful Wick TV program. I want this entire scene re-enacted on television. I want the viewing public to see exactly what went on in this room.

BLANCHE: What!

ANNE: Mr. Wick!

EUGENIA (*With a gasp of happiness*): You mean it?

JONATHAN (*Grins*): It'll be a sensation! You, Miss Dobbs, will take the part of a blindfolded moderator. (*To* BLANCHE.) She'll pretend to ask you questions, Mrs. Kerry, but your daughter will speak for you. Can't you just see it? (*He breaks into loud laughter.*) It'll be a riot!

EUGENIA: Mr. Wick, are you serious?

JONATHAN: Of course I'm serious! (*Beams at* EUGENIA) You argued for a television program, didn't you, Miss Dobbs? Well, it's all yours. (EUGENIA *is breathlessly elated.* JONATHAN *turns to* BLANCHE.) You shall have your new washing machine, Mrs. Kerry. (*Dryly*) You certainly need one. (*To* ANNE) You and your young man will receive regular acting rates.

EUGENIA (*Sinks weakly onto divan*): Oh, my goodness!

ANNE (*Joyfully, to* BLANCHE): Mother, did you hear that?

BLANCHE (*Beams*): The reply is *yes!*

PHIL (*Begins to grin*): Good grief, then we're *all* in the act.

JONATHAN: I shall make my appearance at the end of the program. (*With sudden authority*) All right, everybody, let's snap into a rehearsal. (*To* EUGENIA) Miss Dobbs, your blindfold, please—(*To* BLANCHE) And you, Mrs. Kerry—

PHIL (*Breaks in, as he steps to* JONATHAN): Just a minute, Mr. Wick. (JONATHAN *turns questioningly.*) We'll present this scene on one condition.

JONATHAN: One condition?

PHIL (*Nods*): First we have to see *you* do it again.

JONATHAN: Do *what* again?

PHIL (*Grins*) Squeeze through that basement window! (*The others shout an enthusiastic agreement.* PHIL *grasps a startled* JONATHAN *by the arm. He escorts* JONATHAN *toward exit.* EUGENIA, *beaming broadly, jumps up. As* PHIL *and* JONATHAN *exit, the others gleefully start to follow. The curtain quickly falls.*)

THE END

Production Notes

Characters: 2 male; 3 female.

Playing Time: 25 minutes.

Costumes: Modern dress. Anne, Blanche, and Phil wear informal clothes. Eugenia wears an attractive tailored suit. Jonathan wears a business suit and carries a cane.

Properties: Medicine bottle and teaspoon, for Anne; blindfold, for Eugenia.

Setting: The living room of the Kerry home. Exits at left, right, and center lead to the rear portion of the house, to the sunroom, and outside. The room is comfortably furnished, with a sofa, chairs, tables, etc. On one table is a telephone.

Lighting: No special effects.

Greetings from the Fultons

Characters

JOAN FULTON
CORA FULTON, *Joan's mother*
DANIEL FULTON, *Joan's father*
TED BENSON
WINSTON MAYWOOD, *Daniel's boss*
BESSIE MAYWOOD, *Winston's sister*

TIME: *Morning, several weeks before Christmas.*
SETTING: *The living room of the Fulton home. A gaily decorated Christmas tree stands slightly right of center, and a box of tree decorations is on the divan.*
AT RISE: JOAN *stands on a small stepladder, fastening ornaments on the tree. She hums a lively Christmas carol. As* JOAN *works,* CORA *enters. She moves to the center and inspects the tree in silence for a moment before* JOAN *notices her.*

JOAN (*Gaily*): How do you like the tree?
CORA (*Without too much enthusiasm*): It's nicely trimmed, I suppose.

JOAN (*Smiles*): Hand me the box of ornaments, will you, darling? It's on the divan.

CORA (*Sighs, then moves to divan*): Joan, I don't approve of this. I've told you that before. (*She picks up box from divan.*)

JOAN: But Mother, this is a tremendous idea, and Ted Benson has been so sweet about it.

CORA (*Crosses to tree*): If *I* were dating Ted Benson, I certainly wouldn't ask him to get mixed up in this. (*She raises box of ornaments within reach of* JOAN.)

JOAN (*Selects an ornament from box*): One's enough, Mother. (*She turns to tree.*) Honestly, Ted's terribly enthusiastic about taking the picture. (*She continues speaking as she fastens ornament on tree.*) Can't you just see our Christmas cards this year? A picture of a Christmas tree with a Santa Claus in front of it! Just think! A real photograph taken in our own living room! Ted said he'd make all the prints we needed. I'll mount one on each card and we'll send them out as greetings from the Fulton family.

CORA: Joan, I don't object to the pictures. I don't object to the tree. (*Pointedly.*) But that Santa Claus idea of yours —(*She breaks off with a shake of her head.*)

JOAN (*As* CORA *crosses to divan, places box on divan*): What else could I do, Mother? We simply had to have a Santa Claus in the picture. (*The doorbell rings.*) That's Ted. Please let him in, darling. (CORA *sighs, then opens center door.* TED, *carrying a camera with an indoor flash attachment, enters the room as* JOAN *descends from the stepladder.*)

TED (*Agreeably*): Hello, Mrs. Fulton.

CORA: Good morning, Ted.

JOAN (*Gaily to* TED, *as he moves downstage*): Merry Christmas, Mr. Theodore H. Benson. We're all set for the camera shot.

TED (*Glances at tree, then turns to* JOAN): That tree is dripping with holiday glamour, all right. But where's the stuffed Santa Claus?

JOAN (*A bit uneasily*): Stuffed Santa Claus?

TED (*Nods*): You told me you were using one in the picture.

JOAN (*Vaguely*): Well, you see—(*She pauses, then suddenly smiles brightly.*) But Mother will explain. (*To* CORA.) Won't you, darling? (JOAN *picks up box of ornaments, and exits.*)

TED (*Knowingly*): I can tell by that look in Joan's eyes that something's up.

CORA: Joan discovered she couldn't make a stuffed Santa Claus.

TED: I told her it might be too big an undertaking.

CORA (*Continues*): So she rented a suit and whiskers.

TED (*Puzzled*): Rented a suit and whiskers? What'll she hang them on?

CORA (*Slowly and unhappily*): She's hanging them on *her* father.

TED: Her father? (CORA *nods.*) Do you mean that Mr. Fulton has consented to pose as Santa Claus for the Christmas picture?

CORA (*Nods dryly*): Joan even persuaded him to stay home from the office this morning while you take the photo.

TED: How did Joan talk Mr. Fulton into this?

CORA: Daniel asked Joan what she wanted for Christmas.

She made him promise he'd do something for her—something which wouldn't cost a cent. That part of the proposition sounded attractive to Daniel, so he agreed.

TED: Then Joan told him of the plan?

CORA (*Nods*): She did. Poor Daniel almost hit the ceiling, but what could he do? He couldn't go back on a promise.

TED: Not at the Christmas season, anyway. (JOAN *enters from right. She leaves the door open.*)

JOAN: We're all ready. Did Mother tell you about our Santa Claus?

TED (*Rises*): Joan, how could you do it?

CORA (*Significantly*): I'm wondering how *Daniel* could do it!

JOAN (*Smiles at* CORA): Don't be disagreeable, darling. (*Then she turns, calls loudly toward open doorway.*) Come on in, Father. (DANIEL *enters, wearing a Santa Claus suit and a flowing white beard.* TED *looks on in stunned amazement.*)

TED: Mr. Fulton! Is that *you?*

DANIEL (*With a sudden rafter-shaking roar*): Who do you think it is?

CORA: It's Daniel all right, together with every good pillow in the house. (*Exasperated,* CORA *snatches up the stepladder and exits.*)

JOAN (*Brightly, to* TED): Doesn't Father look wonderful?

DANIEL (*Shouts*): I don't *feel* wonderful!

TED: You *are* quite a sight, Mr. Fulton. You—you— (*Sinking back onto divan,* TED *breaks into loud laughter.*)

DANIEL (*Yells at* TED): Cut that out!

TED (*Attempts to control his laughter*): I'm sorry, sir.

DANIEL: This wasn't *my* idea!

TED: I understand, sir. (*He rises.*)

DANIEL (*Fumes loudly*): What'll my boss think when I don't show up for work?

JOAN: Don't worry about Mr. Maywood, Father. I called your office this morning.

DANIEL (*Startled*): You called my office?

JOAN (*Nods easily*): I thought of everything.

DANIEL: And what did Winston Maywood say? That I was fired or that I'd lost my mind?

JOAN (*Hesitates*): I didn't exactly talk to Mr. Maywood, Father. A woman answered the phone.

DANIEL (*Stubbornly*): Nobody answers Mr. Maywood's phone except Mr. Maywood!

JOAN: Honestly, Father, I don't know who she was. I'd never heard her voice before.

DANIEL (*Thoughtfully*): Somehow I don't like that. (*His voice rises.*) At the moment I don't like anything!

JOAN: Oh, stop fuming! I merely told the woman that you wouldn't be in this morning. (*Smiles.*) I said you were in poor shape. (*Giggling, she pats the padding which augments* DANIEL's *figure.*) Actually, Father, you *are* in poor shape—in spots.

DANIEL (*Groans helplessly*): Well, let's get it over.

JOAN: Ted, have we everything?

TED (*Thoughtfully*): We really ought to use a sheet.

DANIEL (*Hotly*): A sheet? Now see here, if you expect to wrap me in a sheet—

TED (*Hastily*): Oh, no, sir. I meant we should hang a sheet for the background.

JOAN (*To* TED): Mother will get us one. (*She moves to door left. She opens door, calls offstage.*) Mother! Oh, Mother!

CORA (*Offstage*): Yes?

JOAN: Will you bring us a sheet?

CORA (*Offstage*): A sheet? What on earth are you up to now?

JOAN (*Turns from doorway, speaks to* TED): You can pose Father while I get the sign.

TED (*Puzzled*): The sign?

JOAN (*Nods*): Santa Claus is going to hold a big "Merry Christmas" poster. Can't you just see it in the picture? (*She quickly exits right, leaving door open behind her.*)

DANIEL (*Continues to fume*): Do you know what will happen next year? That daughter of mine will want Thanksgiving cards—and she'll use *me* as the stuffed turkey!

TED: I know how you feel, sir—

DANIEL: You have no idea how I feel!

TED (*Politely*): Now if you'll just step over here, Mr. Fulton—(TED *crosses to left.*)

DANIEL (*Sputters, as he moves to* TED): I'll never make another promise as long as I live.

TED (*To* DANIEL): You can stand right here by the tree, in front of this chair. (*He indicates armchair by side of tree.*)

DANIEL: Why don't you just *hang* me on the tree?

TED: Mr. Fulton, please. (DANIEL *stands by Christmas tree as directed. The armchair is immediately behind him.* TED *backs to center, gazing at the effect. He nods in satisfaction.*)

DANIEL (*Sourly*): Well, do something! I don't intend to

stand here until the Fourth of July! By that time I'd probably have to crawl into a firecracker.

TED (*At center, as he peers at* DANIEL): Mr. Fulton, I believe I'll shoot you from here.

DANIEL (*Bellows*): So! It isn't enough that you take my picture. Now you want to *shoot* me! (JOAN *enters. She carries a large cardboard sign on which has been lettered "Merry Christmas."*)

JOAN (*Pauses briefly as she sees* DANIEL): Father, you *are* cute.

DANIEL: I am not cute! I'm crazy! (JOAN *crosses to* DANIEL. *She hands him the sign.*)

JOAN (*As* DANIEL *takes the sign*): Be sure your beard doesn't cover the sign. And give us a big, happy smile when Ted takes the picture, dear.

DANIEL (*Pained*): Big, happy smile! This is worse than making out my income tax return.

TED (*Significantly*): It's fortunate I'm not taking a *talking* picture of this scene. (CORA *enters. She carries a white sheet, folded.*)

CORA: May I kindly inquire as to why anybody in this house wishes a sheet? (JOAN *moves to* CORA.)

TED (*To* CORA): It was my suggestion, Mrs. Fulton.

CORA (*Dryly, to* TED): Don't tell me you're putting Santa Claus to bed.

JOAN (*Takes sheet from* CORA): We're using this as a background, Mother. (*She pats* CORA's *arm.*) Why don't you just sit in the sunroom, darling? We'll be through shortly. I know you'll be happier if you're out of the way.

DANIEL (*Grimly*): She's not the only one!

JOAN (*Turns to* DANIEL): Quiet, Father. (*To* CORA.) Now run along, dear. (CORA *gazes at the others in silent despair. With a deep sigh she then crosses to door.*)

CORA (*Pauses at door, turns to* DANIEL): Daniel, do you know what I think about all this? I think there ought to be a law! (CORA *exits.* TED *snickers in high amusement.* DANIEL *glares at him menacingly.* TED *swiftly erases the grin. The doorbell rings at offstage center.*)

DANIEL (*Startled*): What was that?

JOAN: The doorbell, Father.

DANIEL (*Loudly*): I refuse to see anybody. I flatly refuse to.

JOAN (*Quickly, to* DANIEL): Be quiet, Father!

DANIEL (*Shouting*): I'm always quiet!

JOAN: Sit down! (*She pushes* DANIEL *into armchair.*)

DANIEL (*Sputters*): Now see here!

JOAN (*Attempts to quiet* DANIEL): Sh, Father!

DANIEL (*Hotly*): Do you know what you're doing? You're pushing Santa Claus around!

TED (*Swiftly*): Not so loud, Mr. Fulton.

JOAN (*She begins to unfold sheet*): Ted, help me.

TED (*Steps to* JOAN): What's the idea?

JOAN (*Hands* TED *one end of sheet*): We've got to cover Father. (TED *snaps into action.*)

DANIEL (*Protests*): Now see here! (*The doorbell rings again.*)

JOAN (*In a loud whisper*): Don't shout, Father. (*Hurriedly, to* TED.) Quick, Ted! (JOAN *and* TED *have unfolded the sheet. Now they toss sheet over* DANIEL, *also covering the chair in which he is seated.*)

DANIEL (*Wails, from under sheet*): Stop it! Stop it!

JOAN (*Desperately to* DANIEL, *as she and* TED *smooth the sheet*): Do you want to be seen?

DANIEL: You're smothering me!

TED (*To* DANIEL): You're all right, Mr. Fulton. (JOAN *and* TED *work swiftly as they tuck the sheet around* DANIEL *and the chair. The doorbell rings a third time, loudly and impatiently.*)

DANIEL (*Groans*): Oh! Oh!

TED (*To* DANIEL, *in an emphatic whisper*): Don't move, Mr. Fulton!

JOAN (*Urgently, to* TED): Get your camera out of here.

TED (*Looks swiftly around the room*): Where?

JOAN (*Indicates door right*): The sunroom. (TED *nods. He rushes to divan, snatches camera.*)

TED: Joan, isn't your mother in there?

JOAN: Tell her nothing! (TED *exits right with camera, closing the door behind him.* JOAN *dashes to center door and throws it open.* BESSIE MAYWOOD *stands majestically in the doorway.*)

BESSIE (*Sputters in annoyance*): Well, young lady! (JOAN *is startled.*)

JOAN: Good morning.

BESSIE (*Demandingly*): Is your doorbell out of order?

JOAN: No.

BESSIE: I have been pushing the button for hours.

JOAN (*Upset*): I'm sorry.

BESSIE: Aren't you going to ask me to enter?

JOAN (*Puzzled*): Why, of course. (BESSIE *steps into the room. She glances around with considerable distaste.*)

BESSIE: No doubt this is the place. (*She takes a few steps downstage.*)

JOAN (*Still puzzled and confused*): The place?

BESSIE: According to my information, this is the residence of one Daniel Fulton and family. Am I correct?

JOAN: Yes.

BESSIE: Are you Mr. Fulton's daughter? (JOAN *nods vaguely.*) Then your name is Joan. Our records indicate that you are the only child of—(*At that moment* TED *steps into the room through doorway right. He has left his camera in the sunroom.*)

TED (*Stops abruptly*): Oh!

BESSIE (*Turns to* TED, *speaks in a shattering tone*): And who are you?

TED (*Confused*): I'm Ted Benson.

BESSIE (*Majestically, to* TED): I have no record of you, young man.

TED: Is that supposed to be good or bad?

BESSIE (*To* TED): Are you related to any member of this family?

TED: No. (*After a slight pause.*) At least not yet.

BESSIE: Kindly do not enlarge upon your answers.

JOAN (*Annoyed, as she turns to* BESSIE): Now just a minute! (BESSIE *turns to* JOAN.) I don't know who you are. You haven't even given me the courtesy of an introduction.

BESSIE (*Draws herself up*): I am Bessie Maywood. My brother is Winston Maywood. This morning I went to work in Winston's office.

JOAN (*Amazed*): You did?

BESSIE: No comments, please. You're simply clouding the issue.

JOAN: Miss Maywood, I know your brother of course. But I'm certain I've never heard of you.

BESSIE (*To* JOAN): You heard my voice this morning. *I* took your phone call.

JOAN (*Startled*): You did?

BESSIE (*Nods*): Since nine o'clock, I have been a member of my brother's organization. I arrived from the West last night. I felt that Winston needed my capable assistance in the business world, which is the reason I left my home and former activities. (*Suddenly* CORA *enters from right.* CORA *looks at* BESSIE *and pauses abruptly.* BESSIE *peers majestically at* CORA.) Good morning, madam. Are you by chance the wife of one Daniel Fulton?

CORA: I am, but chance had nothing to do with it.

JOAN (*Swiftly makes the introductions*): Mother, this is Miss Maywood. (*Slowly and significantly*) Miss Maywood is Winston Maywood's sister.

CORA (*Aghast*): His sister?

BESSIE: Certainly.

TED (*To* CORA, *with emphasis*): She has been working in Mr. Maywood's office since nine o'clock this morning.

CORA (*To* TED): She has?

TED (*Nods*): One of the old employees. (CORA *is greatly upset. She turns nervously to* BESSIE.)

BESSIE (*To* CORA): Winston was not expecting me. I merely walked into his office and said, "Winston, I am here to manage your business."

CORA: You did?

TED (*Dryly*): That must have been a surprise.

BESSIE (*To* CORA): Your daughter phoned our office this

morning. She informed me that your husband was in poor shape. Those were her words, I believe. Prior to the call I had decided that all reported illnesses would be promptly investigated. That is why I am here.

CORA (*Aghast*): Oh, dear! (JOAN *and* TED *are thrown into panic.*)

JOAN: Miss Maywood, did your brother send you here?

BESSIE: Young lady, since nine o'clock this morning, *I* have been making the decisions in Winston's office. (*She turns to* CORA.) I now wish to interview your husband.

JOAN (*Gasps*): But you can't! (CORA *is speechless.*)

TED (*Hurriedly*): Mr. Fulton is resting.

CORA (*In confusion*): Resting? Why, I thought Daniel was —(CORA *breaks off. She dashes to the Christmas tree. Now for the first time she discovers* DANIEL, *his figure covered by the sheet. She stops short in horror.*)

BESSIE (*Remains standing where she still cannot see* DAN-IEL): I shall not leave this house until I have inspected Mr. Fulton. (BESSIE *marches down to divan.* CORA, *at left, remains in front of* DANIEL *as she unsuccessfully attempts to hide him from* BESSIE'S *view.* BESSIE *prepares to sit on divan; she suddenly discovers him. Straightening up with a start, she points to* DANIEL.) What is *that*? (*For a moment no one answers.* CORA, JOAN *and* TED *stand frozen.*)

CORA (*At last, feebly*): Where?

BESSIE (*Commandingly*): Behind you, Mrs. Fulton. (CORA *slowly turns to* DANIEL. *She makes a feeble attempt at surprise.*)

CORA (*Desperately*): It's nothing. Just Santa Claus.

BESSIE (*With a horrified start*): *Santa Claus?*

TED (*Attempts to ease the situation*): A *stuffed* Santa Claus.

BESSIE (*With rising anger*): Am I to understand that this family is celebrating the Christmas season with a stuffed Santa Claus?

JOAN: We're not exactly celebrating—

TED: Not at the moment!

BESSIE (*In cold fury*): I wish it to be known that I am completely and forever opposed to Santa Claus! (*The others are shocked.*)

CORA: You are?

BESSIE (*Nods emphatically*): Tall or short, small or large, living or stuffed.

CORA (*With a gasp*): Oh, my!

BESSIE: This morning I ordered all of Winston's employees into my office. I told them there was to be no Santa Claus at the office party this year. Nor would I permit such a character to be displayed in the homes of the employees. (BESSIE *turns to* CORA, *points to* DANIEL.) You will do away with that stupid figure at once.

CORA (*In panic*): But Miss Maywood, you don't understand—

BESSIE: Mrs. Fulton, I have appointed myself the personnel director of Winston's office. I made that appointment at exactly two minutes past nine o'clock this morning. From now on I shall do all the hiring and the firing. (*Significantly.*) Your husband is on our payroll, Mrs. Fulton. I strongly suggest that you follow my command if you wish him to remain there.

CORA: Miss Maywood!

JOAN (*Confused*): Please—

TED (*Suddenly steps forward, speaks agreeably to* BESSIE):

Of course, Miss Maywood. We'll do exactly as you desire.

CORA (*Shocked*): We *will?*

BESSIE (*Nods approvingly to* TED): A most sensible decision.

TED (*To* BESSIE): The dummy shall be removed immediately.

BESSIE (*To* TED): Young man, I approve of your attitude—though as a general rule, I am *not* the approving type.

TED (*Steps to door right, opens door*): Perhaps you would wish to wait in here, Miss Maywood. (*He smiles brightly.*) The destruction of Santa Claus is likely to be a rather messy job. (CORA *gives a little shriek.*)

JOAN (*To* TED): Ted!

BESSIE (*To* TED): I understand your attitude. And I do not wish to observe the dismantling of such a ghastly figure. I would suggest, however, that you burn it in the alley.

TED (*Nods*): A remarkable idea, Miss Maywood.

BESSIE (*Crosses to door right, then speaks to* TED): In any event, I shall expect you to act quickly. I must still interview Mr. Fulton. (*She exits.*)

TED (*In an urgent whisper*): Quick! Let's get him out of here! (CORA, JOAN *and* TED *rush to* DANIEL. *Wildly they throw back the sheet which has covered him.* DANIEL *is near collapse. He still holds the "Merry Christmas" sign.* TED *speaks to* DANIEL *in a subdued voice.*) Hurry, Mr. Fulton!

CORA (*Breathlessly and indignantly to* DANIEL): Daniel, did you hear what that woman had the nerve to say? She insists you're stuffed!

DANIEL (*Loudly*): I heard everything!

JOAN (*Attempts to silence* DANIEL): Not so loud, Father!

DANIEL (*Jumps up, pulls off the false beard*): That woman is Winston Maywood's sister! Winston Maywood is my boss!

JOAN (*Attempts to soothe* DANIEL): Yes, Father, we know.

DANIEL (*Wild-eyed*): She hates Santa Claus! (*Trembles violently*) Don't just stand there! Somebody hide this suit!

CORA (*Suddenly concerned*): Daniel, you're shaking!

DANIEL: Why shouldn't I shake?

CORA: You're not well.

DANIEL (*Sputters*): I'm trembling like the last leaf. I can't breathe! I'm burning up! My heart's beating in calypso rhythm! My blood pressure's gone off on a roller coaster ride!

JOAN: Father, stop it! (*Swiftly* CORA *places her hand on* DANIEL's *brow.*)

CORA: Daniel, I think you have a fever!

DANIEL: I'm catching something! I know I am. (DANIEL *sneezes, a roof-shaking, vibrating sneeze.*)

TED (*Jumps violently*): Mr. Fulton!

BESSIE (*Loudly, offstage*): What was that? (*Wildly* TED *pushes* DANIEL *back into the chair.* JOAN *and* CORA *toss the sheet over* DANIEL's *head. Then* BESSIE *marches into the room through doorway right. She leaves the door open behind her.* JOAN, CORA *and* TED *weakly face* BESSIE.) I heard a sneeze! (BESSIE *advances to center. As the scene progresses,* TED *silently and unobtrusively backs upstage and across the room to doorway right. Unnoticed by the others, he at last exits right. The door remains open.*)

CORA (*Trembles, as she answers* BESSIE): Really, Miss Maywood?

BESSIE: The vibration rattled the windows in the sunroom.

CORA (*Vaguely*): I thought I heard a faint noise myself.

BESSIE: *Faint?* (*Pause.*) Mrs. Fulton, did your husband sneeze?

CORA: It's possible.

JOAN (*Desperately*): When Father sneezes—well, he sneezes.

BESSIE (*To* CORA): Take me to him at once!

CORA: But, Miss Maywood—(*Then* DANIEL *sneezes again. Now the vibration shakes his entire body. Involuntarily, but vigorously, he throws his hands in the air. The sheet flies back from his head. The Christmas poster and the white beard lie across his knees.* JOAN *and* CORA *stand in horrified silence. Wildly* DANIEL *snatches up his beard and holds it in front of his face in a feeble attempt to hide.* BESSIE *gazes at* DANIEL *in shocked amazement.*)

BESSIE (*After a tense pause, speaking explosively to* DANIEL): Put down that beard! (*Slowly* DANIEL *obeys.*)

DANIEL (*To* BESSIE, *as he smiles weakly*): Good morning. (BESSIE *advances to* DANIEL. *Menacingly she pauses in front of him.*)

BESSIE (*Angrily*): Are you one Daniel Fulton?

DANIEL: I'm Santa Claus.

BESSIE (*Acidly*): You're not even a *stuffed* one! (*She turns to* CORA.) Is this *object* your husband?

CORA (*Speaks stoutly and indignantly*): All right, so he's my husband. But don't you dare call him an object!

BESSIE (*Ironically to* DANIEL): Dressed as Santa Claus! (*She reaches down, snatches the Christmas poster from his knees.*) And *this!* (*She gazes grimly at the sign, then turns to* CORA.) So your husband is ill, is he?

CORA (*With sudden spirit*): Yes, he is!

BESSIE (*Breaks in*): Silence, Mrs. Fulton! (*She turns to* DANIEL.) It was serious enough that you stayed away from our office this morning. And now, when I make a routine investigation, I find you—(*She breaks off, moans dramatically.*) Give me strength!

JOAN: That's what we all need right now—a little strength.

BESSIE (*To* DANIEL): I shall return to my office at once. I shall instruct our cashier to—(*The doorbell rings off center.* BESSIE *pauses.*) What was *that* interruption?

CORA: *Not* another sneeze, I can assure you.

JOAN (*To* BESSIE): It was the doorbell, Miss Maywood. (JOAN *moves upstage.* DANIEL *rises with effort.*)

BESSIE (*Thoroughly annoyed*): This place is a madhouse! (JOAN *opens center door.* WINSTON MAYWOOD *stands at doorway.*)

JOAN (*Gasps*): Mr. Maywood! (BESSIE *swings around with a start as* WINSTON *steps into the room.* DANIEL *takes one look at* WINSTON *and almost faints.*)

BESSIE (*With a shriek*): Winston! (TED *appears at the open doorway, carrying the camera and flash attachment. He pauses at doorway. He is unnoticed by those in the room.*)

WINSTON (*Expressionless, to* BESSIE): Yes, Bessie, it's your brother.

BESSIE (*To* WINSTON, *as she points a menacing finger at* DANIEL): Winston, see what I found! Take a look at that *spectacle!*

WINSTON (*In a friendly tone*): Good morning, Daniel. (BESSIE *continues to stand near* DANIEL. *She holds the "Merry Christmas" sign in front of her.*) According to Bessie, you were ill. I dropped by to check up.

JOAN: I phoned your office, Mr. Maywood, but I didn't exactly say father was sick. I just said he was in poor shape.

WINSTON: Poor shape? (*He peers closely at* DANIEL, *then grins.*) I declare, he is at that. (WINSTON *begins to chuckle.*)

BESSIE (*To* WINSTON): This is not humorous, Winston. You know very well the decree I handed down to our employees this morning. I'm certain they now understand my feelings regarding Santa Claus. (*She points to* DANIEL *as she continues to speak to* WINSTON.) Then I walk into this house and find *that!*

DANIEL (*Humbly, to* WINSTON): I'm mighty sorry.

BESSIE (*To* WINSTON): We are discharging Mr. Fulton as of today. (BESSIE *and* DANIEL *stand side by side downstage left. They face* WINSTON *who is slightly upstage right.* BESSIE *holds the holiday poster.* JOAN *and* CORA *are a few steps upstage, to left of center.*)

WINSTON: Now, Bessie, let's not be hasty.

BESSIE (*With supreme authority*): *I* am handling the office personnel, Winston. As I told you when I arrived this morning, I shall take complete charge of that. (*A bright flash of light fills the room.* TED, *standing at doorway right, has taken a flash photo of* DANIEL, *the decorated Christmas tree, and* BESSIE. *Startled by the sudden flash of camera bulb, those in the room turn swiftly toward*

TED, *who, holding camera, takes a step into the room.*)

JOAN (*Gasps*): Ted!

BESSIE (*Loudly and indignantly*): What was that flash of light?

TED (*Easily*): I took a picture, Miss Maywood.

BESSIE: A picture?

TED (*Nods*): The Fultons wanted a photo of Santa Claus and the tree. They expect to use the prints on their Christmas cards.

BESSIE (*Suddenly concerned*): But you included *me* in that picture!

TED (*Smiles*): That's right. You see, I couldn't wait any longer, and there you stood, Miss Maywood, facing the camera.

BESSIE: Facing the camera?

TED (*Nods*): You were at the side of Santa Claus, holding the "Merry Christmas" sign.

BESSIE (*In rising alarm*): Now, see here, young man!

TED (*Continues easily*): Of course, even though you have fired Mr. Fulton, he'll still wish to send Christmas cards to the office employees.

BESSIE (*Horrified*): But he can't send them a picture of me posing with Santa Claus! Not after what I said this morning! (BESSIE's *rising panic is evident.* CORA, DANIEL *and* JOAN, *at first stunned, now begin to appreciate the situation. Desperately* BESSIE *turns to* WINSTON.) Winston, do you realize what has happened?

WINSTON (*With a twinkle of amusement in his eye*): I think I do.

BESSIE (*Hotly*): That negative must be destroyed!

WINSTON: Bessie, I'm afraid we can't do much about it.

BESSIE (*Wildly*): But if the employees receive a picture of Santa Claus and me—

WINSTON (*Nods*): It *will* cause comment, Bessie, especially after that speech you delivered. (*He shakes his head sadly.*) I declare, I'd hate to see my dear sister end up as the joke of the office.

BESSIE (*Storms*): I won't have this!

WINSTON (*Affects a deep sigh*): I guess we'll just have to face it, Bessie. Of course, you can't expect our employees to take you seriously in the future. As soon as one of those greeting cards is posted on the office bulletin board—

BESSIE (*Wild-eyed*): Winston, no one would dare do such a thing!

WINSTON: I'm afraid so, Bessie.

BESSIE (*Suddenly and explosively*): Then I resign!

WINSTON: *Resign?*

BESSIE: As of this moment! And you needn't ask me to go back to your office, Winston, now or ever!

WINSTON (*Protests mildly*): Why, Bessie!

BESSIE: I'm returning home. There's a noon train out of here. (BESSIE *throws the cardboard sign to the floor. She marches hastily upstage, then turns to* WINSTON.) Don't bother to see me off, Winston! (*She throws open center door, then plunges through doorway.*)

CORA: My goodness!

DANIEL (*Thoroughly shaken*): Oh, dear!

TED (*Steps to* WINSTON): Mr. Maywood, I'm sorry. I should apologize.

WINSTON (*Breaks in with sudden emphasis*): Don't you dare apologize! (*Then he breaks into loud laughter.*)

JOAN (*Amazed*): Mr. Maywood, you're *laughing!*

WINSTON: I've never been so relieved. Bessie could have wrecked my organization. (*He extends his hand to* TED. *Vigorously he shakes* TED's *hand.*) Young man, thanks to you and your camera, this will be a mighty happy Christmas season for me. (TED *grins.*)

CORA (*Still stunned*): Does this mean that Daniel isn't fired?

WINSTON (*Chuckles*): Of course he isn't fired. (*To* DANIEL, *as he moves to center.*) And I'm giving you an additional job, Daniel. At the Christmas office party, you are to be our Santa Claus. (WINSTON *smiles broadly.* DANIEL *is delighted.*)

JOAN (*Suddenly to* WINSTON): Mr. Maywood, why is your sister so opposed to Santa Claus?

WINSTON (*Shakes his head*): I wish I knew.

JOAN: Something has certainly sent her off the beam.

WINSTON (*Nods*): It must have happened since I saw her last. (*A bit sadly.*) Actually, I feel sorry for her. (*The center door opens and* BESSIE *enters.*)

BESSIE (*Somewhat subdued*): Winston—

WINSTON: Bessie! (BESSIE *moves down center, then hesitates.*)

BESSIE (*To* WINSTON): You thought I walked out, didn't you?

WINSTON (*Confused*): You *did* give us that happy impression— (*Quickly corrects himself.*) I mean, that *impression—*

BESSIE: Before I leave, Winston, I feel it my duty to make a final statement.

WINSTON: You were always one to make the final statement, Bessie.

JOAN (*To* BESSIE, *with sudden concern*): Miss Maywood, are you coming back to work for your brother?

BESSIE: I certainly am not! (*With dignity she turns to* WINSTON.) Winston, I wouldn't return to that office for all the—

TED (*With a sly grin*): For all the whiskers on Santa Claus?

CORA (*Sharply, to* TED): Ted! You know how Miss Maywood feels about that—that subject.

WINSTON (*To* BESSIE): Bessie, I insist upon knowing *why*.

BESSIE: That's the reason I returned. (*Pause.*) Winston, I made the trip to this town because I was fed up with the Christmas spirit.

WINSTON (*Startled*): Fed up?

BESSIE (*Nods*): Fed up with the Christmas party at the orphanage, fed up with the annual December bazaar, fed up with the holiday festival for the underprivileged.

WINSTON: But Bessie, you have always taken an interest in such things. They're all worthy causes, and you're a robust and active woman.

BESSIE (*Cuts in*): And because I'm active—(*She breaks off.*) Anyway, do you know what job I'm always given?

WINSTON: No.

BESSIE: At any holiday activity, I'm expected to play the role of Mrs. Santa Claus!

WINSTON (*Amazed*): *Mrs. Santa Claus?*

BESSIE: Every Christmas *I'm* the one who's unanimously selected. Those women may bicker and argue among themselves, but they all agree upon one thing—that Bessie Maywood shall appear as Mrs. Santa Claus.

WINSTON: So that's the reason!

BESSIE (*Cuts in*): Yes! But considering what has happened around here and at that office of yours—I've had quite enough of your organization, Winston. I'm going back home to my holiday duties.

WINSTON (*Attempts to hide a grin*): I declare, Bessie, this is amazing. You leave me speechless—as usual. (BESSIE *turns from* WINSTON. *She moves to* TED.)

BESSIE (*Stoutly, to* TED): Young man.

TED (*Uneasily*): Yes, Miss Maywood?

BESSIE: That picture you just took— (*She hesitates.*) If it's any good, you might send me a print.

JOAN (*Steps to* BESSIE): He'd be delighted, Miss Maywood.

BESSIE: Goodbye, Winston—(*She marches upstage to center, then turns. She remains dignified and majestic, but there's a slight smile on her lips as she speaks to* DANIEL.) And to you, Santa Claus, a Merry Christmas from *Mrs. Santa Claus!* (BESSIE *exits. The others break into broad and amused smiles, as the curtain quickly falls.*)

THE END

Production Notes

GREETINGS FROM THE FULTONS

Characters: 3 male; 3 female.

Playing Time: 25 minutes.

Costumes: Modern dress for all except Daniel, who wears a Santa Claus costume and a long white beard. Joan wears a blouse and skirt. Cora wears a housedress. Ted wears sports clothes and a student jacket. Bessie wears a severe, tailored suit. Winston wears a conservative business suit.

Properties: Christmas decorations and a sign reading "Merry Christmas," for Joan; camera with flash attachment, for Ted; sheet, for Cora.

Setting: The living room of the Fulton home. There are three entrances to the room—the outside door, upstage center; the left door, which leads to the rest of the house, and the right door, which leads to the sunroom. A divan and coffee table are downstage right. Downstage left is an armchair. Slightly upstage and to the immediate right of the armchair is a decorated Christmas tree. The tree is located in such a position that characters standing at upstage center must move well downstage before they can see the armchair. When the play opens, a small stepladder is beside the Christmas tree, and a box of tree ornaments is on the divan. Additional furniture and lamps may be added to furnish the room comfortably.

Lighting: No special effects.

Hold Your Hat

Characters

JUDITH ASHBY
MISS GRANT
PARK STODDARD
SAM NELSON
HELEN BARNES
MRS. HORTENSE LIVINGSTON

TIME: *Saturday morning.*
SETTING: *A corner of the millinery section of Miss Grant's Fashion Shoppe.*
AT RISE: JUDITH *enters enthusiastically, carrying a new hat. She crosses to a hat display table, removes a hat from one of the standards on the table, then replaces it with the hat she carries. She steps back slightly, viewing the result with high satisfaction.* MISS GRANT *enters briskly, carrying a small dust cloth.*

MISS GRANT: Judith!
JUDITH (*Swings around*): Oh, it's you, Miss Grant.

189

MISS GRANT: I thought you were waiting on a customer.

JUDITH: Not yet. (*Beams*) But I'm ready for anybody—just anybody. (JUDITH *continues to arrange the hats, as* MISS GRANT *begins to dust.* JUDITH *is happily excited.*) Goodness, Miss Grant, you *do* have a lovely store. It's the smartest ladies' shop in this town. (*Sighs with pleasure*) And here I am—one of your clerks. I'm simply rippling with enthusiasm.

MISS GRANT (*Crosses to* JUDITH, *hands her the dust cloth*): Then you can ripple over to this table and start dusting. (*She indicates table left.*)

JUDITH (*Takes dust cloth*): Of course. (JUDITH *moves to table, stoops down, and begins to dust the furniture.* MISS GRANT, *at display table right, arranges the hats. After a slight pause* JUDITH *straightens up, speaks expectantly.*) Miss Grant—

MISS GRANT: Yes?

JUDITH: When I'm out of high school this spring, would you consider taking me on as a full-time employee?

MISS GRANT (*Slightly annoyed*): My dear girl, this is your first day in my store. After all, this is a temporary arrangement. You're to come in on Saturdays and after classes. I can't answer your question until you've proved yourself.

JUDITH: I will prove myself! Why, I won't let a single customer walk out of this department without a new hat.

MISS GRANT (*Sourly*): You wouldn't say that if you'd been in this business as long as I have.

JUDITH: I'm sure it's a marvelous business. I can't imagine you'd ever have trouble with anybody.

Miss Grant: If you think I've no troubles, you should meet Mrs. Hortense Livingston.

Judith (*Startled*): Mrs. Livingston? *The* Mrs. Hortense Livingston? (Miss Grant *nods.*) I'm always reading about her in the social column of the paper.

Miss Grant: Mrs. Livingston purchased a dress from this store. She wore it to an affair out of town. (*Shudders*) Wouldn't you know—when the hostess opened the door, *she* had on an exact duplicate.

Judith (*Grins*): I'll bet Mrs. Livingston almost lost her eyebrows.

Miss Grant: You should have heard her when she phoned me the next morning. (*Sighs*) I've offered to make a full refund when she returns the dress. (*Sadly*) But I've lost her as a customer. She was the best one I had. Now she'll never make another purchase in this store.

Judith (*Hopefully*): If she *does* come in again, maybe I could float up to her, give her a big toothy smile and—

Miss Grant (*Steps to* Judith, *snatches dust cloth from her*): If Hortense Livingston ever enters this store, you'd better take my advice. (Miss Grant *starts for door.*)

Judith: Advice?

Miss Grant (*Turns to* Judith): Run for the nearest *exit.* (Miss Grant *exits. With considerable misgivings,* Judith *watches* Miss Grant *go out. Then,* Park Stoddard *hesitantly enters from right. He pauses, obviously embarrassed*).

Park (*At last speaks to* Judith, *whose back is to him*): Good morning. (Judith *swings around. She gazes at* Park *in open surprise.*)

Judith: Why—why—

PARK (*Grins weakly*): Hello.

JUDITH (*Takes a step forward*): My goodness, aren't you Park Stoddard?

PARK (*Nervously*): I think so. (*He pulls out handkerchief, wipes his forehead.*)

JUDITH (*With increasing friendliness*): Why, you play football on our high school team. (*Smiles*) I'm Judith Ashby. We don't attend the same classes, but I'm always bumping into you in the halls, just as if I were playing center for the opposition.

PARK (*Nods*): I thought I recognized you.

JUDITH (*Enthusiastically*): Everybody in school calls you "Iron Muscle" Stoddard. (*Hesitates, as she gazes critically at* PARK.) Although you certainly don't look iron muscled at the moment. What do you want in here?

PARK (*With effort*): I think I want a saleslady.

JUDITH: A saleslady? (*Suddenly she dashes to* PARK, *grabs his arm.*) Iron Muscle, you have one!

PARK (*Upset*): Hey, wait!

JUDITH (*Pulls* PARK *to center*): I'm the girl you're looking for.

PARK: You mean you'd wait on me?

JUDITH (*With conviction*): Conditions being as they are at the moment, I'd wait on the Statue of Liberty.

PARK: I didn't know you worked in this store.

JUDITH (*With a flourish*): I'm one of the fixtures. I'v been here for, let's see, for several minutes. Now, what's on your mind?

PARK: I'm looking for something.

JUDITH: The lost-and-found department is on the second floor.

PARK (*Increasingly uneasy*): I mean, I'm looking for a hat.

JUDITH: Sorry, Iron Muscle, but we don't carry men's hats.

PARK: Not a man's hat. (*Pause*) A woman's hat.

JUDITH (*Pays scant attention*): If you'll go down the street to—(*But she breaks off suddenly as she realizes what PARK has said. She turns with a violent start.*) What did you say?

PARK (*Pained*): I said I was looking for a woman's hat.

JUDITH (*Gazes unbelievingly at PARK*): You? (PARK *nods nervously. Suddenly* JUDITH *breaks into hilarious laughter, but she quickly attempts to hide her amusement.*) Excuse me, Iron Muscle. For a minute you swept me off my feet, but not from a touchdown run.

PARK: I know it sounds unusual.

JUDITH: Unusual? It sounds fantastic.

PARK: I have to buy a hat for my girl friend.

JUDITH (*Suddenly*): My goodness, then that makes you a legal customer! (*Again she plunges at* PARK, *grasps his arm. She pulls him toward chair in front of table left.*) Come on, Iron Muscle! Sit down, sit down! (*She roughly pushes a nervous and weakly protesting* PARK *into chair.*) You're just the person I've been waiting for since the store opened. (*She gazes happily at* PARK.) Now tell little Judith all about it.

PARK (*With effort*): While I was driving my girl to a party last week, the wind blew her hat off. It was ruined. (*As an afterthought*) The hat—not the wind.

JUDITH (*Nods understandingly*): I've always said this was the windiest town in the state.

PARK: She was pretty mad—my girl friend, not the wind.

So was her mother. Now I have to get a replacement for her. (*Pause*) A hat—not a mother.

JUDITH: You certainly came to the right place, Iron Muscle. Our hats look perfect on everything from a parakeet to an elephant.

PARK (*With sudden spirit*): Betty *isn't* either one.

JUDITH: Betty?

PARK (*Nods*): Betty Livingston. She's the girl I had the date with. The girl with a hat.

JUDITH (*Excited*): Betty Livingston was our homecoming queen, wasn't she? (PARK *nods*.) I don't know her personally, but she's terribly cute. So *she's* your girl friend.

PARK: She *was* my girl friend. But after this hat deal, her mother put her foot down.

JUDITH (*Nods sympathetically*): That's the way some mothers are—always coming down feet first.

PARK: You should have heard what she said. Not Betty, but her mother—Mrs. Hortense Livingston.

JUDITH (*Startled*): Mrs. Hortense Livingston? Is Betty her daughter?

PARK (*Nods*): Do you know Mrs. Livingston?

JUDITH: No, but I've heard enough about her to send the National Guard into action. (*Then she smiles at* PARK, *pats him on the shoulder.*) Don't you worry, Iron Muscle. We'll fix you up in no time.

PARK (*As* JUDITH *moves briskly to table*): Thanks. I wish you would.

JUDITH (*Who now stands before display of hats*): Did you have something special in mind?

PARK (*Sighs*): The only thing I have in mind is getting back in the good graces of Mrs. Livingston.

JUDITH (*Selects a large hat from table, holds it up for* PARK'S *inspection*): How do you like this hat?

PARK (*Gazes at hat*): I'm afraid it's a bit too overwhelming.

JUDITH (*Replaces hat on table*): For Betty, I suppose you're right. (*She selects a second hat from table, holds it up.*) How about this one?

PARK (*Doubtfully*): No, not exactly.

JUDITH (*Breaks in*): All right, so you don't like it. (*She drops hat on table, picks up a third. This one is small, smart and striking.*) Take a look at this one, Iron Muscle. (*She displays hat.*)

PARK (*Looking suddenly pleased*): Now, that's more like it! (*Holding hat,* JUDITH *crosses to* PARK.) You know, it sort of reminds me of the one Betty was wearing—the night of the breeze. (*Gazes with satisfaction at hat.*) I believe she'd approve of that one.

JUDITH (*Hesitates*): Are you sure, Iron Muscle?

PARK (*Firmly*): I'm positive.

JUDITH (*Somewhat upset*): Well, I—I—

PARK (*Swiftly*): I'll take it—no matter what it costs. (*But for a moment* JUDITH *doesn't move.* PARK *looks at her questioningly.*) What's the matter? Don't you want to make a sale?

JUDITH: I sure do. That's what I'm here for. Only—(*She pauses, then speaks with determination.*) All right, Iron Muscle. You're my first customer and I have to make good. If you want that hat, it's yours.

PARK (*Grins*): Great! (*Hesitates.*) There's just one thing missing.

JUDITH: Something missing on this hat?

PARK: Yes.

JUDITH (*With spirit*): My goodness, what do you expect—
strawberries and a barbecue pit?

PARK: I mean, it needs a veil.

JUDITH: A veil?

PARK (*Nods*): Betty's hat was decorated with a little veil.

JUDITH: Iron Muscle, this hat isn't supposed to have a veil.
(*Sighs*) If you want a veil, I'll get a veil. (*She hands the
hat to* PARK.) Here, hold it. I'll find something in the
stock room. (*She moves to door, turns to* PARK.) Don't
you drop that hat!

PARK (*Meekly*): I won't.

JUDITH: Remember, you're not kicking goal for the extra
point! (*She exits.* PARK *holds hat carefully, but awkwardly. He turns the hat slowly as he examines it in
detail. Obviously he is entirely satisfied with his purchase. In a few moments* JUDITH *enters. She carries a
long length of veiling.* JUDITH *indicates veiling.*) This is
all I could find. (*She moves to* PARK.) It's too long, but
we'll cut it down after we get a fit. (*She takes hat from*
PARK.) Now, we'll try it on.

PARK (*Smiles gratefully*): Say, I wish you would! It'll give
me an idea how—

JUDITH (*Breaks in, surprised*): *Me* try it on? (*Firmly*) Iron
Muscle, *you're* going to try it on.

PARK (*With a violent start*): What!

JUDITH (*With determination*): Certainly. (*She moves behind* PARK'S *chair.*)

PARK: Now hold on! (*He starts to rise, but with one hand*
JUDITH *grabs his shoulder. She forces him back into
chair.*)

JUDITH: Just relax.

PARK: I can't put that—

JUDITH (*Cuts in*): Did you ever hear of anybody buying a hat without first trying it on?

PARK (*After a pause*): No, but I—

JUDITH: You'll have to substitute for Betty.

PARK (*Desperately*): I tell you, I can't.

JUDITH: Don't argue, Iron Muscle. For years I've been selecting my own hats, and no saleslady ever sold me one before I'd first tried it on.

PARK: Good grief!

JUDITH: Now hold still.

PARK: Is this necessary?

JUDITH (*Calmly and efficiently*): I'm following instructions. We salesladies have our unshakable rules.

PARK: You're certainly shaking me!

JUDITH (*Scoffs*): That's silly.

PARK (*Greatly upset*): I hadn't counted on this.

JUDITH: When you're buying a woman's hat, you have to be prepared for anything. (*She raises hat above* PARK's *head.*) Stop squirming, Iron Muscle. (PARK *is in silent agony, but completely helpless. With a flourish,* JUDITH *places the hat on* PARK's *head. The result is definitely startling.* JUDITH *steps in front of* PARK. *She takes one look—and suddenly bursts into a loud giggle.*)

PARK (*Angrily*): Stop laughing!

JUDITH (*Controls her mirth*): I'm sorry. It's just that I've never seen you wear a woman's hat, Iron Muscle. (*She starts to giggle again.*)

PARK (*Attempts to remove hat*): And you won't again!

JUDITH (*Swiftly and firmly holds hat on his head*): No, you don't, not yet! We have to see how it looks with a veil.

PARK: I don't care *how* it looks! I only want to—

JUDITH (*Cuts in with dignity*): *I* care how it looks, and I'm your saleslady. I'm here to wait on customers. You have to show proper respect. (*With a hopeless sigh,* PARK *sinks back into chair. Now* JUDITH *covers his face and the hat with the length of veiling. She draws the ends back tightly, then firmly ties veil at the back of* PARK's *neck. There is no way by which he can remove either veil or hat without assistance.* JUDITH *finishes her shattering project, then again steps in front of* PARK. *Her expression is sober and critical.*)

PARK (*Threateningly*): See here, if you laugh at me again—

JUDITH: I'm not laughing. If you want my opinion, Iron Muscle, the veil doesn't do anything to that hat.

PARK (*Groans*): It doesn't do anything to *me!*

JUDITH (*Thoughtfully*): You might take a look at yourself. (*Firmly*) I don't think you'll approve of the veil, either.

PARK (*Jumps up*): I don't approve of anything!

JUDITH (*Always the efficient saleslady*): You'll find a mirror in there. (*She indicates door left.*)

PARK (*Desperately*): Can't I just buy the hat without looking at myself?

JUDITH: It simply isn't done, Iron Muscle. (*She points to door.*) Through that door, please. (PARK *sighs deeply. Then unhappily he moves to door. He turns to* JUDITH.)

PARK (*Grimly*): All I can say is, there ought to be a law against women's hats! (*He exits, slamming door. Immediately* HELEN BARNES *enters from right. She carries a large business folder.*)

HELEN (*Brightly*): Hello, Judith.

JUDITH (*Swings around*): Helen—Helen Barnes!

HELEN: I thought I saw you back here.

JUDITH (*Suddenly excited*): Darling, you've come to buy at hat! (JUDITH *leaps at* HELEN, *grasps her arm, starts to pull her toward table at right.*) Here, let me show you—

HELEN (*Laughs, as she frees herself*): Judith, stop it!

JUDITH: But Helen—

HELEN: Darling, I'm not buying a hat. I'm here to ask Miss Grant for an ad in our school annual.

JUDITH (*Disappointed*): Is *that* all?

HELEN: Sam Nelson came along with me.

JUDITH: Sam Nelson?

HELEN (*Nods*): You know, the editor of the school paper. (*Smiles*) I have a happy surprise for you.

JUDITH (*Stoutly*): Nothing will make me happy until I sell a hat.

HELEN: Sam wants an interview with you.

JUDITH (*Showing more interest*): An interview? With me?

HELEN (*Nods*): All about your first day as a saleslady in this store. He thought it would make a cute feature in next week's edition.

JUDITH (*Startled, but pleased*): My goodness! (*Immediately* SAM NELSON *enters. He carries a small notebook and a pencil.*)

SAM (*Breezily*): Hi ya, Judith.

JUDITH (*Smiles*): Hello, Sam.

SAM: I'm looking for a story. Did Helen tell you?

JUDITH: Yes.

SAM: It shouldn't take long. If you'll just answer a few questions for me—

JUDITH: Well, I—(*Suddenly*) Sam, you'd better get permission from Miss Grant. She's the boss.

HELEN (*Glances around*): Where *is* the great lady?

JUDITH: Here in the store some place.

HELEN (*To* JUDITH): Then we'll find her. (*Turns to* SAM.) I have to talk with Miss Grant, too. (*She moves to right.*) She ought to be receptive to an ad in the annual. (*Sighs*) Although she has already turned me down three times.

SAM (*To* JUDITH): We'll see you in a minute, Judith.

HELEN: Unless Miss Grant tosses us out the front door. (HELEN *and* SAM *exit right. Her eyes bright,* JUDITH *watches them as they leave. Immediately there's a sharp commotion offstage left. The door at left swings open.* PARK *plunges into the room. He still wears the hat and veil. He's in utter panic.*)

JUDITH (*Turns as* PARK *enters*): Well, Iron Muscle? (*With a start as she sees* PARK's *expression.*) Iron Muscle! (PARK *groans.*) Did you look at yourself?

PARK (*Wildly*): Get me out of this thing! (*In vain he attempts to loosen the knot in veil.*) Get me out of it, I say!

JUDITH (*Crosses to* PARK): My goodness, you *are* in a state.

PARK (*Trembles with anger*): I took one look at myself, and I almost collapsed!

JUDITH: *You*—Iron Muscle?

PARK (*Loudly*): Untie this veil! I can't do it by myself. (*For a moment* JUDITH *doesn't move.*) Don't just stand there!

JUDITH: Please, Iron Muscle, not so loud. (*She steps behind* PARK, *prepares to untie the veil.*)

PARK (*Indicates door*): A couple of women bounced in there to try on coats. They took one look at me, and screamed like a pair of Indians! (*Wildly*) For Pete's sake, hurry.

JUDITH (*Fumbles with knot in veil*): From the very first I felt you wouldn't like the veil effect.

PARK (*Shouts loudly*): I don't like *any* of the effect! (SAM *enters.* HELEN *follows him.*)

SAM (*As he enters*): If Miss Grant's in this store, we can't find—(*But he breaks off in horror as he looks at* PARK.) Good grief!

HELEN (*Stops, then shrieks*): Sam—*look!* (*Aghast, she points at* PARK. *For a moment no one speaks.* PARK *stands frozen in horror.*)

SAM (*At last, almost speechless*): No! It can't be!

HELEN: It is! It's Iron Muscle Stoddard himself!

PARK (*Hotly*): Now, you see here!

SAM: I don't believe it!

JUDITH (*With spirit*): Certainly it's Iron Muscle. He's buying a hat.

HELEN: *That one?* (*Gasps*) Good heavens! (*Suddenly* SAM *breaks into a wild laugh.*)

PARK (*Shouts at* SAM): Stop it! (HELEN *begins to laugh uproariously.*)

JUDITH (*Steps to center, speaks stoutly to* HELEN *and* SAM): He's my first customer.

HELEN (*Continues to gaze at* PARK): This can't be real. I'm seeing things. It's a mirage.

JUDITH (*To* HELEN): I see nothing funny about this.

HELEN (*Again bursts into laughter*): Then you haven't taken a good look at him!

PARK (*Desperately*): Get out of here! Everybody get out!

SAM (*Suddenly*): What a story for the school paper!

PARK: School paper? (*Hotly*) If you so much as dare to—

SAM (*Cuts in enthusiastically*): Can't you see the flaming headlines? "Iron Muscle Stoddard Selects New Hat for Next Saturday's Crucial Game."

PARK (*Wildly, to* SAM): You shut up!

HELEN (*Fascinated, as she continues to look at* PARK): He's in evening clothes. Look at that veil!

SAM (*Snickers loudly*): All he needs now is a basket of flowers.

PARK (*In a fury as he steps to* SAM, *raises his fist menacingly*): You get out of here or I'll—

JUDITH (*Rushes to* PARK, *grasps his arm*): Iron Muscle, don't!

PARK (*Roughly pushes* JUDITH *aside, steps closer to* SAM): Sam Nelson, if you print one word of this, I'll—(MISS GRANT *enters hurriedly. She stops abruptly, takes one long look at* PARK, *then shrieks in horror. All turn toward her.*)

MISS GRANT (*Wildly, as she points to* PARK): What's *that?*

JUDITH (*To* MISS GRANT, *with spirit*): My first customer.

SAM (*With hilarity*): Isn't he simply darling? (MISS GRANT *is speechless.*)

PARK (*In panic, as he attempts to unfasten veil*): Somebody untie this thing!

HELEN (*Gleefully*): We can't. We've fainted from shock.

MISS GRANT (*Regains her speech, as she plunges to* JUDITH): Judith Ashby, are you responsible for this exhibition?

HELEN: Exhibition? It's a three-ring circus!

MISS GRANT (*To* JUDITH): Judith, did you do this?

PARK (*Shouts at* MISS GRANT): I'll say she did!

HELEN (*Near hysteria*): If we only had his picture, we'd hang it in the study hall.

SAM: Every freshman would quit school!

HELEN: They'd have to fumigate the building!

MISS GRANT (*Furiously, to* JUDITH): So *you're* responsible!

JUDITH (*To* MISS GRANT): I—

MISS GRANT (*To* JUDITH): Young lady, you're fired!

JUDITH (*Aghast*): Fired?

MISS GRANT: As of now. This minute!

JUDITH (*Shocked*): But Miss Grant—

PARK (*Wildly, to* MISS GRANT): Stop yapping and untie this veil!

MISS GRANT (*Continues to speak to* JUDITH): You'll get one day's wages—and you'll leave this store as soon as I get your pay! (MISS GRANT *moves swiftly toward door.*)

PARK (*With a loud groan*): Come to my rescue, somebody!

JUDITH (*Completely unnerved, as she starts to follow* MISS GRANT): Miss Grant, please! (MISS GRANT *exits. Immediately the voice of* MRS. HORTENSE LIVINGSTON *is heard.*)

HORTENSE (*Explosively, from off right*): Where is she? (*Her voice nears.*) Where is she, I say! Where's Miss Grant? (*Those in the room turn toward right.*) Tell her I want to see her. Tell her that Mrs. Hortense Livingston demands her immediate presence!

JUDITH (*Gasps*): It's Mrs. Livingston! (PARK *groans wildly.*)

HELEN: Mrs. Livingston?

JUDITH (*Breathlessly*): Hortense the Terrible! (*In panic*) Run for the nearest exit—everybody! (*Thoroughly alarmed,* JUDITH *backs upstage left.* PARK *is in complete confusion. He looks wildly around the room, then dives to the far side of table. He drops on his knees in an effort*

*to hide behind the enclosed end of table. However, the
hat he wears is on a level with top of table.* HELEN *and*
SAM *back upstage.* HORTENSE *charges into room from
right. She carries a suitbox.*)

HORTENSE (*Calls as she enters*): Miss Grant! Miss Grant!
(HORTENSE *gazes around the room.*) Where is she?

JUDITH (*Steps forward cautiously*): Were you looking for
somebody?

HORTENSE: I am Mrs. Hortense Livingston. I want an immediate refund on this dress! (*She indicates suitbox.*)
What is more, I shall never trade in this store again as
long as I breathe. In addition, when I get through with
that Miss Grant character—(HORTENSE *breaks off abruptly. She has now seen the hat which* PARK *is wearing.
From her location,* HORTENSE *does not discover* PARK,
only the top of the hat. HORTENSE *drops suitbox to floor,
points to hat.*) That *hat!*

JUDITH (*Turns, gazes at hat on* PARK's *head*): Over there?

HORTENSE (*Takes a step forward*): It's just what I want!

JUDITH (*With a gasp*): My goodness!

HORTENSE (*Her eyes still on hat*): I've never seen anything
like it.

SAM (*Chuckles*): Neither has anybody else.

HORTENSE: It's exactly what I've been looking for. (*Takes
another step toward table.*) I want it, and I shall have it.
(*She moves nearer hat.*) I'll take it with me. Send me a
bill and I shall—(*As* HORTENSE *reaches table,* PARK *suddenly rises.* HORTENSE *stops in horror, then shrieks
wildly. Immediately* MISS GRANT *rushes into room. She
stops, frozen.*)

PARK (*To* HORTENSE, *with a weak smile*): Hello, Mrs. Livingston.

HORTENSE (*Aghast*): Oh, no!

PARK: Oh, yes—

HORTENSE: What on earth are you doing?

HELEN (*Speaks brightly*): He's selecting his trousseau.

MISS GRANT (*Steps forward, speaks to* HORTENSE): Mrs. Livingston, pay no attention—

SAM (*Grins at* HORTENSE): We know exactly how you feel, madam.

MISS GRANT (*To* HORTENSE): If you wish to speak to me—

HORTENSE (*Points to hat which is still tied on* PARK's *head*): I want that hat! (*Significantly, to* MISS GRANT.) Even if it *does* come from this store.

JUDITH (*To* HORTENSE): I've already sold it to Iron Muscle.

SAM (*Grins*): It's the latest model in football helmets.

HORTENSE (*To the world at large, as she gazes at hat*): I must have it, I tell you.

JUDITH (*To* HORTENSE): Then you'll have to deal with him. (*She indicates* PARK. HORTENSE *turns to* PARK.)

PARK (*To* HORTENSE): Mrs. Livingston, I bought this hat for Betty.

HORTENSE (*Shocked*): Betty—my daughter?

PARK: To take the place of the hat which was ruined.

HORTENSE (*To* PARK): Then it belongs to you?

PARK (*Swallows*): Yes.

HORTENSE (*Suddenly excited*): Park, you're wonderful!

PARK (*Shocked*): Wonderful?

SAM (*Gleefully*): He's sweet and dainty, too.

HORTENSE (*Steps to* PARK): Let me have that hat and you can—(*She pauses.*)

PARK (*To* HORTENSE): I can *what?*

HORTENSE (*Breathlessly*): You can date Betty as often as you wish.

PARK (*Elated*): Mrs. Livingston! Do you mean that?

HORTENSE (*Nods*): I mean whatever I say.

MISS GRANT (*Steps forward grimly, speaks to* HORTENSE): Mrs. Livingston, just a minute. (HORTENSE *turns questioningly to* MISS GRANT.) The young man does not own that hat.

HORTENSE (*With a start*): What did you say?

JUDITH (*To* MISS GRANT): Miss Grant, I told Iron Muscle he could have it. He was my first customer.

MISS GRANT (*Firmly, to* JUDITH): You are not connected with my store, Judith Ashby. I've fired you. Therefore, I refuse to recognize any transaction you may have made verbally.

HORTENSE (*Turns angrily to* MISS GRANT): Hold on, Miss Grant—

MISS GRANT (*Draws herself up*): The young man did not pay for that hat. It still constitutes merchandise in this store. I am not selling it. (*Significantly*) Not to *you,* Mrs. Livingston.

HORTENSE (*Sputters*): Why—why!

JUDITH (*Suddenly, to* MISS GRANT): Miss Grant—

MISS GRANT: Keep out of this, Judith.

JUDITH (*Desperately*): That hat *doesn't* belong to this store.

MISS GRANT (*Suddenly turns to* JUDITH): What's that?

JUDITH (*With effort*): The hat belongs to *me.*

MISS GRANT (*Aghast*): To you?

JUDITH (*Nods*): I laid it on the display table when I came

to work this morning. It was the one hat Iron Muscle liked. Because he was my first customer—

HORTENSE (*To* JUDITH, *in sudden triumph*): If the hat's yours, I can buy it!

JUDITH (*To* HORTENSE): I don't want to sell it, now that I'm fired. It's my best hat and I have to keep it.

HORTENSE (*To* JUDITH): Young lady, if you were still working here, would you sell it?

JUDITH (*Hesitantly*): Yes.

HORTENSE (*Turns, steps to* MISS GRANT): Miss Grant, if you will rehire this young lady, I'll start trading at this store again. I'll run up an account with you that will look like the national debt.

MISS GRANT (*Amazed*): You will?

HORTENSE: On my word of honor.

MISS GRANT (*Weakens*): Maybe—

HORTENSE: It's up to you, Miss Grant.

MISS GRANT (*Hesitates, then turns to* JUDITH *with a smile*): Judith, you're on the payroll.

JUDITH (*Beams*): Miss Grant!

PARK (*Groans as he drops into chair in front of table*): All right, all right, everybody's happy. (*Desperately*) Will somebody please get me out of this thing?

SAM (*Steps forward with a broad grin*): Not until we get a picture of you, Iron Muscle.

HORTENSE (*Turns to* SAM): Just who are you, young man?

SAM: I'm editor of the high school paper. I'm writing up the entire story. (HORTENSE *gasps*.) It'll be the biggest news item since the San Francisco earthquake.

HORTENSE: Do you mean you expect to print an article on this affair?

HELEN (*To* HORTENSE): With names and dates, and a banner heading across Page One.

HORTENSE (*Sputters*): It's impossible! I refuse to be a part of such publicity. Consider who I am!

SAM: That's just it. (*Grins*) Maybe we'll use your picture, too.

HORTENSE: No, no! (*Desperately*) I'll do anything—

PARK (*Rises wildly*): Then get me out of this hat!

HELEN (*Suddenly, to* HORTENSE): Mrs. Livingston, I'm selling advertising space in the school annual. If Sam doesn't print this story, will you buy an ad?

HORTENSE: Buy an ad? I'll take an entire page.

HELEN (*Overjoyed*): Mrs. Livingston!

HORTENSE: The ad will be a recommendation for this store —under my signature. (MISS GRANT *beams happily.*) I'll write a testimonial. I'll sign an affidavit.

SAM (*Suddenly, to* HORTENSE): What about the story I don't print? I'm out on a limb—hatless.

HORTENSE (*To* SAM): Then I'll *buy* you a hat.

PARK (*With a malicious grin*): Exactly! A woman's hat! (PARK *dashes to* SAM, *grabs his arm.*)

SAM (*Yells in horror*): Wait a minute! (PARK *holds* SAM *firmly.* HELEN *nods in approval. Quickly* JUDITH *goes to* PARK's *assistance. She and* PARK *lead a wildly protesting* SAM *to chair at table.*) Don't! Stop it! (*Now* HELEN *gleefully joins them.* JUDITH, PARK *and* HELEN *force* SAM *into chair.*)

HORTENSE (*To* MISS GRANT): Find the young man something large and colorful.

HELEN (*To* MISS GRANT, *as* SAM *groans*): With flowers and feathers—

MISS GRANT: I have just the model. (MISS GRANT *rushes to table, picks up a heavily decorated hat.*)

SAM (*Shrieks*): I won't, I tell you! (MISS GRANT *moves to* SAM *with the hat.*)

JUDITH (*Suddenly, to* MISS GRANT): Miss Grant—

MISS GRANT (*Beams at* JUDITH): Yes, dear?

JUDITH: We'll tie down that hat with a *ten-yard veil!* (SAM *yells wildly.* MISS GRANT *starts to place hat on* SAM's *head.* JUDITH, HELEN *and* PARK *hold* SAM *firmly in chair.* HORTENSE *looks on with majestic approval. The curtain quickly falls.*)

THE END

Production Notes

Characters: 2 male; 4 female.

Playing Time: 25 minutes.

Costumes: Judith and Helen wear smart, youthful dresses. Miss Grant wears a smart dress. Hortense wears expensive, extreme clothing. Sam wears typical high school apparel. Park wears slacks and a sport sweater with a school letter or team number.

Properties: Hats and veiling, for Judith; dust cloth, for Miss Grant; business folder, for Helen; notebook and pencil, for Sam; suitbox, for Hortense.

Setting: A corner of the millinery section of Miss Grant's Fashion Shoppe. Downstage left is a table for trying on hats, behind which stands a small chair. The ends of the table are enclosed. At right is a larger table on which are displayed an assortment of hats, some on display stands. There are two entrances to the stage: one at right, leading to the rest of the hat department, and one at left, leading to the stock room.

Lighting: No special effects.

Luncheon for Three

Characters

DIANA WORTH, *an attractive high school senior*
NEIL REYNOLDS, *Diana's ex-boy friend*
NANCY TUCKER, *another senior*
JUNE MANNING, *Neil's fourteen-year-old cousin*
PETE, *the delivery man*

TIME: *Saturday afternoon.*
SETTING: *Miss Clayton's apartment.*
AT RISE: *The stage is unoccupied. After a pause, the silence is broken by a knock on door at center. The knock is repeated. Then the door opens.* NANCY TUCKER, *a pretty, vivacious girl of seventeen, stands in the doorway.*

NANCY (*Peering into room*): Miss Clayton! Miss Clayton—! (*Receiving no answer,* NANCY *turns from doorway and calls to someone offstage right in hall.*) Come on, Diana —(NANCY *enters the room, moving downstage right.* DIANA WORTH, *attractive, with a somewhat dramatic personality, appears at center doorway.*)

DIANA (*Pauses at doorway, glances into room*): Where is she?

NANCY: Miss Clayton? Probably at the corner market. She said we were to walk right in.

DIANA (*Entering*): Then I suppose it's all right.

NANCY: Of course, Diana.

DIANA (*A bit uneasily*): You're certain Miss Clayton is expecting us for lunch? After all, Nancy, this invitation came through you.

NANCY (*Indicates table right*): Well, take a look at this table. It's set for the three of us—you, Miss Clayton and me.

DIANA (*Not too enthusiastic*): It was nice of her to invite us, I suppose.

NANCY: Miss Clayton is always doing nice things—especially for young people. When any high school student has a problem, Miss Clayton is ready to help.

DIANA (*Sinks onto divan at left*): But why should she invite me to her apartment for lunch?

NANCY: She probably thought it would raise your spirits. (*Significantly.*) After all, you *have* been terribly depressed since you and Neil had a quarrel and broke up—

DIANA (*Cuts in hotly*): Don't even mention Neil Reynolds' name to me!

NANCY: But darling, who has a better right? I'm your best friend.

DIANA (*Firmly*): That makes no difference.

NANCY: Honestly, Diana, I can't understand it. You and Neil had been going steady for two years. And then all at once—

DIANA: I said kindly do not mention his name!

NANCY (*Continues determinedly*): You two made such a perfect pair. Everybody in high school said so. Why, you and the boy-whose-name-I'm-not-to-mention played the leads in all the plays. When you two were on the stage together, you were sensational!

DIANA (*Rises*): Nancy Tucker, get this straight once and for all—I never want to be with Neil Reynolds again, on or off the stage. Don't even discuss him with me. (*She marches down left to end table. In grim silence she idly picks up vase.*)

NANCY (*Sighs*): But if girls can't discuss boys, what *can* they talk about?

DIANA: Plenty of things. (*Coolly, as she inspects vase*) This vase, for instance. I could do without the hearts and flowers, but it's beautiful.

NANCY: And expensive.

DIANA (*Turns to* NANCY): How do you know?

NANCY: I've been here before.

DIANA: This is my first visit to Miss Clayton's apartment.

NANCY: Do you want to see the rest of the place?

DIANA (*Replaces vase on table*): I guess so, if Miss Clayton won't mind.

NANCY: She'd be glad to have you look around. (*Moves toward door at right*) Come along—

DIANA (*Crosses right*): Nancy, are you just trying to entertain me?

NANCY (*Reaches door, turns to* DIANA): Frankly, I am—without bringing a certain individual into the conversation—which is about as easy as climbing the Washington Monument! (*She exits right, followed by* DIANA. DIANA *closes the door behind her. After a brief pause, there is a knock on center door. The door opens and* JUNE MANNING *steps into the room and moves down left, glancing around.* NEIL REYNOLDS *appears in open doorway at center.* NEIL, *seventeen, is good-looking and well-groomed. At the moment, however, he appears grim and unhappy.*)

NEIL (*At doorway*): So this is the place—

JUNE (*Turns impatiently to* NEIL): Well, don't just stand there, Neil.

NEIL (*Enters, closes door behind him*): Why isn't Miss Clayton here?

JUNE: She told me she might not be in when we arrived. We were to make ourselves at home.

NEIL (*Glances at table*): At least she's expecting us—places for three at the table.

JUNE: Neil Reynolds, of course she's expecting us!

NEIL: I still think it's funny she didn't invite me herself.

JUNE (*Exasperated*): After all, I *am* your cousin. One invitation was enough. Miss Clayton simply asked me to bring you over to her apartment for lunch today. (*Pointedly*) And don't act so—so gloomy.

NEIL (*Stoutly*): June Manning, I am not gloomy.

JUNE: I know what's wrong—(*Sits on divan*) You're still singin' the blues because you and Diana—

NEIL (*Flares up*): I told you to stop babbling about Diana Worth! (*Moves to* JUNE, *glares down at her.*) Diana and I have broken up for good. It's over—ended—terminated!

JUNE: At least you seem to be definite about it.

NEIL: I certainly am!

JUNE (*Sadly*): When I think of how you and Diana used to take the leads in all the school plays—

NEIL: I'll never appear in another play, (*Grimly he begins to pace the floor.*) and I'll never have another date with Diana!

JUNE: All right . . . all right. But for goodness' sakes, stop pacing.

NEIL: I'm waiting for Miss Clayton—and lunch.

JUNE: You wouldn't look so stormy if you'd sit down. (*She indicates space on sofa beside her.*) Here—(NEIL *sits down.*)

NEIL (*Grimly*): What do I do now?

JUNE (*Uneasily*): Well, you—you—(*Suddenly she sees the knitting bag beside her on divan.*) I know! (*Picks up bag*) Here's Miss Clayton's knitting bag. I'll teach you to knit—(*Swiftly she removes ball of yarn and needles from bag.*)

NEIL (*Crossly*): Do I look as if I wanted to knit?

JUNE: It might take your mind off your troubles.

NEIL: I don't have troubles!

JUNE: You don't even have a mind. And let me tell you something else—(DIANA *enters from right.*)

DIANA (*Speaking over her shoulder through doorway*): Miss Clayton *does* have a lovely bedroom—(*She turns, then sees* NEIL. *With a violent start she stops short.* NANCY *enters from right.* NEIL *takes one look at* DIANA *and jumps angrily to his feet. After a short pause,* JUNE *rises nervously.*)

NANCY (*At last, with an effort at brightness*): Well, look who's here!

JUNE (*Giggles, to hide her uneasiness*): That's just what I was about to say, Nancy—look who's here. You practically took the mouth out of my words.

NANCY (*Pleasantly*): This—this *is* a surprise.

JUNE (*Giggles*): I was about to say that, too.

NEIL (*Turns hotly to* JUNE): Keep quiet! (JUNE, *frightened, quickly backs upstage from* NEIL. NEIL *again faces* DIANA.)

DIANA (*To* NEIL): What are you doing here?

NEIL (*Equally cold*): What are *you* doing?

JUNE (*Giggles*): Isn't that cute? They both asked the same question—

NEIL (*Shouts at* JUNE): Keep *quiet!*

DIANA (*Draws herself up*): For your information, Mr. Reynolds, Nancy and I were invited here for lunch.

NEIL: That's impossible, Miss Worth. It so happens that my cousin and I are having lunch here. (*Indicates* JUNE)

DIANA: You will notice that the table is set for three.

NEIL (*Grimly*): Exactly. For June, Miss Clayton and myself.

DIANA: No, sir! Nancy and I are dining with Miss Clayton.

NANCY (*With forced gaiety*): I suppose the dear lady just made a mistake.

JUNE: Even I make mistakes at times.

NANCY (*In a bright, friendly tone*): Well, now that we're all here, we might as well—

DIANA (*Coldly, to* NEIL): I told you that Nancy and I are having lunch with Miss Clayton. Just the three of us.

NEIL (*Stands his ground*): Miss Clayton invited June and me.

NANCY: Suppose we all sit down and talk it over—(*Sits in chair to right of table*)

JUNE (*Agrees*): Like one big happy family—(*Sits on divan*)

NEIL: We're not a family.

DIANA: And we're not happy.

NEIL (*Steps toward* DIANA): Now see here, *I* was invited to Miss Clayton's for lunch.

DIANA (*Moves to* NEIL): Not today you weren't.

NEIL (*Turns to* JUNE): June, where's our invitation?

JUNE (*Vaguely*): Why, I—

DIANA (*Turns to* NANCY): Where's our invitation, Nancy?

NANCY: We—we didn't receive a written invitation. It was verbal.

JUNE (*Quickly, to* NEIL): Ours was verbal too, Neil. You know—Miss Clayton wagged her tongue and I said yes.

NEIL (*Angrily, to* DIANA): Well, Miss Worth, you have the wrong day.

DIANA: Wrong day? Do I look that stupid, Mr. Reynolds?

NEIL: Frankly—yes!

DIANA: Why—why—

NANCY (*Rises*): Now see here, both of you—(*Moves quickly to* DIANA *and* NEIL, *attempts to step between them.*)

NEIL (*To* NANCY): Keep out of this, Nancy. (*Gestures her aside.*)

JUNE (*Rushes to* DIANA *and* NEIL): Everybody just relax and count up to fifty thousand—

NEIL (*To* JUNE): One more word out of you, and you won't be able to count!

DIANA: Neil Reynolds, you deliberately plunged into this apartment—

NEIL: I did not plunge. I walked in like a gentleman.

DIANA: That must have been an effort.

NANCY (*About to weep*): Stop it—both of you!

NEIL (*To* DIANA, *paying no attention to* NANCY): That's just the sort of remark I'd expect from you, Diana Worth.

DIANA: It's the way any girl would talk, after dating you for two years.

NANCY (*Above the confusion*): Stop this bickering, I tell you!

JUNE (*To* DIANA *and* NEIL): If you knew how silly you both looked—

DIANA (*To* NANCY): I'll bicker as much as I like!

NEIL (*To* JUNE): If I want to look silly, I'll look silly!

NANCY (*Groans*): Oh, I give up! (*Throws her hands in the air, starts upstage.*) Once and for all, I give up!

JUNE (*To* NANCY): Nancy, where are you going?

NANCY (*Reaches center door, turns to* JUNE): I'm going to learn to train wild animals. That'll be easier! (*She exits center, slamming the door behind her.*)

JUNE (*Her voice trembles*): See what you've done? Nancy walked out—

DIANA (*To* NEIL): You can start walking too, Mr. Reynolds.

NEIL: I certainly will. (*He crosses to chair at left of table. Grimly, he sits.*) Right here. (*He folds his arms.*)

DIANA: Now just a minute—

NEIL: I was invited for lunch. I'm sitting at this table until Miss Clayton arrives.

DIANA: *I* was invited for lunch, not you, and I have no intention of leaving this apartment. (*She marches to*

divan, sits. She too grimly folds her arms. Cold silence.
NEIL *and* DIANA *gaze stonily into space, neither looking
at the other.*)
JUNE (*Unnerved and near tears*): You two can't just sit
around forever.
DIANA: I'm staying.
NEIL: I refuse to budge.
JUNE (*Helplessly*): But—but what am I supposed to do?
NEIL (*Loudly*): *Get out!* (*In terror* JUNE *gazes at* DIANA
and NEIL. *Then she turns and wildly exits at center back,
leaving door open.*)
DIANA (*To* NEIL, *after a pause*): Really, Mr. Reynolds,
you're wasting your time.
NEIL (*Smugly*): When Miss Clayton returns, a certain
person is going to be without an invitation, and I know
who that person is.
DIANA (*Equally smug*): So do I.
NEIL: It will be rather embarrassing for you, watching me
eat lunch.
DIANA: You'll do the watching, Mr. Reynolds.
NEIL (*With confidence*): Oh, no, Miss Worth.
DIANA: You won't be sitting in that chair when Miss Clay-
ton serves lunch.
NEIL: I shan't have to move. Of course, if you insist upon
staying, I won't object to your looking on while I enjoy
my meal. I'm broad-minded.
DIANA: I'm not at all worried about who will do the
watching.
NEIL: Miss Clayton's knitting bag is there on the divan.
If you're a knitter, you'll have plenty of time to turn
out a sweater or a pair of socks. (DIANA *picks up knit-*

ting needles and ball of yarn.) That's it—just take up the needles and enjoy yourself.

DIANA (*Indicates knitting needles*): You can use these needles, Mr. Reynolds, while I'm using my knife and fork.

NEIL: That should be interesting. I don't believe I've ever seen anyone knit with a knife and fork. (*He rises, picks up knife and fork from table, starts to cross to* DIANA.) I'll be delighted to help you get started—

DIANA (*Cuts in*): Stay where you are!

NEIL (*Pauses*): Are you trying to dictate to me—

DIANA: If you're determined to wait for Miss Clayton, that's your business. But in the meantime, don't come near me.

NEIL: Always the actress, aren't you? Either on stage or off.

DIANA: At least I was good enough in every play to carry you along. Otherwise, you would have flopped.

NEIL (*Ironically*): Ha! (*He turns, tosses knife and fork on table.*)

DIANA: And let me tell you something else—

NEIL (*Swings around to* DIANA): Let me tell *you* something—this is a free country, and I'll move around as I wish.

DIANA (*Jumps up angrily*): That's what you think! (*She tosses needles and knitting bag onto divan, retaining ball of yarn.*) I see I'll have to settle this myself. (*Holding ball of yarn, she steps to center as she speaks to* NEIL.) Keep on the other side of this room. (NEIL, *puzzled, backs to right.*)

NEIL: And why, may I ask?

DIANA: You'll see. (DIANA *steps to downstage center. She*

*stoops, placing free end of yarn on floor. Then she begins
to unroll ball of yarn directly upstage. The single strand
of yarn, lying on floor, divides the room.*)

NEIL (*Aghast*): What—what are you doing?

DIANA (*With cool confidence*): I'm dividing this apartment.

NEIL (*Chokes*): Dividing the—(*Breaks off*) Oh, no! (DIANA
*extends the yarn to within a few feet of center door. She
places the unused portion of ball on the floor. Then she
straightens up and steps to left of dividing line.*)

DIANA (*Indicates yarn*): There! That's the partition. Until
Miss Clayton returns, you will stay on your side and I'll
stay on my side.

NEIL (*Angrily*): So that's your stupid idea!

DIANA: Don't you dare step into my territory.

NEIL: I wouldn't be caught dead over there! (NEIL *peers
at dividing line. Suddenly he drops to his knees before
a section of the yarn, gazing closely at the line.*) Miss
Worth, this line bulges—right here. (*Points to yarn.
DIANA rushes to the other side of dividing line, just
across from NEIL. She peers intently at yarn.*)

DIANA (*Indignantly*): That line is perfectly straight!

NEIL (*Pushes a section of yarn toward DIANA*): Now it is.

DIANA: Mr. Reynolds, stop moving the partition!

NEIL: I'm entitled to half of this apartment. (*He rises,
still glaring at DIANA.*) You were cheating.

DIANA: I was not cheating! And don't you speak to me
again. (*She turns from NEIL, then marches to divan
where she sits.*)

NEIL: Don't you talk to me! (*He walks to chair at right of
table; sits. Neither looks at the other.*)

DIANA (*At last—dramatically, as though speaking to her-*

self): What a wonderful luncheon Nancy and I will have.

NEIL: You're not supposed to speak to me.

DIANA (*With affectation*): I seem to hear an unpleasant sound from the other side of the partition—as though the kitchen drain had clogged up. (NEIL *sputters.*) Yes —Miss Clayton, Nancy and I will have a lovely afternoon.

NEIL (*Pretends to talk to himself*): I feel sorry for certain people who are going without lunch today.

DIANA (*Forgets herself, speaks directly to* NEIL): You needn't feel sorry for me, Neil Reynolds!

NEIL (*Dramatically, as he places hand to his ear*): Methinks I hear noises through the partition. Sounds like old plaster falling from the ceiling. (DIANA *chokes angrily.* PETE *appears at open doorway center. He is in his late twenties, big and muscular. At first neither* DIANA *nor* NEIL *sees him.*)

DIANA (*With continued affectation*): Any moment now a certain individual is going to be tossed bodily from this apartment.

NEIL: We who were invited for lunch will remain. Certain others will be asked to leave.

PETE (*Suddenly steps through doorway*): O.K., folks— (NEIL, *startled, turns toward* PETE. DIANA, *equally surprised, rises.*) Here I am. (PETE *closes door behind him.*)

NEIL (*To* PETE): Sir, what do you mean, barging in here?

PETE (*Moves down right of dividing line*): I never knock when the door's open.

NEIL: If you've come for lunch, you might as well get out. This place is overloaded with uninvited guests already.

PETE (*Puzzled*): Lunch? Say, what's the matter with you?

NEIL: I'm tossing the question right back at you.

PETE (*Hesitates*): W-well, Mr. Squires sent me over here.

NEIL: Who is Mr. Squires?

PETE: He—he owns the gift shop down by the post office. He told me to make a pickup at this here apartment.

NEIL: I'm certain no one is in the mood around here to be picked up.

PETE: I'm talkin' about a vase.

NEIL: A vase? I wouldn't know anything about it.

PETE (*Growing impatient*): I was sent to pick it up, I tell you. Mr. Squires described the vase to me. He said it was a—(*Suddenly* PETE *sees vase on end table.*) That's the one, over there—(*Points to vase*)

NEIL (*Becoming suspicious*): Just a minute—(*Pause*) You say you were sent to Miss Clayton's apartment to pick up a vase?

PETE: 'Course I was.

NEIL: Frankly, I don't believe you.

PETE (*Protests*): Now, look—!

NEIL: I'm certain Miss Clayton doesn't wish to return any merchandise.

PETE (*Becoming hard-boiled*): Listen, junior, I'm here to get a vase. I'm a delivery man, I am—and I'm not in the habit of makin' mistakes.

NEIL: Now you say you're a delivery man. How quaint!

PETE: And I'm supposed to return a vase to the gift shop. (*Points to vase*) I know it's that one, sittin' over there.

NEIL (*Rises, looks blankly toward vase*): Where?

PETE (*His voice rises*): Right over there, standin' on that little table— (*Takes a step toward the dividing line.*)

NEIL (*Hurriedly*): But, sir, hold on—! (PETE *pauses.*)

PETE (*Turns to* NEIL): What's the matter?

NEIL: I think I should call your attention to something—

PETE: You don't have to call my attention to nothin'! (*Turns, as though to move toward vase*)

NEIL (*Urgently*): But sir, you couldn't possibly see a vase. You're looking at a blank wall.

PETE (*Turns angrily to* NEIL): If you don't—(*Breaks off with a start as* NEIL's *remark sinks in*) What?

NEIL (*With a prim smile*): I said you were merely gazing at a blank wall. And it *does* look a little odd. (*Slowly* PETE *turns from* NEIL. *He gazes first at the vase, then at* DIANA *who still stands silently in front of divan.*)

PETE (*At last*): There's no wall here— 'cept the one on the other side of the room.

NEIL: Oh, but there is, and you couldn't possibly see through the partition. (PETE *turns suspiciously to* NEIL. PETE *is becoming slightly unnerved.*)

PETE: What partition?

NEIL (*With affected patience*): My dear man, the partition which divides this room down the center.

PETE (*Disturbed in spite of himself*): I don't see a partition —(*Again gazes across the room.*) All I see is that vase— and a girl standin' by the divan.

NEIL: Girl? (*With a smile of pity.*) I'm afraid it's just your imagination. (PETE *is shaken. Uneasily he points at* DIANA.)

PETE: But she—she's right there—loomin' up like the Rock of Gibraltar.

NEIL (*Peers across room, shakes his head sadly*): All I can see is the blank wall. It was erected down the center of the room. It cuts the apartment in half.

PETE: Now look here, buddy—you just have to see more than that.

NEIL: But I don't, and neither would any sane person.

PETE (*Shocked*): Sane? Are you tryin' to accuse me of—

NEIL (*Hastily*): My good man, I'm not trying to accuse you of anything. I was just pointing out that a partition extends down the middle of this room. (NEIL *smiles brightly.*)

PETE (*His alarm increasing*): There's no partition down the middle of this here room! (DIANA *has grasped the situation. Amused, she attempts to hide a smile. Quietly she sits on divan.*)

NEIL (*To* PETE): Oh, but there is. (*Suddenly*) Let me show you—(*Moves swiftly around table to left*)

PETE: Now you keep away—

NEIL (*Brightly*): But sir, I'm afraid you're confused, and it always saddens me when I see an individual in—well, in your mental condition. (PETE *is becoming more and more upset.* NEIL *pauses in front of yarn on floor. He looks down at it.*) Do you see this yarn?

PETE (*Peers closely*): 'Course I see it.

NEIL (*Sighs deeply with relief*): At least you can be thankful for that.

PETE: What do you mean—at least I can be thankful for that?

NEIL: It indicates you're not—completely crazy.

PETE (*Loudly*): Now wait a minute—!

NEIL (*Raises his hand for silence*): Careful, my good man. Keep a firm grip on yourself. (PETE, *wide-eyed, swallows nervously.*) Now the partition rises from the yarn. It extends across the room and to the ceiling. (NEIL *looks up, as though gazing at the partition.* PETE *fearfully does likewise. Then* NEIL *pushes with both hands against the imaginary partition. He grunts and strains. With hands against the unseen wall,* NEIL *turns to* PETE.) See? Solid as a rock.

PETE (*Desperately, to* NEIL): I tell you there's nothin' there but air!

NEIL (*As though to calm* PETE): Please, mister—mister— (*Pause*) My goodness, I don't believe you've introduced yourself.

PETE (*With effort*): I—I'm Pete. (*Gruffly*) And I have a reputation!

NEIL (*Nods brightly*): How nice! (*In a friendly tone*) Now, Mr. Pete, why don't you push against this partition yourself? Just to prove I'm right.

PETE (*Stoutly steps forward*): That's just what I'm goin' to do!

NEIL (*Significantly*): Of course, Mr. Pete, if you *don't* feel anything when you push against the wall—(*Breaks off*)

PETE (*Eyes* NEIL *significantly*): So if I don't?

NEIL (*Shudders*): Please, Mr. Pete, let's not consider such a tragic possibility.

PETE: What're you drivin' at?

NEIL: Well, if you pushed against the wall—and you still insisted the wall wasn't there—(*Breaks off sadly, then smiles hopefully.*) But I'm sure you're not insane, not violently insane, anyway.

PETE (*Wipes his brow with his arm*): I—I'm not crazy, I tell you!

NEIL: I'm so glad, Mr. Pete. (*Pause*) Of course, the way you keep seeing impossible things—

PETE (*His confidence slipping fast*): Nothin' wrong with me—(*Pause*) I think.

NEIL (*Sadly*): That's what they all say at first. (*He steps back, permitting* PETE *to come forward.*) Now, put your hands to the wall, Mr. Pete, and we'll both hope for the best. (PETE *doesn't move. He's a shaken and terrified man, but with supreme effort he at last slowly raises his hands and starts to put them forward to the "wall". His hands freeze in mid-air. He just can't take the risk. Slowly he drops his hands.*)

PETE (*Feebly*): I—I'll take your word for it. (*Then* PETE *attempts to shake off his fears. Swinging around to* NEIL, *he speaks loudly.*) Look here, you're just wantin' to mix me up. And don't try to tell me there's no girl on the —on the other side of the—the partition.

NEIL (*Pleasantly*): Oh, but there is— a Miss Diana Worth. A lovely person, too. (DIANA *is surprised and pleased.*)

PETE (*Points with trembling finger at* DIANA): And she's settin' there on the divan—

NEIL: I wouldn't know about that, of course. (*With increasing concern*) Really, Mr. Pete, I'm uneasy about you. (*Smiles*) But I'll be glad to ask Diana where she's sitting—that is, if I can make her hear through the wall. (NEIL *steps to the dividing line. He calls loudly.*) Diana! Oh, Diana! (DIANA, *always the actress, quickly pretends she has heard a faint call. Entering completely into the "act", she puts a hand to her ear as though listening. Slowly she rises. She moves to her side of the dividing line. Then she places her ear to the imaginary wall.*)

DIANA (*Answers loudly*): Did someone call me from over there?

NEIL (*Raises his voice*): *I* called you, Diana. It's Neil—
Neil Reynolds. (*Actually* NEIL *and* DIANA *are close to
each other.*)

DIANA (*Pleasantly*): Of course. What is it, Neil?

NEIL: Have you been sitting on the divan?

DIANA (*Pretends to be startled*): Why, yes, I have. How did
you know? (PETE *looks on in complete confusion.*)

NEIL: I have a friend over here. Somehow he guessed you'd
been sitting on the divan.

DIANA: He did? My goodness, he must have a peculiar
mind. (*With concern*) You want to be careful, Neil.

PETE (*In rising panic*): Now—now look—! You two are
standin' there right close—shoutin' at each other—

DIANA (*Calls to* NEIL): Did I hear another voice, Neil?

PETE (*To* DIANA, *loudly and desperately*): I'm standin'
right here. Standin' big as life! Can't you see me?

NEIL (*To* DIANA, *disregarding* PETE's *outburst*): You heard
my friend, Mr. Pete. (*Sadly*) Poor, poor man.

DIANA (*With a little gasp*): You mean he's—he's—?

NEIL: I'm afraid so, Diana.

PETE (*Yells*): I'm not, either!

DIANA (*Calls to* NEIL): Come over soon, Neil.

NEIL (*Smiles broadly*): Indeed I will, Diana.

DIANA (*Suddenly*): Why not drop in now?

NEIL: I'd be delighted. (*Pause.*) Mind if I bring along Mr.
Pete? I don't think he should be left alone—in his condition.

DIANA: I'd be glad to have him, if you think it's safe. (*She
moves left from dividing line.*)

NEIL (*Turns to* PETE): Diana wants to meet you. Her door
is the next one down the hall, but remember, you must

promise to come quietly—(NEIL *takes* PETE *by the arm, but with a sudden shriek,* PETE *breaks away.*)

PETE (*In open panic*): Get your hands off me! (PETE *jumps back. He turns from* NEIL *and plunges upstage. Wildly he exits at center. There is a pause as* DIANA *and* NEIL *gaze in silence toward center doorway. At last* DIANA *turns to* NEIL.)

DIANA (*Hesitantly*): Neil, you—you were wonderful—

NEIL (*Shrugs*): It was nothing.

DIANA: I'm certain that man was a thief. He must have planned to—to—(*She breaks off.*)

NEIL: At least I couldn't take any chances.

DIANA: I know he gave an excuse for coming in here, but —(*Her voice trails off. Slowly she moves to extreme downstage left. She pauses, her back to* NEIL.) Anyway, Neil, I—I want to thank you.

NEIL (*With affected unconcern*): Always glad to be of service—(*He moves to extreme right downstage. His back is to* DIANA. *When* NEIL *at last speaks, his voice is hesitant but deeply sincere.*) I—I guess I'd do anything for you, Diana—

DIANA (*With a happy little gasp*): Neil! (*Slowly* NEIL *and* DIANA *turn toward each other. Their expressions reflect forgiveness and devotion. Each takes a step forward. Obviously the battle has come to an end, but at that moment* JUNE *and* NANCY *enter at center doorway.* NEIL *and* DIANA *pause abruptly.* JUNE *and* NANCY *take a few steps downstage, then stop. They are gloomy with defeat.*)

JUNE (*At last*): You were right, Nancy. They're both still here.

NANCY (*Nods*): And as mad at each other as ever.

JUNE (*Sadly*): Nancy decided we'd better come back and tell you something.

NANCY (*Sighs*): You might as well know the truth. (DIANA *and* NEIL *remain silent.*)

JUNE: There isn't any lunch. There never was going to be any lunch. Miss Clayton isn't even in town today. (NEIL *and* DIANA *are startled.*) We had a marvelous plan, but it didn't work.

NANCY (*Continues the explanation*): Miss Clayton let June and me have the apartment. We were the ones who invited you two for lunch. We thought if we could get you together, you'd stop quarreling.

JUNE (*Weepily*): But instead of forgiving each other, you just got madder and madder.

NEIL (*After a tense pause*): But what—what difference did it make to either of you?

NANCY (*Exasperated*): You idiots, don't you understand? You two have always played the leads in the high school plays. Now the senior play's coming up, but we knew neither of you would take a part if you were enemies.

JUNE: So we thought we could work out a reconciliation—

NANCY: I was doing it in behalf of the high school.

JUNE (*Sighs*): And I was doing it in behalf of a beautiful romance. (DIANA *and* NEIL *are speechless.*)

NANCY (*Firmly, to* DIANA *and* NEIL): Well, now you know the facts. We tried—and failed. And so far as I'm concerned, you two can go on battling the rest of your lives! (*She turns, starts upstage toward center door.*)

JUNE (*To* DIANA *and* NEIL): Sure, go right on fighting. We don't care any more! (*Starts upstage*)

NEIL (*Suddenly*): But wait! Diana and I aren't fighting.
(JUNE *and* NANCY *pause abruptly. Slowly they turn.*)

NANCY: What—what did you say?

DIANA (*To* NANCY): Of course we're not fighting.

NEIL: We're the best of friends.

DIANA (*Smiles*): In fact, we're devoted. (*Quickly* DIANA *crosses to* NEIL.) Aren't we, Neil?

NEIL (*Grins happily, as he takes* DIANA'S *hands*): Totally —completely—and forever!

NANCY (*Amazed*): Why—why—Oh, dear!

JUNE: But I don't get it—

DIANA (*Smiles significantly at* JUNE): Neither did Pete.

NANCY: You mean you two are—are back together?

NEIL: What does it look like?

JUNE (*Weakly*): Somebody's crazy around here, and I'm beginning to think I'm it.

NANCY (*Breathlessly*): This—this is wonderful!

NEIL: You're telling us! (*He slips his arm around* DIANA'S *waist.*)

NANCY: I—I've never been so relieved in my life—

JUNE (*Enthusiastically*): I'm just bubbling over!

NANCY (*Suddenly*): Then that vase— (*She indicates vase on end table.*) It can stay here.

NEIL (*With a sudden start*): Vase?

DIANA (*Equally startled*): Stay here?

NANCY: We bought Miss Clayton that vase when she said we could use her apartment to get you two together. It's all hearts and flowers—to symbolize the occasion.

JUNE: But when it looked as if you two were going to be enemies for life, we decided to exchange the vase for a black panther Miss Clayton had admired in Mr. Squires' gift shop. (*Grimly*) The panther seemed more appropriate, anyhow.

NANCY: So I went downstairs and phoned Mr. Squires. He didn't have the panther any more, but he was going to order another, and he said he'd send his delivery man over here for the vase. Good thing the guy didn't show up. (DIANA *and* NEIL *stand frozen in amazement.* NANCY *looks at them curiously.*) What's the matter with you two?

DIANA (*With a gasp*): Oh, my goodness! That poor guy . . .

NEIL (*Weakly*): I—I—Good grief! (*At that moment* PETE *re-enters at center back. He is wild-eyed and trembling violently. Moaning, he staggers down center.*)

DIANA (*As she sees* PETE): Pete! (PETE *collapses into chair at left of table.* NANCY *and* JUNE *are thrown into confusion.*)

NANCY (*To* PETE): Who—who are you?

JUNE (*To* PETE): What do you want?

PETE (*Pays no attention to* NANCY *and* JUNE *as he begins to sob*): I—I ran into Mr. Squires out in front of this building. I—I told him I—I could see through people's partitions. He—he thinks I'm crazy—and so do I! (*Desperately, with a loud wail.*) I know I'm losin' my mind . . . so please, somebody call the police! After what I been through in this here place, all I want is a nice padded cell! (PETE *lays his head on the table. He sobs loudly.* JUNE *and* NANCY *look on in amazement. Then suddenly* NEIL *and* DIANA *break into loud laughter. The curtain quickly falls.*)

THE END

Production Notes

LUNCHEON FOR THREE

Characters: 2 male; 3 female.

Playing Time: 30 minutes.

Costumes: Modern clothes. Diana, Neil, Nancy, and June are dressed up for the occasion. Pete wears working clothes.

Properties: Vase decorated with hearts and flowers; knitting bag containing needles and one or two balls of wool.

Setting: The living room of Miss Clayton's apartment. There are two entrances to the room—a door at center back, which opens into the outer hallway of the apartment building, and a door to right of stage which leads to the other rooms of the apartment. The room is bright and cheerful. To right of stage is a small dining table covered with a gay luncheon cloth. Three place settings have been carefully arranged on the table. A chair stands in front of each setting, one chair behind table upstage, another at right of table, and the third at left. To left of stage is a divan with a knitting bag on it. At downstage end of divan is a small table, on which stands a vase decorated with hearts and flowers.

Lighting: No special effects.

Keep It Under Cover

Characters

CAROL FLEMING
BILL HEDGES
MRS. HEDGES
SHIRLEY RICH
DOROTHY MADISON
MIKE JACKSON

TIME: *Saturday afternoon.*
SETTING: *Living room of the Fleming residence.*
AT RISE: CAROL FLEMING *is unwrapping a box which lies on the table. She opens the box and takes out a pair of boxing gloves, which she inspects carefully. The doorbell rings and* CAROL *swiftly puts gloves into box and closes it.* BILL HEDGES *enters.*

CAROL: Bill! Thank goodness, it's only you.
BILL: Only? That's a pleasant greeting. Were you expecting Santa Claus or the F.B.I.?

CAROL (*Laughs lightly*): After all, a girl can't be too careful.

BILL: You *did* phone this morning. Remember? You asked me to drop by.

CAROL: I know. I'd just unwrapped your package when the doorbell rang.

BILL: Carol! Then you did buy those boxing gloves for me!

CAROL (*Proudly*): Indeed I did. (*She indicates box.*)

BILL (*Going to table*): Carol Fleming, you're a genius!

CAROL (*Removes lid of box*): One pair of boxing gloves —secretly purchased for a certain Bill Hedges. (*She removes a glove from box.*)

BILL (*Excited*): Perfect! (*He takes glove from* CAROL.) You had enough money?

CAROL: Sir, you gave me the exact amount.

BILL: You know, Carol, it was entirely your idea—making this purchase for me. (*Smiles*) You're about the smartest girl a fellow could have.

CAROL: Why shouldn't I help you? For weeks you've secretly been taking boxing lessons. Now you're in condition for the amateur tournament at Westwood City next Saturday night. Since you couldn't tell your family and you needed a new pair of gloves, I simply walked into Mr. Wiggins' Sport Shop and bought them myself.

BILL: Did Mr. Wiggins wait on you?

CAROL: Yes, but I didn't tell him the gloves were for you. Of course, he *was* curious.

BILL: If I'd bought those gloves myself from Mr. Wiggins, he'd have told my mother within an hour. That would have ended everything. (*He sinks onto divan.*) I do hate to keep these plans from the family.

CAROL: I know, but what else can you do? I know how opposed your mother is to boxing.

BILL: If I could just win one of those bouts at Westwood City, maybe Mother would change her mind.

CAROL: By then it would at least be too late for a protest. (*The doorbell rings.* BILL *rises.*)

CAROL: Give me that glove! (*She takes glove.*)

BILL: Who's at the door?

CAROL: How could I know? I'm not equipped with X-ray vision. (*She puts the glove into box and hands* BILL *the box.*) Here—hide it!

BILL (*Takes box*): Where?

CAROL: Any place! (*She goes toward center door.* BILL *nervously looks around the room. As* CAROL *opens door,* BILL *places box behind divan.* SHIRLEY RICH *enters. She carries a large knitting bag which contains an embroidered pillow slip, embroidery hoops and thread.*) Shirley Rich!

SHIRLEY: Hi, Carol. (*She sees* BILL.) Look who's here—the dashing vagabond in person!

BILL: Hi, Shirley.

SHIRLEY: I hope I didn't interrupt anything.

CAROL (*Hastily*): Bill's here on business.

SHIRLEY: Business?

BILL (*To* SHIRLEY): I just dropped by to pick up a package.

SHIRLEY: Don't mind me, my little chicks. (*She moves to divan, sits. She places knitting bag at her side, speaks to* CAROL.) You're my best friend, so you know I'm likely to pop in anytime. Just pay me no heed.

CAROL (*Uneasily*): Shirley, do you expect to spend the afternoon over here?

SHIRLEY: Of course! (*Smiles*) Rather a ghastly idea, isn't it? (*She removes pillow slip and embroidery materials from bag.*) I'm embroidering a pair of pillow slips for Jean Humphrey. Poor Jean—she goes to college just one year, and then what happens? She decides to get married. Of course I was invited to the wedding. (*Sighs*) Everybody sends me an invitation—and everybody I know seems to be getting married. I really have nothing against weddings (CAROL *and* BILL *pace nervously*), but it *does* seem to me that a girl of Jean's age could find something more amusing to do than to look for an unclaimed man. (*To* CAROL) Take you and Bill, for instance. You're both interested in all sorts of—(*She breaks off suddenly.*) That reminds me! I heard all about you this morning.

CAROL: You heard about me?

SHIRLEY (*Nods*): I was in Mr. Wiggins' Sport Shop, and do you know what Mr. Wiggins told me? He said you'd been in a few minutes earlier for a pair of *boxing gloves!* (CAROL *and* BILL *look uneasy.*) Mr. Wiggins said you were terribly vague, so I simply couldn't wait to get over here for a report on the gruesome details.

BILL (*Groans*): I might have known Mr. Wiggins would talk!

SHIRLEY: Then it *is* true! (*To* CAROL) How exciting! I've heard of girls who carry some mad money, but you're the first one I've known who takes along a pair of boxing gloves.

CAROL (*Annoyed*): Now, Shirley!

BILL (*Turns to* CAROL): You might as well tell her, Carol. She won't rest until she knows.

SHIRLEY: This is breathtaking! I feel quivery all over. (CAROL *goes behind the divan and picks up the box.*) I simply adore secrets, and unless they're terribly, terribly confidential, I never breathe a word.

CAROL: All right, Shirley. I bought these gloves, but they're not for me.

SHIRLEY: Not for you?

CAROL: Bill has been taking boxing lessons. Next Saturday, he's entering the tournament at Westwood City.

SHIRLEY: Bill Hedges, you're not!

BILL: It's true, but I have to keep my plans a secret—particularly from Mother.

CAROL (*To* SHIRLEY): When Bill needed a new pair of gloves, I offered to make the purchase for him; otherwise, Mr. Wiggins would have spread the glad tidings.

SHIRLEY (*Enthusiastically*): Bill, I think this is wonderful! You're the first boxer I've known socially. And in no time you'll probably win the heavyheaded title and become another Man o' War.

BILL (*Grimly*): Don't you breathe one word of this, Shirley Rich!

SHIRLEY: I wouldn't think of it. (*Suddenly*) But, Bill, why must you keep this from your mother? I'd think she'd be terribly proud.

BILL (*Gloomily*): Not Mother!

CAROL (*To* SHIRLEY): She doesn't approve, Shirley. Bill's father was quite a boxer in his youth.

BILL (*To* SHIRLEY): Mother never did like the idea. Just before she and Dad were married, Dad met a really rough opponent. It was a tough fight.

SHIRLEY: He lost?

BILL (*Nods*): Yes, and he almost lost Mother, too. Mother made Dad promise he'd never box again. She's still bitterly opposed to the sport.

CAROL (*Breaks in*): Of course she'd be furious if she thought Bill had taken up boxing.

SHIRLEY: My, this *is* revealing!

BILL: Of course, if I'm lucky enough to come out a winner at Westwood City, I'll tell Mother and Dad.

CAROL (*To* SHIRLEY): Until the tournament, Bill must keep his plans under cover.

SHIRLEY (*Beams*): I *am* happy to be a part of all this hush-hush. I simply adore secrets. (*Suddenly*) Bill, I have an idea—you can put on an exhibition for us right now. (*She stuffs pillow slip and accessories back into knitting bag.*)

BILL: Hold on here!

SHIRLEY: Carol can be your savage opponent.

BILL: That's impossible!

CAROL: Of course it is.

SHIRLEY (*Places knitting bag on divan*): I still think it's a jolly suggestion. After all, you should put on *some* sort of a performance for us, Bill. That's the best thing I know for keeping me mum.

BILL: Oh, all right.

CAROL (*Hands a glove to* BILL): Here, Bill—

BILL (*Suddenly backs away*): But I can't—

CAROL (*Hesitates*): Can't? Why not?

BILL: There isn't time. I have to go now.

SHIRLEY (*To* BILL): Don't tell me you're booked for a match this afternoon.

BILL: It isn't that. Carol, I'm supposed to be home. I

promised Mother I'd get back by the time she returned from the station.

CAROL (*Puzzled*): From the station? What do you mean? (BILL *doesn't answer.*)

SHIRLEY (*To* CAROL): Carol, I have a feeling your boy friend has something on his conscience besides a pair of boxing gloves.

BILL: Of course I haven't! (*He turns to* CAROL) It's just that Mother has invited a guest for the weekend. She's coming in by train.

CAROL: *She?*

BILL: Well—Dorothy Madison. Dorothy's mother and my mother were girlhood friends. So they thought it—it would be nice if—if Dorothy came over for a little visit.

CAROL (*Coolly, after a pause*): I see.

BILL (*With spirit*): But you don't see! This wasn't my idea. I've never even met Dorothy Madison. I don't want to meet her! She's refined—she's intellectual—she's cultured—

CAROL (*With irony*): So different from *me,* of course.

BILL: Now you listen to me, Carol Fleming!

CAROL (*Breaks in*): Really, Bill, you needn't raise your voice. I'm sure Dorothy Madison would consider that terribly unrefined. (*There is a pause.*)

SHIRLEY: I do hope I'm not intruding, but if anybody wants me to leave before the battle, just say so. (*After another pause*) Well, since no one has spoken, I'll gladly stay.

CAROL (*To* BILL): I suppose you just forgot to mention your weekend plans with this—this friend.

BILL: She isn't a friend! I didn't happen to forget. I just

thought it wasn't important. If I *had* told you about
Dorothy, you wouldn't have tried to understand.

CAROL: I'm sure I understand perfectly.

BILL: Carol, you have to be reasonable! All this was something that Dorothy's mother cooked up. Dorothy has
had a fight with her boy friend—Charles something-or-
other. So her mother thought if Dorothy came over here
for a weekend—

CAROL: She could dig up another boy friend. How quaint!

BILL: I tell you, that isn't the idea at all!

SHIRLEY: Carol, you're not being fair.

CAROL (*Paying no attention to* SHIRLEY): Shouldn't you be
on your way, Bill? I'm sure dear Dorothy is waiting for
you, and you mustn't disappoint her, must you?

SHIRLEY: Now, Carol—

BILL (*To* CAROL) So! You're trying to run me out of here,
are you?

CAROL (*Startled*): Run you out? Certainly not, but you—

BILL (*With an affected scoff*): Oh, it's plain enough. You
just don't want me around here.

CAROL: Bill Hedges! Of course I want you around here,
but you plainly said—

BILL (*With emphatic finality*): Then I'm staying.

CAROL: But, Bill—

BILL: Hand me that glove. (CAROL *hands him the glove.*
BILL *turns to* SHIRLEY.) Help me with this glove.

SHIRLEY (*Enthusiastically*): I'll be your able second. (*She
slips glove over* BILL's *right hand.*)

CAROL (*To* BILL): But, Bill, if you're going to meet this
Dorothy Madison person—

BILL: I said I was staying, didn't I? I don't care whether

I *ever* meet Miss Madison. (*Suddenly*) Maybe I'll just settle down and spend the rest of my life right in this house.

SHIRLEY (*Gasps*): My goodness! What a shattering thought!

CAROL (*Shrugs*): I'm sure this is of no concern to me.

BILL: But it *is* your concern, Carol Fleming! You're my girl, aren't you? (CAROL *doesn't answer.* BILL *waves his arms vigorously.*) Well, aren't you?

SHIRLEY: Bill, stop waving your hand until I get you laced up. You're as bad as a girl dressing for her first prom.

BILL: Carol, listen to me. I told Mother I'd spend the afternoon with Dorothy—simply as a matter of courtesy. But that was all, positively all! If you're not sympathetic enough to believe me—(*Doorbell rings.*)

SHIRLEY: Someone's at the door! Carol, hide that box! (*To* BILL) Get out of that glove, you chump! (BILL *begins to fumble with the glove.* CAROL, *seeming to pay no attention to* SHIRLEY *or* BILL, *goes to door.*) Carol, stop! (CAROL *keeps moving.* SHIRLEY *snatches up box.* BILL *attempts to remove the glove.*)

BILL (*Groans*): I can't get this glove off.

SHIRLEY: Keep pulling! Carol, wait! (SHIRLEY *puts box behind sofa.* CAROL *opens center door.* MRS. HEDGES *and* DOROTHY MADISON *stand in doorway.* BILL *quickly hides gloved hand behind him.*)

CAROL: Mrs. Hedges!

MRS. HEDGES: Carol, my dear. (*She enters, followed by* DOROTHY. DOROTHY *is quiet and serious.* MRS. HEDGES *sees* BILL, *who keeps his gloved hand behind him.*) Hello, William. (*She notices* SHIRLEY.) And Shirley

Rich. How nice! Carol, this is Dorothy Madison. (*She indicates* DOROTHY. CAROL *smiles with effort*) Carol Fleming, Dorothy, and Shirley Rich.

SHIRLEY (*Weakly*): Hello.

MRS. HEDGES (*To* BILL): William, this is Dorothy! (BILL *is unable to speak.* MRS. HEDGES *turns to* DOROTHY.) Dorothy, this is my little William.

DOROTHY (*Without much enthusiasm*): I'm glad to know you, Bill.

MRS. HEDGES (*To* DOROTHY): William is simply overjoyed to meet you!

CAROL (*With effort*): Mrs. Hedges, won't you and Dorothy sit down?

MRS. HEDGES: Only for a moment, my dear. (*To* DORO- THY) Come, Dorothy. (*She and* DOROTHY *sit down.*) Dorothy is the daughter of my dear, dear school chum, Jessie Watts. (*To* CAROL) No doubt William has spoken to you often of Dorothy.

CAROL: Well, certainly not *too* often.

MRS. HEDGES: Dorothy lives in Crest Ridge. She's spend- ing the weekend with us. William said he had to stop here on a matter of business, so we dropped by to pick him up.

SHIRLEY: How enchanting! I'm certain Bill is equally de- lighted. (*To* BILL, *with a sweet smile*) Aren't you, Bill?

BILL: Yes—yes, indeed.

MRS. HEDGES: Dorothy was *so* anxious to be with us for a few days.

DOROTHY: Remember, Mrs. Hedges, this wasn't *my* idea. You and Mother made the plans.

MRS. HEDGES (*To* DOROTHY): We knew the change would give you a lift, my dear. (*To* CAROL) Dorothy hasn't been quite herself lately.

DOROTHY (*To* MRS. HEDGES): I'm sure no one is interested in my personal affairs, Mrs. Hedges.

MRS. HEDGES: William.

BILL: Yes?

MRS. HEDGES: What *is* wrong with you?

BILL (*Nervously, as he keeps his hand behind him*): Wrong?

MRS. HEDGES: I'm certain you've kept your hand behind your back from the moment we arrived.

BILL (*Affecting surprise*): I have?

SHIRLEY (*To* MRS. HEDGES): It's a high school custom in these parts. Instead of covering his face, a gentleman always hides one hand. (*Smiles*) A sign of modesty, you know.

MRS. HEDGES: How strange! I'm sure I knew nothing about it.

SHIRLEY: That's not half of what you don't know, Mrs. Hedges.

CAROL: Shirley!

MRS. HEDGES (*To* DOROTHY): Is this hidden-hand business a school custom in Crest Ridge, too?

DOROTHY: I've never seen Charles act like that.

MRS. HEDGES: Charles is Dorothy's boy friend.

DOROTHY: Not any more, he isn't!

MRS. HEDGES: Custom or no custom, I still don't approve. (*To* BILL) You have no idea how foolish you look, William, standing there like an ostrich with his head in the sand.

SHIRLEY: Goodness, what a wonderful idea for a nickname

—Bill "Ostrich" Hedges! (CAROL *goes to divan.* BILL's *gloved hand is now within easy reach of* CAROL.)

MRS. HEDGES (*Ruffled*): I hardly think this is amusing. "Ostrich"!

DOROTHY: Charles has always been highly opposed to nicknames. He says it cheapens one.

SHIRLEY: It's better to be caught red-handed with a nickname than with a—a—

MRS. HEDGES: With a what?

SHIRLEY: Never mind, never mind.

MRS. HEDGES (*To* BILL): Really, William, I can't understand your total lack of conversation. (*To* DOROTHY) My son is usually so talkative.

SHIRLEY: This just isn't one of Bill's talkative days. (*During the following conversation,* CAROL *slips her hand into* SHIRLEY's *knitting bag on the divan, quietly removes the pillow slip. Unnoticed by the others in the room, she places the pillow slip over* BILL's *gloved hand.* BILL *glances around, realizes what* CAROL *is doing, but he keeps silent.* CAROL *smiles.*)

MRS. HEDGES: My son is really a remarkable young man, Dorothy.

DOROTHY (*Flatly*): Indeed?

MRS. HEDGES: He never gives his father or me a moment's concern. We know his every plan and desire.

SHIRLEY: At least, it's an intriguing thought.

MRS. HEDGES (*To* DOROTHY): William *is* quiet and reserved —so like you, my dear. I suppose it's because of his father's rather—well, rather violent activities as a youth. I do think that's what completely settled William.

DOROTHY (*Interested*): Violent activities?

MRS. HEDGES (*Nods*): I suppose you didn't know. But William's father wanted to be a boxer.

DOROTHY: A boxer? How awful!

MRS. HEDGES: Of course I was firmly opposed. Just before we were married, Sam entered the ring for the last time. My dear, it was slaughter, simply slaughter, but probably it was just as well. Sam came out of that fight in distressing condition. He even ended up with a misplaced nose.

DOROTHY: How dreadful!

MRS. HEDGES: Of course his opponent took unfair advantage. I didn't see the fight, but I've always felt there was something underhanded about it. But be that as it may, I was horribly angry at Sam.

DOROTHY: Boxing, imagine!

MRS. HEDGES: After that, I put my foot down completely. And when I put my foot down, it stays down. I said that Sam should never box again. I have been equally firm with William.

DOROTHY: I'm certain that Charles would never engage in such a sport.

SHIRLEY: If you ask me, Charles sounds like something out of a wax museum on a hot day.

MRS. HEDGES (*Shocked*): My dear!

DOROTHY (*Suddenly flares up*): No Charles isn't! (*Stops*) I mean, it doesn't make the slightest difference to me— not now it doesn't.

MRS. HEDGES (*Uneasily, as she turns to* DOROTHY): My dear, we really should be on our way. (*She rises.*) Come along, William. (*There is a pause.* BILL *remains in front of divan, his hand still behind him.*) William, we simply must be on our way.

CAROL (*Rising*): So soon, Mrs. Hedges?

MRS. HEDGES: Really, William, I'm afraid you're not well. (*She crosses to* BILL) Since Dorothy and I arrived, you've been simply speechless.

BILL: Mother, I—

MRS. HEDGES (*Insistently*): And do take your hand from behind your back. (*She grasps* BILL *by the right shoulder, and swings him around, speaking as she does so.*) Dorothy will think you possess only one arm—(*She breaks off with a horrified gasp as she sees* BILL's *hand, covered by the pillow slip.*) William Hedges, what on earth! William, you've been injured! Your hand!

BILL: I have *not* been injured!

DOROTHY (*Points to pillow slip*): Mrs. Hedges, that's a *pillow slip*—and he's wearing it!

BILL (*Desperately*): I'm not wearing it! I mean, I—I—oh, what'll I do!

DOROTHY (*Peers closer at pillow slip*): Mrs. Hedges, someone has been hand-embroidering that pillow case.

BILL (*To* DOROTHY): So what? (*To* MRS. HEDGES) Mother, I've been hiding something from you.

MRS. HEDGES: William Hedges, you've taken up *sewing!*

BILL: Mother, I didn't mean that. (*He pauses, confused, then turns to* CAROL.) Carol, tell them! (CAROL *doesn't speak.*) Say something! Say something!

CAROL: Well, I *do* think it's a lovely pillow slip and the handwork is adorable. (*She smiles at* MRS. HEDGES *and* DOROTHY.) Don't you both think so?

DOROTHY (*To* MRS. HEDGES): This certainly explains your son's business over here today.

BILL: Now wait a minute—

CAROL (*Lightly, to* MRS. HEDGES): Bill drops in often. I'm always so interested in his progress. He has even been taking lessons—secretly, of course.

MRS. HEDGES: Lessons?

SHIRLEY: Carol keeps me posted on all of Bill's delightful little secrets. (SHIRLEY *picks up knitting bag.*) Don't you simply *love* this knitting bag? It's so handy for one's embroidery.

BILL (*To* SHIRLEY): You cut that out!

CAROL (*To* MRS. HEDGES *and* DOROTHY): I suppose this *is* rather unusual.

DOROTHY (*Emphatically*): I'm certain Charles has never embroidered a pillow slip!

CAROL (*To* MRS. HEDGES): Our house is simply full of the sweetest little pieces of fancywork—all handmade, of course. (*Suddenly*) Perhaps you'd like to see them, Mrs. Hedges.

MRS. HEDGES: Do you mean the—the fancywork that—that my son—(*She breaks off.*) Oh, dear!

CAROL (*Smiles*): I shan't be a moment. (*She exits.*)

BILL: Mother, you don't understand. It isn't like this, but I'm in a spot!

MRS. HEDGES: You certainly are!

DOROTHY: Charles has never been in a single spot in his life.

BILL: Look, Mother, I can't say anything—

MRS. HEDGES (*With dignity*): Under the circumstances, you certainly don't need to say anything.

SHIRLEY (*Steps to* BILL, *smiles down at him*): Just relax, Bill. When you told me your little secret, I promised not to open my mouth. Remember? Of course I didn't know then that—(*Doorbell rings*) The doorbell. You'll excuse me? (SHIRLEY *goes to door, opens it.* MIKE JACKSON *enters quickly.*)

MIKE (*Speaks quickly to* SHIRLEY): Are you Carol Fleming?

SHIRLEY (*Puzzled*): No—(MIKE *moves quickly to* DOROTHY.)

MIKE: Are you Carol Fleming?

DOROTHY: I certainly am not!

SHIRLEY (*To* MIKE): See here—who are you and what do you want? (MIKE *pays no attention. He steps to* MRS. HEDGES, *peers at her closely.*)

MIKE (*To* MRS. HEDGES): No—you couldn't possibly be Carol Fleming.

BILL (*Jumps up, speaks to* MIKE): Just a minute, sir.

MIKE (*Turns to* BILL): Take it easy, buddy. (*He turns to* SHIRLEY) Is Carol Fleming in this house?

SHIRLEY: Yes, she is. But—(*At that moment* CAROL *enters from left. She carries several pieces of embroidery.*)

CAROL (*As she enters*): I didn't bring everything, Mrs. Hedges—(*She stops abruptly as she sees* MIKE.) Oh!

SHIRLEY (*To* CAROL): Carol, either you have a caller or we're being auditioned for a quiz show.

MIKE (*Faces* CAROL): So you're Carol Fleming.

CAROL (*Steps forward*): Yes.

MIKE (*After a pause*): You thought you could put it over, didn't you?

CAROL: Put it over?

MIKE (*Nods*): I'm here to stop you. As promoter of the fights, I have a right to reject anyone who—

CAROL: Promoter? Fights?

MIKE: I'm from Westwood City. I'm managing the amateur boxing matches over there next Saturday night.

MRS. HEDGES (*Suddenly sits up*): What's this?

MIKE (*To* CAROL, *paying no attention to* MRS. HEDGES): I've just come from Mr. Wiggins' Sport Shop. I placed a poster in his window. (*Slowly and significantly*) He told me all about it.

BILL (*Takes a step forward*): Now, hold on, sir.

MIKE (*To* BILL): I asked you to keep out of this. (*He points to* BILL's *hand.*) Frankly, you look as though you've been in enough trouble already.

MRS. HEDGES (*To* MIKE): Sir, my son has *not* been in trouble. He has simply been embroidering a pillow slip.

MIKE (*Startled*): What?

MRS. HEDGES (*To* MIKE): I know. I was just as surprised as you are. I think he turns out fancywork, too. It was all a secret until—

MIKE: Madam, please! (*To* CAROL) Yes, I talked with this Mr. Wiggins. He told me that you were in his shop this morning. Is that correct?

CAROL (*Uneasily*): Well, yes.

MIKE: He said you bought a pair of boxing gloves.

MRS. HEDGES: *Boxing gloves?*

DOROTHY (*Amazed*): Carol purchased boxing gloves?

CAROL (*To* MIKE): Yes, I did. But I—

MIKE (*Cuts in*): Mr. Wiggins said you refused to explain the reason. But Wiggins has an idea, and I think he's right.

BILL (*To* MIKE): Mr. Wiggins is full of ideas, most of which are half-witted. If you want my opinion—

MIKE: Young man, from what I've seen of you, I wouldn't take your opinion on the correct answer to one and one.

MRS. HEDGES: Sir, don't you speak like that! He's my son.

MIKE (*Turns to* MRS. HEDGES): Then you have my sympathy, madam. (*Faces* CAROL *again*) Mr. Wiggins has convinced me that you purchased those boxing gloves for the single purpose of entering my tournament next Saturday night.

CAROL (*Shocked*): What!

SHIRLEY: Carol—enter a boxing tournament?

MIKE (*To* CAROL): I'm here to tell you that no ladies are allowed to fight in any matches I promote.

DOROTHY (*Amazed*): Does this mean that Carol is a lady boxer?

BILL: Of course it docsn't!

MIKE (*To* CAROL): I've been putting on tournaments for ten years, and this is the first time a girl has ever tried to muscle in. (*His voice rises emphatically.*) Do you know what would happen if you entered the ring? You'd bring down the roof, that's what you'd do. You'd cause a riot.

BILL: You listen to me, you big chump—

MIKE: Don't you call Mike Jackson a chump!

MRS. HEDGES (*With a sudden gasp*): Mike Jackson? (*She jumps up.*)

BILL (*To* MIKE): Carol Fleming is my girl! Do you hear? She's my girl. She wouldn't enter your old tournament for a free ticket to the moon!

MIKE: Get back to your embroidery, junior. That's about your speed.

BILL (*Explosively*): Is that so! (*He snatches off the pillow slip, exposing the boxing glove.*) Well, I'll show you—! (MIKE *sees the glove just as* BILL *takes a swing in the direction of* MIKE's *jaw.* MIKE *jumps back and* BILL's *blow misses him.* MIKE, *startled, trips and falls to a sitting position on the floor.*)

CAROL: Bill!

MIKE (*On floor, as he looks up at* BILL *in complete amazement*): Why—why—

MRS. HEDGES: William! (*Eagerly*) Do you know what you did? You socked Mike Jackson!

DOROTHY (*Wide-eyed*): Mrs. Hedges!

BILL: Mother!

MRS. HEDGES (*To* BILL): You hit him! You hit Mike Jackson!

BILL (*Confused*): But, Mother, I didn't really—

MRS. HEDGES: He's on the floor, isn't he?

BILL: Yes, but—

MRS. HEDGES (*Triumphantly*): I've waited twenty-five years for this golden moment!

MIKE (*On floor, as he gazes up at* MRS. HEDGES): Madam, you're off your rocker!

MRS. HEDGES (*Looks down at* MIKE): I didn't know who you were until I heard your name!

MIKE (*To* MRS. HEDGES): You'd better keep out of this.

MRS. HEDGES: I won't keep out of anything! Do you know who you are?

MIKE (*Aghast*): Do I know who I—? (*He breaks off.*) You *are* crazy!

MRS. HEDGES (*Grimly*): Weren't you a boxer?

MIKE: A boxer? Why, sure, 'way back in—

MRS. HEDGES (*Victoriously*): Exactly! You're Mike Jackson. You're the big brute who knocked out my husband in his last fight—twenty-five years ago!

CAROL: Mrs. Hedges!

BILL: Mother!

SHIRLEY: Oh, good grief!

MRS. HEDGES (*To* MIKE): I didn't see that fight, but I heard all about it. *You're* the one who misplaced my husband's nose! And it's the only one he ever had. (MRS. HEDGES *rushes to* BILL *and throws her arms around him.*) I was never so proud of you in all my life.

BILL: But, Mother, I didn't really hit him.

MRS. HEDGES (*Pays no attention to* BILL): My dream come true! Mike Jackson on the floor—just where he put my dear Sam twenty-five years ago!

MIKE (*With a sudden and violent start*): Sam? Sam? (*He jumps up, faces* MRS. HEDGES.) Is Sam Hedges your husband?

MRS. HEDGES (*Nods*): Indeed he is.

MIKE (*Grins*): Say, this *is* a small world! Good old Sam Hedges. Well, what do you know!

MRS. HEDGES (*Proudly*): It took our son to make you bite the dust.

BILL (*Urgently*): But, Mother, I tell you I didn't—

CAROL: Mrs. Hedges, you don't know all the facts. Bill has been taking boxing lessons. He even planned to enter the Westwood City tournament.

MRS. HEDGES: He did? (*Stoutly*) Well, who's keeping him from it?

BILL (*Grins broadly*): Mother, do you mean it? (MRS. HEDGES *nods.*) You're absolutely great!

CAROL (*To* MRS. HEDGES): You're wonderful!

SHIRLEY (*Wipes her brow with her hand*): Boys and girls, am I all shook up! (DOROTHY *steps to* MRS. HEDGES *and pulls her arm to gain attention.*)

DOROTHY: Mrs. Hedges.

MRS. HEDGES (*Without interest*): What is it, dear?

DOROTHY: I want to say good-bye.

MRS. HEDGES (*Startled*): Good-bye?

DOROTHY (*Nods*): I'm taking the next train back home. That's certainly where I belong—back home with Charles. (*She smiles.*) Thanks for everything. This experience has opened my eyes. So I'm on my way back to Charles—bless his quiet, simple, peaceful little heart! (DOROTHY *turns. She exits right.*)

SHIRLEY: What do you know!

MRS. HEDGES: A nice girl, but terribly reserved. (*She turns to* MIKE.) Mike, you're coming home with us for a meal. Of course Sam will want to see you again.

MIKE: Mrs. Hedges, I'd be tickled crimson!

MRS. HEDGES: But first, we're doing it once more.

BILL: Doing *what* once more? (MRS. HEDGES *steps to* BILL. *She grasps his gloved hand, raises it slightly.*)

MRS. HEDGES (*To* BILL, *as she indicates* MIKE): You're giving Mike one tender little hook on the jaw, Bill Hedges. (*To* MIKE) And you'd better fall flat when he does it. (*Triumphantly, to them all.*) Before Bill enters that tournament next week, I want to be able to say he's scored a triple-decker, home-run knockout! (MRS. HEDGES, *holding* BILL's *arm, begins to push it toward* MIKE's *jaw.* BILL *and* MIKE *grin. Quick curtain.*)

THE END

Production Notes

Keep It Under Cover

Characters: 2 male; 4 female.

Playing Time: 30 minutes.

Costumes: All wear modern dress. Mrs. Hedges wears tailored dress or suit. Dorothy wears travelling outfit. Mike may be dressed in flashy jacket or sweater.

Properties: Wrapped box containing boxing gloves; knitting bag containing embroidered pillow slip, embroidery hoops and thread; pieces of embroidery.

Setting: The living room of the Flemings. There are two entrances: the outside door is at center back; door at left leads to rest of house. There are a divan, a table, and as many other furnishings as desired.

Lighting: No special effects.

Take Care, Anne

Characters

SUSAN WOODLEY ⎱ *high school*
ANNE HILLMAN ⎰ *students*
FREDDIE HILLMAN, *Anne's brother*
MARTHA HILLMAN, *their mother*
BARTON HILLMAN, *their father*
HORACE BOUNCE
DON MEEKER, *a high school student*
CLARA MEEKER, *his mother*

TIME: *Late Saturday morning.*
SETTING: *Living room of the Hillman home.*
AT RISE: *The stage is empty. Door at right is open. After a pause, the doorbell rings off-stage. Then center door opens.* SUSAN WOODLEY *enters, pauses, glances around the room.*

SUSAN (*Calling*): Anne! Anne, are you home? (*She closes the door behind her and raises her voice.*) Paging Anne

Hillman, paging Anne Hillman! (ANNE *enters from left.*)

ANNE (*Enthusiastically*): Susan!

SUSAN: I *did* attempt to be a perfect lady. I rang the door-bell. I even waited a full split second before entering.

ANNE (*Walks to center*): I was in the kitchen helping Mother. She's entertaining the officers of her club this afternoon. You know, she's the new president.

SUSAN: I certainly have no desire to break in on the club ladies' reservation—but when you phoned that you had to see me, I dropped everything.

ANNE: Susan, I have the most exciting news!

SUSAN (*Sits in chair*): All right, here I am. Give me the shattering details.

ANNE (*Excitedly*): It's about Don Meeker.

SUSAN: Don Meeker? Our high school heartthrob? The guy with the palpitating personality?

ANNE (*Slowly, and with a hint of triumph*): Susan, I'm ex-pecting him to ask me for a date to the school prom.

SUSAN (*Amazed*): Don Meeker ask *you* for a date? (ANNE *nods.*) Listen, you're a sweet child and my best friend and my next-door neighbor, but you and Don Meeker —(*Breaks off*) Why, he could have his pick, from Helen of Troy to the Pioneer Mother. After all, you two are only casual acquaintances.

ANNE: We were—until yesterday afternoon, but things have changed, Susan.

SUSAN: Don't tell me you're trying to stake out a claim on Don Meeker simply because his mother and your mother happen to be officers in the same club.

ANNE: No. Although that's how we got into conversation —about Mother's entertaining the club officers here today. One thing led to another, and Don happened to mention that he'd made an important purchase downtown. It was something he didn't want his parents to see—at least not yet. Then I had my inspiration. (*Pause*) I suggested that Don have the package sent here.

SUSAN: Sent here, to this house? (ANNE *nods.* SUSAN *rises.*) Anne, you didn't!

ANNE: I did. Don protested at first. He said it would be too much bother for me and that he wouldn't think of putting me to all that trouble. But I insisted. (*Proudly*) So I am to be custodian of his purchase.

SUSAN: Anne Hillman, I've never heard of such a thing!

ANNE: Don't you see? Don and I will have a common interest. He'll even feel obligated. After the package is delivered here, he'll drop by, maybe several times. That's the way beautiful friendships begin, and if all goes well, he's certain to ask me for a date to the prom.

SUSAN (*Grimly*): Anne Hillman, you'd better take care!

ANNE (*Triumphantly*): That's exactly what I'll be doing —taking care of Don's purchase. I'll admit it wasn't easy to convince him.

SUSAN: What do you suppose he is sending over?

ANNE: I haven't the slightest idea.

SUSAN: You don't know what he bought?

ANNE: Of course not. It was enough just to get his consent, but when the package arrives, I'll just slip it into a dresser drawer.

SUSAN: You won't slip it into a drawer if it's an oil well or a second-hand tugboat! (*From off-stage left comes a wild yell. Startled,* SUSAN *and* ANNE *turn. The left door opens, and* FREDDIE HILLMAN *charges into the room.*

He carries a long-handled spear. Holding spear in front of him as an attacking weapon, he moves towards the girls. Susan *shrieks, then dashes behind chair.*)

ANNE (*Cries out*): Freddie Hillman! (*Rushes toward* FREDDIE) Stop that! (*She reaches* FREDDIE *and grasps spear.*) Stop it, I say!

FREDDIE (*Tugs desperately*): You let go of my spear!

ANNE: Mother and Father warned you!

FREDDIE: I'm not hurting anything. (*He pulls spear from* ANNE.)

SUSAN (*From behind chair*): Anne, what is your brother up to this time?

FREDDIE (*To* SUSAN): I'm a jungle hunter! Don't I remind you of a genuine African explorer?

SUSAN: You remind me of somebody out to harpoon a bowl of goldfish.

ANNE (*To* SUSAN): From the moment Freddie got that spear, nothing in this house has been safe.

FREDDIE: Now, sis—

ANNE (*To* SUSAN): Freddie has punctured everything from sofa pillows to lamp shades.

FREDDIE: They were only discards—

ANNE (*To* FREDDIE): Father has already threatened to take away your allowance for the next three months.

FREDDIE (*With dignity*): Dad isn't home this morning. He's out to collect a bill somebody owes him. (SUSAN *moves from behind chair.*)

ANNE (*To* SUSAN): Father phoned the house an hour ago. He told Mother that he'd been able to get something in payment for an overdue account—not cash, but I don't know what it was. When Mother told him that

Freddie was wearing that horrible outfit again, he just groaned and hung up.

SUSAN: I'd not only groan and hang up—I'd leave for Siberia.

ANNE (*To* FREDDIE): I've had enough of this, Freddie Hillman. I'm going to bring Mother in here.

FREDDIE (*Smugly*): Huh, Mom's not home either. She went to the market a minute ago.

ANNE: I'll see for myself. (*To* SUSAN) Excuse me, Susan. (*Crosses left, then turns to* FREDDIE) I'm reminding you, Freddie, if Mother hears you've used that weapon, it will be the end of your hunting days. *And* of your allowance! (*Exits left*)

FREDDIE (*To* SUSAN): A fine family! A man can't even breathe around here. How does anybody expect me to teach the other members, if I don't have a spear?

SUSAN: What members?

FREDDIE (*Importantly*): I am project chairman of the Little Dynamite Club. I'm the one who decided those guys were going to learn to be jungle fighters.

SUSAN: No doubt my mentality is slipping—but why jungle fighters?

FREDDIE: Because I own the costume and the spear. I've been saving box tops. Some of the kids wanted to be cowboys, but I voted them down. After all, you can't get a horse with box tops.

SUSAN: You should know, Freddie.

FREDDIE: So we're jungle hunters. (ANNE *enters from left.* FREDDIE *grins in triumph.*) What'd I tell you, sis? Mom *isn't* in the kitchen.

ANNE (*Annoyed*): All right, she went to the market, but I hope she returns in time to see you with that spear. (*The doorbell rings off-stage.* FREDDIE, *still clutching spear, jumps up.*)

FREDDIE: Who's at the door?

ANNE: I hope it's a tribe of African cannibals in search of a juicy meal. We have just their dish! (*She glares at* FREDDIE, *then goes to door.* ANNE *opens the center door, and* HORACE BOUNCE *enters, staggering under the weight of a large burlap bag.* ANNE, SUSAN *and* FREDDIE *watch, amazed.*)

HORACE: Is this the Hillman residence? (ANNE *nods mutely.*) I thought so. (*He drops sack onto floor.*)

FREDDIE (*Calls out*): Hey, you!

ANNE (*To* HORACE): What are you doing?

SUSAN (*To* HORACE): This is a living room!

HORACE (*Straightens up*): That's no concern of mine.

ANNE: But, sir—

HORACE (*Facing* ANNE): My name isn't "sir." It's Bounce —Horace Bounce.

ANNE: But, I don't understand—

HORACE: I was told to make a delivery to the Hillman house. Your garage door is locked. Couldn't find a porch —front or back. Looks like rain, too, so there it is. (*He points to sack.*)

ANNE: But I didn't order anything. You've made a mistake.

HORACE: I'm a deliveryman—and I never make a mistake.

SUSAN (*With a sudden gasp*): Oh, my goodness! (*To* ANNE) Anne! Anne, don't you see?

ANNE: See what?

SUSAN (*Points to bag*): That must be Don Meeker's purchase!

ANNE: Don Meeker's purchase?

FREDDIE: What are you girls gurgling about?

ANNE (*Pays no attention to* FREDDIE): Susan, do you honestly think—

SUSAN (*Nods*): You told Don to send his purchase out here, and you admitted you didn't know what it was.

FREDDIE (*Points to bag in amazement*): You mean that belongs to Don Meeker? (*He goes over to the bag.*)

HORACE: Wish folks would stop rushing around. Makes me nervous. (FREDDIE *groans as he reads tag attached to sack.*)

SUSAN: Freddie, what is it?

FREDDIE: According to the tag, this is a sack of stock feed.

ANNE: Stock feed?

HORACE (*Sourly, as he steps downstage*): What'd you think it was—dusting powder?

ANNE: Why should Don Meeker buy stock feed?

HORACE (*Impatiently*): That's no business of mine. (*He takes a step toward door.*)

ANNE: Mr. Bounce, you can't leave that sack in here!

HORACE (*Turns majestically*): I was told to deliver one bag of feed to the Hillman address. I have discharged my duty.

ANNE: No, you haven't! (*The phone rings off-stage.*)

SUSAN: Anne, that's the phone—

ANNE: Freddie, see who it is! (*Phone rings again.* FREDDIE *exits right, closing door behind him.* ANNE *steps quickly to* HORACE.) Mr. Bounce, please listen to me! My mother is entertaining this afternoon—

SUSAN (*To* HORACE): Indeed she is—right here in the living room!

ANNE (*To* HORACE): This is no place for a sack of stock feed!

HORACE: If there aren't enough chairs, somebody can sit on it.

ANNE: You'll have to put it in the garage!

HORACE: But the garage door is locked.

ANNE: Freddie will open it! (*She steps to* HORACE.) Please pick up that bag and take it away! If Mother finds stock feed in the living room, she'll have hysterics.

SUSAN: And so will her guests. They'll think it's the refreshments!

HORACE (*Mutters*): All right, all right. (*He leans over and lifts the sack.* FREDDIE *enters from right.*)

FREDDIE: Mr. Bounce, Mr. Bounce! The phone—it's for you.

HORACE: For me? Well, what do you know?

ANNE (*Quickly*): Freddie, just tell whoever it is that Mr. Bounce is busy and that he'll call back—

HORACE: No you don't! (*He drops sack back to floor.*) I'm never too busy for a good chat on the telephone. (*He moves toward doorway right.*)

ANNE: But Mr. Bounce! Suppose Mother walks in here. She'd absolutely faint!

HORACE (*Turns*): A good helping of stock feed never made anyone faint. (*He exits right, closing door after him.*)

ANNE (*Desperately*): Freddie, carry out that sack—before Mother shows up!

FREDDIE: I couldn't even lift it.

ANNE: Then I'll help you. (*She goes to bag and turns to*

Susan.) Give us a hand, Susan. There isn't a moment to spare. (*Suddenly* Martha Hillman's *voice is heard off-stage left.*)

Martha (*Offstage*): Anne! Oh, Anne!

Susan: Your mother!

Freddie: It's Mom! (*He gazes at spear, then dashes to divan, drops to his knees, and slips the spear under divan.*)

Susan: Anne, what'll we do? (Anne *looks around wildly. She sees the throw rug in front of divan.*)

Anne (*Pointing to rug*): That rug! (*Runs to divan*) Help me, Susan! (*She leans over, grasps one end of rug.*) We have to cover the sack! (Susan *picks up other end of rug.*)

Martha (*Off-stage*): Anne, where are you? (Anne *and* Susan *carry rug upstage and toss it over the sack.* Freddie *jumps up.* Martha *enters from left, leaving door open.*) Anne, dear, I'm back from the—(*Pauses abruptly*) Why, hello, Susan. (Susan *smiles weakly.*) I didn't know you were here. (*She moves toward center.*) I'm entertaining the officers of my club this afternoon, but I had to run over to the market. (*She breaks off and points at rug.*) What on earth is *that?*

Anne (*After a pause*): It—it's just our rug, Mother—

Martha: It's certainly covering something more than the floor. (*She takes a step upstage.*)

Anne (*Swiftly steps in front of* Martha): Mother—don't!

Susan (*To* Martha, *with affected brightness*): It's nothing, Mrs. Hillman—just an old sack.

Martha: An old sack? In my living room—today? (*Turns to* Anne) Really, Anne—

Anne: Don't get upset, Mother. It—it belongs to Don Meeker.

MARTHA: *What* belongs to Don Meeker?

FREDDIE: That old sack full of feed.

MARTHA: Feed? *Feed?*

ANNE (*Desperately*): Freddie means it's like a bag of cereal —that's it—cereal.

MARTHA: Anne, what in the world are you doing with a bag of cereal that belongs to Don Meeker? And in my clean living room, with guests expected soon?

ANNE (*Soothingly*): Don't worry, Mother. It was just delivered, and we're putting it in the garage.

FREDDIE: Mr. Bounce is taking it out.

MARTHA: Mr. Bounce? Who is Mr. Bounce?

ANNE: Mother, you mustn't give this another thought. I'll take care of everything. (*She grasps* MARTHA'S *arm, and begins to lead her toward door at left.*)

MARTHA (*Protesting*): But, Anne, I—I don't understand—

ANNE: We'll have the place in perfect order in no time. (*She gives* MARTHA *a little push through doorway.*) That's it—just run along. I'll be right in to help you. (ANNE *closes the door behind* MARTHA.)

FREDDIE: Whew! Was that a close one!

ANNE (*Urgently*): Freddie, get Mr. Bounce off that phone. Tell him to come in here. (HORACE *enters from right.*)

HORACE (*Grumbles*): Well, if that isn't the everlasting limit!

ANNE: Mr. Bounce, you have to hurry. You can dash out to the garage with the sack and—

HORACE (*Interrupting*): No, I can't.

ANNE: What?

HORACE: I have to take that bag of feed back to the store. That was my boss calling. Seems the guy who purchased the feed has changed his mind about having it sent out here.

ANNE: Changed his mind?

HORACE: He's going to make other arrangements, and after seeing what goes on around this house, I don't blame him. (*Moves to sack, and throws back rug which covers it.*) What do you mean by covering up this nice bag of feed with an old rug?

ANNE: Mr. Bounce! Are you trying to say that you're returning this purchase to the store?

HORACE (*Scowling*): What do you *think* I'm talking about —the price of whale meat in Alaska?

SUSAN: Don't stop him, Anne. You're lucky. This means Don Meeker has made other plans and—

ANNE: You say he has changed his mind and is making some other arrangement?

HORACE (*Nods*): My boss said the guy even apologized for making so much trouble.

ANNE: Mr. Bounce, you are *not* returning that bag of feed! (HORACE *looks startled.*) So! Don is making other plans, is he? (*Turns to* SUSAN) It's plain enough! He thinks I'm not capable of taking care of a sack of feed. He's trying to squirm out of his promise! Well, I am entirely qualified to look after that purchase!

SUSAN: Of course you are. But—

ANNE: This was to be my big opportunity—(*Turns to* HORACE) That purchase is not to be returned, Mr. Bounce!

HORACE: Now hold on—

ANNE (*To* HORACE): Do you want to wreck the beginning

of a romance? Do you want to ruin a perfect date to the high school prom?

HORACE: I only want to take back this bag of feed! (*He leans over, begins to pick up sack. Suddenly* ANNE *reaches under divan and pulls out spear. She approaches* HORACE, *holding spear in front of her.*) Stop it, Mr. Bounce! (HORACE *looks at* ANNE *in horror. He drops the bag to the floor.*)

FREDDIE: Hey, that's my spear!

ANNE (*To* HORACE, *as she advances*): I am custodian of that purchase! (*She reaches bag.* HORACE *backs away.* ANNE *thrusts spear downward for emphasis.*) And I expect to prove to Don Meeker that I—(*She accidentally plunges head of spear into the side of feed sack. The sack rips slightly, and a bit of the contents seeps onto floor.*)

SUSAN (*Shrieks*): Anne, you've torn the bag!

HORACE: Ripped it wide open with that weapon!

ANNE (*Gazes at bag and backs away*): Oh—oh—!

SUSAN: It'll spill all over the floor—

HORACE (*To* ANNE): You've ruined a bag of stock feed, that's what you've done!

ANNE: I'll pay for the damage—

HORACE: You sure will! I'm not returning a bag full of holes to the store.

ANNE (*Desperately*): All right, all right! Just take it to the garage and—

HORACE: I'm not touching it. It's yours! (*He turns and marches toward center door.*) And if I ever have another delivery for this address, I'm going to put in a complaint for unfair labor practices! (*He exits.*)

FREDDIE (*To* ANNE): Now you've done it!

SUSAN (*Taking spear from* ANNE): Give me that—before another redskin bites the dust!

ANNE: We'll have to move the sack to the garage.

FREDDIE: With feed spilling out all through the house? Mom's guests would think we were raising chickens in the living room.

ANNE: Then we'll sew up the hole. (*To* SUSAN) Run next door for a needle and thread. I don't dare disturb Mother. (*To* FREDDIE) And, Freddie, you put your fingers in the hole until Susan gets back. Don't let any more feed spill on the floor! (FREDDIE *falls to his knees at side of bag, and* ANNE *pushes his fingers into the hole.*)

FREDDIE: I'm not responsible for this!

ANNE (*Desperately*): Freddie, you have to help me. I tell you what—I'll guarantee that you receive your weekly allowance. If Father won't pay you, I will.

FREDDIE: You will? (*Grins*) Well, that being the case—(*He thrusts his fingers further into the torn bag.*)

ANNE (*To* SUSAN): Hurry, Susan—Hurry! (SUSAN *nods, steps to center door, still carrying the spear. She opens door, swings around, and slams door behind her.*)

SUSAN (*Horrified*): Anne! He's here!

ANNE: Who?

SUSAN: Don Meeker—coming up the walk!

ANNE: Oh, no!

SUSAN: If he discovers you've stabbed his purchase in the back—

ANNE: He won't discover it! (*She snatches up the rug which had previously covered sack.*) Susan, this rug—

SUSAN: Again? (ANNE *nods.* SUSAN *snatches up one end of rug.*)

FREDDIE: What about *me?*

ANNE: Stretch out on that sack!

FREDDIE: Gee whiz—!

ANNE: And don't you move!

SUSAN: And keep your finger in that hole in the dike!

FREDDIE: But I—(*The doorbell rings off-stage at center.*)

ANNE (*To* FREDDIE): Remember, I can save your allowance! (FREDDIE *sprawls on top of feed sack, with his fingers in the torn portion.* ANNE *and* SUSAN *throw rug over* FREDDIE *and the bag. The doorbell rings again.* SUSAN *gazes at spear in her hand. Then she runs to door right and exits.* ANNE *moves upstage and throws open center door to* DON MEEKER.)

DON (*Smiling at* ANNE): Greetings!

ANNE (*Affecting surprise*): Why, Don Meeker! My goodness, this is a surprise. Come in. (DON *enters. He does not notice rug upstage.*)

DON: I guess you weren't expecting me so soon.

ANNE: But I *was* expecting you. Indeed I was. Your purchase arrived, Don.

DON: I dropped by the store this morning. I was told the package was already on the delivery truck.

ANNE: I know everything about it, Don—even what you said, but I'm keeping your purchase right here until you're ready to take it home.

DON (*Puzzled*): Why, of course. (*Smiles*) After all, this was your suggestion.

ANNE: You can depend upon me, Don. You needn't change

your plans. Just forget about making other arrangements.

DON: Other arrangements? (SUSAN *enters from right, without spear.*)

SUSAN (*Without enthusiasm*): Hello, Don.

DON: Susan! I didn't know you were around.

SUSAN (*Dryly*): I am—unfortunately.

DON (*To* SUSAN): Did Anne explain about my little purchase?

SUSAN: I love that word "little." (*She moves near center.*)

ANNE (*To* DON): You didn't mind my telling Susan?

DON: Of course not. (*Smiles*) Then we needn't keep anything under cover.

SUSAN (*Pointedly*): That's what you think. (DON *sits in chair right.*)

DON (*To* SUSAN): I want to keep this a secret from my parents. You can understand, can't you?

SUSAN: A thing like this would paralyze *my* parents.

DON (*To* SUSAN): Wasn't it thoughtful of Anne to take it in for me?

SUSAN: Not only thoughtful, but overwhelming.

DON: Dad and Mother are going to be surprised, all right, especially Mother.

SUSAN: I can just see the expression on her face.

DON: Anne tells me the delivery has already been made. (*He turns to* ANNE.) I suppose it arrived safely? (ANNE *nods nervously.*) I hope you could slip it away without difficulty—I've been thinking—if this should cause you any trouble or embarrassment—

ANNE: It won't. That's why I refused to let Mr. Bounce return it.

DON: Return it?

ANNE (*Smiling*): I'm entirely capable, Don. Now, I don't want to hear another word on the subject.

DON: What did you do with it?

ANNE (*With effort*): Do with—what?

DON: My purchase, of course. (*There is a strained pause.*)

ANNE (*Points unsteadily at rug upstage*): It's over there. (DON *turns, glances upstage, and sees the rug. He rises.*)

DON: Where?

ANNE: Under that rug. I didn't want Mother to see it! She's entertaining in this room today—the officers of her club.

DON: Yes, I know. My mother is one of the officers. (*He gazes at rug.*) Under that rug, you say? I'm afraid my purchase turned out larger than I expected. From the beginning I had a feeling that perhaps I shouldn't send it out here—

ANNE: Don't you even say that, Don Meeker!

DON: Do you think Mother will like it?

SUSAN (*Starts*): Your *mother*?

DON: She's crazy about this sort of thing. She really eats it up.

SUSAN: Oh, no!

DON (*Suddenly*): But this is stupid of me. You girls haven't even had a chance to look inside it. Let me show you— (*He takes a step upstage toward rug.*)

ANNE (*Dashing in front of* DON): No! I mean—if somebody walked in, it—it might be difficult to explain.

DON: I suppose you're right—especially if I had to admit I'd purchased it for Mother.

SUSAN: People wouldn't believe you.

DON: I'm giving it to Mother as a birthday present. (*Doorbell rings off center.*) Was that the bell?

ANNE: Someone is at the door!

SUSAN: Probably a hungry group from the stockyards. (ANNE *opens center door.* CLARA MEEKER *stands in doorway. She does not see* DON, *who has paused near open doorway right.*)

ANNE (*Gasps*): Mrs. Meeker! (DON *gives a violent start, and exits right, closing the door behind him silently.*)

CLARA (*Brightly*): How are you, Anne? (*She steps into the room, and sees* SUSAN.) Why, hello, Susan! (*She moves down center, without noticing rug upstage.*)

SUSAN: Hello, Mrs. Meeker. (ANNE *follows* CLARA *downstage.*)

CLARA: I've heard that you had a wonderful time at the music camp last summer.

SUSAN: That's where I should have stayed—under the murmuring pines and hemlocks.

CLARA (*To* ANNE): I thought perhaps I could help your mother if I came early. (*She sits in chair right.*)

ANNE (*With effort*): It was sweet of you. I'll call her. (*Exits.*)

CLARA (*Turns to* SUSAN): Is anything wrong with Anne? Somehow I have a feeling she isn't quite up to par today.

SUSAN: That's a common ailment around here. (SUSAN *glances upstage at rug.*)

CLARA (*Cheerfully*): Of course you knew that Anne's mother is entertaining the new officers of the club? (SUSAN *nods.*) Such a task! I hope everything is covered.

SUSAN: I know *something* that is. (MARTHA *enters from left.*)

MARTHA: Clara!

CLARA (*Rises*): Martha, my dear! (*As* MARTHA *and* CLARA *speak,* SUSAN *silently moves to door right and exits.*) I know you weren't expecting anyone so early, but I thought I might be able to help.

MARTHA: You *are* a dear. (*Glances around the room*) Although I'm certain that everything is under control— (*Breaks off as she sees the rug upstage*) Oh, dear!

CLARA: What's the matter?

MARTHA (*Points at rug*): Look at that—still in the living room! (CLARA *turns and gazes at rug.*)

CLARA: My goodness—what is it?

MARTHA: Anne promised she'd have it out of here before the meeting. Excuse me, Clara. (*She crosses left, opens door, calls.*) Anne—Oh, Anne! (*Turns, closes door behind her.*) I don't mind telling you, Clara—at times a daughter can be a problem.

CLARA: A son, too, for that matter. (*She sits in chair right.*) Although my Don *is* a wonderful boy. (MARTHA *sits on divan.*) He's so conscientious and dependable. For weeks he has been staying overtime at school.

MARTHA: He's not falling behind in his studies!

CLARA: Of course not! Don has been simply head over heels in research.

MARTHA: Research?

CLARA: He's written an essay, and he needed the reference books in the library. You can imagine how late he has been in getting home, day after day. Hasn't Anne mentioned the contest?

MARTHA: Contest? No—not that I remember.

CLARA: The essay contest was on the subject, "Wholesome

Diets for the Modern Student." I suppose Don hasn't a chance to win, but wouldn't it be exciting if his essay *should* take first place?

MARTHA: When will the winner be announced?

CLARA: I don't know. The contest is sponsored by a break-fast food manufacturer. (*Laughs*) But I don't know what we'd do with the top prize. I believe it's a year's supply of cereal.

MARTHA: I'm sure you'd be proud if—(*Breaks off suddenly*) Cereal? Clara, did you say the first prize was *cereal?*

CLARA: Yes. (MARTHA *rises slowly and gazes at rug.* CLARA *looks puzzled.*) Martha, what's wrong?

MARTHA: Clara, let me get this straight—is the winner of the best essay to receive a year's supply of cereal? (CLARA *nods.*) Then—then Don won the prize!

CLARA (*Jumps up*) What!

MARTHA (*Steps to center, indicates rug*): There it is— under that rug.

CLARA (*Almost speechless*): Martha, you're joking!

MARTHA: I am not joking. Anne told me she's keeping something under there which belongs to your Don. It was delivered this morning. And Anne did admit it was cereal.

CLARA: Martha!

MARTHA: She wouldn't let me look at it, but she promised to put it in the garage.

CLARA: Martha, I'm simply speechless!

MARTHA (*Peers again at bag*): Really though, I didn't re-member it was so large—or such a strange shape—

CLARA: I've never been so excited in my life! Don must be

keeping it as a surprise for me. I *do* have a birthday next week—(*Takes a step toward rug*) I simply can't wait to—(*Breaks off, pauses*) Oh, but I mustn't peek, I know. I wonder what sort of cereal it is.

MARTHA: As top prize in a breakfast food contest, it should be terribly nutritious.

CLARA (*Points to rug*): My, how I'd like to get my teeth into that! Martha, I've an idea. Let's serve samples of it this afternoon—along with your refreshments.

MARTHA: Serve it to the other officers?

CLARA: We'll make it an announcement party in honor of Don. It'll be ever so much more exciting than keeping it as a secret for my birthday. We might as well start eating it at once.

MARTHA (*Doubtfully*): I wouldn't want to do anything which might upset Anne or Don—

CLARA: They won't mind! And can't you just see the ladies when they begin gobbling up those delicious goodies? (*She takes a step toward rug, then pauses.*) Do you suppose it's an assortment? I do hope we can uncover plenty of big, chewy raisins. (ANNE *enters from left.*)

ANNE (*Weakly*): Did—did you call me, Mother?

CLARA (*Turns to* ANNE): Anne, my dear, we know all about it!

ANNE (*Startled*): About what?

CLARA: We've guessed what's under the rug!

ANNE (*Aghast*): What!

CLARA (*Triumphantly*): It's a year's supply of breakfast cereal!

MARTHA (*To* ANNE): You said it was cereal, darling, and you admitted it belonged to Don—

CLARA (*To* ANNE): The dear boy won it on his essay, didn't he? But we shan't wait for my birthday. We'll unveil it this afternoon.

ANNE: Unveil—this afternoon—?

CLARA: Your mother and I will serve bowls of cereal to the guests. (ANNE *stands in horrified silence.*)

MARTHA (*Soothingly, to* ANNE): I know the award was meant as a secret, dear, but I'm sure Don will understand.

ANNE (*Gasps*): But you—you can't! I mean—you don't realize what's under that rug! (*The center door opens.* BARTON HILLMAN *enters.*)

BARTON (*As he removes his hat*): Am I in time for the party?

MARTHA: Barton!

CLARA: Mr. Hillman, my dear man! You'd never guess! We're serving heaping bowls of breakfast cereal!

BARTON (*Startled*): What's that?

MARTHA (*Indicates rug upstage*): It's under that rug, Barton.

BARTON: Cereal—under the rug?

CLARA (*Triumphantly*): A year's supply!

BARTON: See here, I don't get this.

ANNE (*Suddenly steps forward*): Father—

BARTON: What's the matter with *you?*

CLARA: It's really nothing, Mr. Hillman. The dear girl is just upset because we've learned the little secret.

MARTHA: Clara—(*Gazes at rug*) That cereal—I'm certain

it has expanded since I was in here a few minutes ago. Do you suppose it's swelling or something?

BARTON: What in the name of common sense is going on around here?

CLARA (*Pays no attention to* BARTON): It is possible, Martha. You know how this damp weather is.

MARTHA: Perhaps we should crisp it up in the oven.

CLARA: An excellent idea! Mr. Hillman, you're elected to carry the cereal into the kitchen. Then we'll pop it into the oven and—(*From under rug* FREDDIE *gives out with a wild yell.*)

FREDDIE: No, you won't! (*He leaps up, flings back the rug.* CLARA *and* MARTHA *shriek.* BARTON *gasps.*)

MARTHA: *Freddie Hillman!*

FREDDIE (*Wildly*): Lemme out of here! (*He starts to plunge across stage.* BARTON *grasps his arm.*)

BARTON (*Shouts*): Hold on here, young man—!

FREDDIE (*Wails loudly*): Nobody's going to put *me* in the oven! I don't need crisping up! (*Door at right opens, and* SUSAN *and* DON *step silently into room. They pause near doorway.*)

CLARA (*To* FREDDIE): Why—why, *you're* not a year's supply of breakfast cereal!

FREDDIE (*Frees himself from* BARTON *and points at* ANNE): It's Anne's fault! (*Suddenly* ANNE *breaks into a sob. She drops onto divan, weeping loudly.* DON *steps forward.*)

DON: Anne—Anne—

CLARA (*Sees* DON *for the first time*): Why—why, Don!

BARTON (*Loudly and desperately*): I demand to know what's going on!

ANNE (*Between sobs*): Don didn't—didn't win any contest . . . there—there wasn't any breakfast cereal . . . there wasn't anything except Freddie and the—the stock feed. I—I tore a hole in the sack and—and Mr. Bounce wouldn't move it. Then Don showed up, and I—I had to use the rug. And Freddie couldn't move because he —(*She breaks into a loud sob.*)

BARTON: That daughter of mine is out of her mind!

CLARA: But Don, you won the essay contest—you received a year's supply of breakfast cereal.

DON: I did not, Mother. I simply made a purchase for your birthday. I had it sent over here.

SUSAN: You certainly did—a bag of stock feed!

DON (*Startled*): Stock feed? Of course not. Mother, I bought you a dressing gown. It was supposed to arrive here this morning.

SUSAN (*Gasps*): *Dressing gown?* Then somebody has made a horrible mistake!

DON: Mother, you thought I was doing research on the essay. But I've been working after school every day, so I'd have cash to buy you a special gift.

CLARA: Don! (*Begins to smile*) Why that's wonderful! A job is ever so much nicer than a year's supply of breakfast food—even with raisins in it.

FREDDIE: But what about that bag of stock feed? After Mr. Bounce delivered it, he got a call from his store—

DON (*Breaks in emphatically*): I tell you I didn't order stock feed!

BARTON (*Suddenly*): I did. (*All turn to* BARTON *in amazement.*)

MARTHA: Barton—*you?*

BARTON: I had a chance to take over a riding horse on that old debt I've been trying to collect. I figured everything was settled, so I ordered a bag of feed sent over here. (*To* MARTHA) I thought Freddie might enjoy owning a horse.

FREDDIE: *Me*—own a horse?

BARTON: I phoned to break the news to your mother, but she said you were still up to your neck in African spears and jungle helmets. So I gave up. I told them at the feed store to pick up the sack of feed and I'd return the horse. (FREDDIE *stands frozen in amazement.*) Then I came home—and walked into *this!*

MARTHA: Oh, Barton, if I'd only realized—

ANNE (*Weeps again*): Freddie's right. Everything's my fault!

DON: Now, Anne—

ANNE (*Cries softly*): I know you'll never forgive me. For the rest of my life you'll never forgive me—

DON (*Begins to grin*): Young lady, that's something we'll discuss in detail—when we go to the prom.

ANNE (*Looks up*): Prom? Don, do—do you mean that? (DON *nods.* ANNE *rises.* DON *takes her hand. Suddenly* MARTHA *gasps audibly, and points to* FREDDIE, *who stands slightly upstage, in a complete trance.*)

MARTHA: Barton, look! (*All turn toward* FREDDIE) Something's wrong with Freddie! He isn't even moving!

CLARA: My goodness, he's turned to stone!

SUSAN (*Nods*): Like the statue on our Courthouse lawn!

BARTON (*Steps to* FREDDIE, *slaps him roughly on the back*): Freddie! Freddie, snap out of it! You're in a daze, boy. What's the matter?

FREDDIE (*With effort*): I—I—Dad, can you still make a deal for that riding horse?

BARTON: Why, yes—I think so—

FREDDIE (*Suddenly, with a shout*): Then out of my way! Out of my way—everybody! (*He waves his arms, dashes upstage.*)

MARTHA: He *is* alive!

BARTON (*Calls out*): Freddie, where are you going?

FREDDIE (*Pauses at center door, turns*): I'm calling a special meeting of the Little Dynamite Club. My new project—bronco-busting on the Western plains! *Cowboys, here I come!* (*He gives a shattering cowboy yell, then plunges through center doorway. The curtain quickly falls.*)

THE END

Production Notes

Characters: 4 male; 4 female.

Playing Time: 30 minutes.

Costumes: Anne, Susan and Don wear everyday school clothes. Freddie is dressed in a pair of tropical shorts, a T-shirt, and a lightweight helmet. Mrs. Hillman wears a party dress; Mrs. Meeker, a suit and gay hat. Mr. Hillman wears a business suit and hat. Mr. Bounce is dressed in work clothing and a battered hat.

Properties: Long-handled spear; large burlap bag, filled with "feed" (sawdust).

Setting: A neat and attractive living room. There are three entrances to the room: the outside door at center rear, a door at left which connects with the rear portion of the house, and a door at right which leads to the library. Downstage left is a divan. An armchair is downstage right. On floor in front of the divan is a large "throw" rug, of sufficient size to cover both Freddie and the bag of feed. Low tables, extra chairs, etc., may be added to complete the furnishings.

Lighting: No special effects.

Johnny Nightmare

Characters

JOHNNY WELLS, *fourteen*
SUSAN WELLS, *his sister, sixteen*
MRS. WELLS, *their mother*
DAVE CLAYTON, *Susan's boy friend*
EDITH HAWKINS, *a television program director*
BELINDA
CARL

TIME: *A Saturday morning.*
SETTING: *The living room of the Wells home.*
AT RISE: JOHNNY *rushes into the room, carrying a portable typewriter, which he places on a table near center. On the table is a typed manuscript. A few pages of paper are scattered on the floor.* JOHNNY *sits at the table and rolls a page of paper into the typewriter. Deep in concentration, he picks up, from a bowl on the table, a dill pickle in one hand and an apple in the other. He leans back in the chair, thinking. Then an idea strikes him, and he tosses the pickle and apple into the bowl, and*

*begins to type excitedly with two fingers. Then he pauses,
looks around the room. He sees the paper on the floor,
crawls under the table, and begins to pick up the paper.*
MRS. WELLS *enters, carrying a bag of groceries.*

MRS. WELLS (*Startled*): Johnny! Johnny Wells!

JOHNNY: Hi ya, Mom.

MRS. WELLS: What on earth are you doing under that
table?

JOHNNY: Picking up my typing paper. What do you think
I'm doing—looking for uranium?

MRS. WELLS: Get up this minute. (*She places groceries on
table, left.* JOHNNY *picks up final sheet of paper.*) Johnny,
I asked you to get up.

JOHNNY (*Crawls from under table. Sourly*): And you're
always telling sis and me to keep the living room orderly.
(*He rises.*)

MRS. WELLS: I'm also telling you, young man, that I don't
approve of your using this room as a literary workshop.
There's plenty of space in the sunroom.

JOHNNY: Mom, when a man's creating a prize-winning
television script, he has to expand—mentally and physi-
cally.

MRS. WELLS (*Quietly*): Johnny, I want to talk to you.
(*She indicates chair.*) Sit down—over there.

JOHNNY: Mom, this is already Saturday morning. I have
to finish this script.

MRS. WELLS (*Firmly*): Sit down!

JOHNNY: O.K., O.K. (*He sits.*)

MRS. WELLS: Now I know all about this script-writing
contest. I'm quite in favor of it. Our local television

station should be congratulated for offering school students an opportunity to submit scripts.

JOHNNY: The station will televise the winning play.

MRS. WELLS: Yes, I know. I'm glad you were interested enough to want to enter.

JOHNNY: Mom, I'm writing a script that'll melt every picture tube in the state.

MRS. WELLS: That's enough, Johnny. Now, I'm perfectly willing to have you submit a script. I've always argued that young people should express themselves. (*Significantly*) Johnny, you mustn't be disappointed if you don't win.

JOHNNY: Mom, I have to win! It's the only way I can make a name for myself. If I don't do something outstanding before the school term ends, Uncle Ben won't give me a free vacation this summer.

MRS. WELLS: Your Uncle Ben wants you to be as well-known in school as your sister. But when he made you that offer, I'm certain he didn't expect you to write a television script.

JOHNNY (*Grins*): He'll be surprised when he sees my play on TV, won't he?

MRS. WELLS (*Dryly*) : Not only surprised—but stunned. (*She notices dish of apples and dill pickles.*) Johnny, you've been eating again!

JOHNNY: Huh?

MRS. WELLS (*Points at dish*): Apples and dill pickles!

JOHNNY: When a man's writing for television, he has to have something in his stomach.

MRS. WELLS (*Sighs*) : Wouldn't you just as soon nibble on a stick of dynamite? I'm sure it would be safer.

JOHNNY (*Rises*): Mom, you don't take my efforts seriously.

MRS. WELLS: I'm trying to, Johnny. I'm trying to.

JOHNNY: I even got the contest rules from Miss Hawkins herself.

MRS. WELLS (*Turns*): Who's she?

JOHNNY: Edith Hawkins? She's program director at the station. (*Beams*) What would you think if my script were awarded first place?

MRS. WELLS: I'd think something was wrong with the judges.

JOHNNY (*Hurt*): You haven't any confidence in my ability.

MRS. WELLS: Johnny, if you realized how your sister feels about this—

JOHNNY: Sis?

MRS. WELLS: Susan is a leader at high school. She doesn't want you to embarrass her with this creative spree of yours.

JOHNNY: Mom, there's never been a script quite like mine.

MRS. WELLS: That's exactly what Susan's afraid of. (SUSAN WELLS *enters. She carries a vacuum cleaner.*)

SUSAN: Mother! I didn't know you were home.

MRS. WELLS: I just got back, Susan.

SUSAN: Shall I clean this room next?

JOHNNY (*Loudly*): You stay out of here!

SUSAN (*Disgusted*): Mother, are you going to let that juvenile delinquent simply run this house?

JOHNNY: I'm no delinquent! I'm a genius—practically.

MRS. WELLS: I've been talking to your brother, Susan.

SUSAN (*Grimly*): You might as well talk to the pyramids of Egypt.

JOHNNY: Sis, did you read my script—as much as I've written?

SUSAN: I have. I shudder when I think of it.

JOHNNY: Sis let Dave Clayton see it, too.

SUSAN: If you'd like to know what Dave said—

JOHNNY (*Sourly*): Dave would say whatever you wanted him to say. You two are so lovey-dovey, it gives me a pain in my dentures.

MRS. WELLS: That's enough, Johnny.

SUSAN (*To* MRS. WELLS): Mother, if you could hear what that moron has written—

JOHNNY: She hasn't heard what I've created since yesterday. Nobody has.

SUSAN: Really? (*Sarcastically*) Then I wonder how I lived through the night.

JOHNNY: Don't you want to know what's happening to my two leading characters, Carl and Belinda? (MRS. WELLS *sighs resignedly*.)

SUSAN: We do not!

JOHNNY: Keep out of my hair. I don't write for children. Now, Mom, get ready! (JOHNNY *picks up manuscript*.) Today you're headed for another dramatic jolt.

SUSAN: One more of your brainless jolts and I'll scream.

MRS. WELLS: Susan!

JOHNNY (*Proudly*): Now, at the beginning an international spy is operating in the United States.

MRS. WELLS: Yes, I recall.

JOHNNY: A fearless and clever agent by the name of Carl is ordered to find the detestable individual who's endangering the safety of our great country.

SUSAN: At which time we all stand up and sing the national anthem.

JOHNNY: Mom, if you don't make her stop—

MRS. WELLS: Be quiet, Susan.

JOHNNY: So Carl starts tracking down this character. He sets a trap. (*Breaks off*) Guess I read you that part, Mom.

MRS. WELLS: You did.

JOHNNY: Then all at once he's face-to-face with the guilty party. But here's the payoff—the spy proves to be Belinda, Carl's *own* wife. (*Beams*) That's as far as we got yesterday.

SUSAN (*Jumps up*): I'm not going any farther! Stop him, Mother.

JOHNNY: I refuse to be stopped. I'll push and push and push—

MRS. WELLS (*Rises*): That's a good idea, Johnny. The grass in the back yard hasn't been cut for a week. You can spend the rest of the afternoon pushing the lawn mower.

SUSAN (*Applauds*): Bravo! That's what I call a wonderful ending.

JOHNNY (*To* MRS. WELLS): But, Mom—

MRS. WELLS: You'll find the mower on the back porch.

JOHNNY: Gee whiz!

MRS. WELLS: Start moving, Johnny.

JOHNNY: I don't see why I have to do this.

MRS. WELLS (*Firmly*): Johnny!

JOHNNY: All right, if that's all you care about your son. When I'm awarded first prize, don't anybody come crawling to me for my *autograph!* (*He exits.*)

SUSAN: Mother, you simply have to do something with

him. If Johnny enters that horrible script in the contest, he'll ruin me.

MRS. WELLS: Now, Susan—

SUSAN: I'm a candidate for queen of the school annual. (MRS. WELLS *picks up grocery bag.*)

MRS. WELLS: Yes, dear—I know.

SUSAN: Each script that's entered will first be presented in our assembly. Can't you just see that awful Carl and Belinda affair spread out all over the stage in a trial production? Even the authors are to be introduced. There I'll be in the audience—Johnny's sister—with everybody staring and snickering at me. Mother, I'd simply die of humiliation.

MRS. WELLS: I don't believe I've ever heard of humiliation being fatal.

SUSAN: Mother, this isn't like you. If you'd just put your foot down and tear up that manuscript—

MRS. WELLS: Susan, listen to me. I've always encouraged you and Johnny to express yourselves.

SUSAN: Johnny'll do more than express himself. He'll wreck the nation!

MRS. WELLS: As a parent, it's my duty to keep my offspring out of evil activities. I'm certain that writing for a television contest isn't one of them. (MRS. WELLS, *carrying groceries, exits.* SUSAN *sighs hopelessly. She picks up a page of script, gazes at it sourly, then drops it on table. She picks up vacuum cleaner and exits. The doorbell rings.* SUSAN *enters without vacuum. She opens door.* EDITH HAWKINS *enters.*)

EDITH (*Gushing*): Good morning, good morning! Wonderful sunshine—wonderful breeze—wonderful day. Oh, you're not Johnny Wells. (*Smiles*) You must be his sister. I'm Miss Hawkins, Miss Edith Eudora Hawkins, program director for the television station. We're channel six, "televising from the tower with the flashing lights; proved by impartial surveys to be the choice of the masses, for all lads and lasses." (*She breaks off, looks around the room.*) Where is he?

SUSAN: Who?

EDITH: Johnny Wells, that budding author, that creative giant, that intellectual dynamo.

SUSAN: The intellectual dynamo is in the back yard—mowing the lawn.

EDITH: Mowing? Oh, dear! (*Beams*) But we all need physical exercise. I do myself. That's why I flit from hither to yon. (*She looks at table.*) So this is where he writes! I know you're proud of him.

SUSAN: "Proud" is not the word, Miss Hawkins.

EDITH: I suppose he has whispered to you that he plans to enter a script in our television contest?

SUSAN: Whispered? Like a boiler exploding.

EDITH: Johnny *is* enthusiastic, isn't he? He even dashed into our studio, just to get the contest rules. He isn't at all shy.

SUSAN: *That*, Miss Hawkins, is one of the understatements of the year.

EDITH: On this glorious morning, I'm just plunging around, checking up on our possible contestants. We want to be certain we have a wide variety of scripts. (*Smiles.*) We'll give the high school assembly extra publicity on channel six. Simply everybody will be there. At the conclusion of Johnny's play, he of course will be introduced from the stage. (*Dramatically*) After waves of applause for Johnny, the audience will then turn to you. Your purple moment!

SUSAN: Purple? *Black! (The doorbell rings.*)

EDITH: Someone at the door? My goodness, could that be our Johnny?

SUSAN: It could not. When Johnny enters, the roof falls in. (SUSAN *opens door.* DAVE CLAYTON *enters, leaving door open.*)

DAVE: Greetings, beautiful.

SUSAN: Dave!

DAVE: I just dropped by to—(*He breaks off as he sees* EDITH.) Oh!

SUSAN: Dave, I want you to meet Miss Edith Hawkins. This is Dave Clayton.

EDITH (*Beams*): I'm simply overcome!

DAVE: So am I.

EDITH: Of course, you're entering a script?

DAVE: Script?

SUSAN (*To* DAVE): Miss Hawkins is program director at the television studio.

EDITH (*To* DAVE): Channel six. I'm simply in a whirl this morning, checking on the potential entries. I do hope you're bursting with scripts.

DAVE: I don't even have a split seam.

EDITH: Johnny Wells is entering, you know.

DAVE: Are you certain Johnny Wells will have a script in the contest?

EDITH: Why, of course. He even leaped over to our studio, just to get the contest rules.

DAVE: I wouldn't be too sure, Miss Hawkins. (SUSAN *appears puzzled.*) Johnny is a rather peculiar person.

EDITH: Peculiar?

DAVE (*Nods*): A genius one moment—mad as a hatter the next.

SUSAN: Dave!

EDITH: My goodness, he *is?*

DAVE (*To* EDITH): The boy has hallucinations at times. (*Smiles*) But he's usually quite harmless.

EDITH (*Alarmed*): You mean, he's—(*She jumps up.*) Really, I must dash along. Tell your brother I'll return when he has completed—er—digging the cistern or whatever he's doing in the backyard. (*She moves to center. She notices dish containing apples and pickles.*) My goodness!

SUSAN (*To* EDITH): What's the matter, Miss Hawkins?

EDITH (*Points at dish*): This dish—apples and pickles!

DAVE: That's right—apples and dill pickles—Johnny's favorite combination. (EDITH's *increasing alarm is evident.*)

EDITH: He eats them at different meals?

DAVE (*Heartily*): Oh, no! He takes a big bite of apple, then he washes it down with a juicy hunk of dill pickle. (EDITH *takes a final look at the apples and pickles. She exits quickly.* DAVE *breaks into a loud laugh.*)

SUSAN: Dave, you shouldn't have talked to her like that. She thinks Johnny is crazy.

DAVE (*Chuckles*): Did you watch the old girl? Her eyebrows almost fell off.

SUSAN: She's scared. She shot out of here like a Roman candle on the loose.

DAVE: That was the idea. I didn't care to have her meet my friends.

SUSAN: Your friends?

DAVE (*Nods*): On the front porch.

SUSAN: What are you talking about?

DAVE (*Steps to* SUSAN): Listen, Susan, you want Johnny out of that contest, don't you?

SUSAN: Of course I do. Yesterday when you read his script, you agreed with me.

DAVE: I still do. That's why I've worked out a plan.

SUSAN: A plan?

DAVE (*Nods*): A plan which I hope will end Johnny's literary ambitions. Johnny won't embarrass you at school, Susan—because Johnny's script won't be produced.

SUSAN: Dave, I don't understand. (DAVE *turns from* SUSAN, *moves upstage.*)

DAVE (*Calls off-stage*): Come on in. (BELINDA *and* CARL *appear. They hesitate, then step into room.* SUSAN *is amazed.*)

CARL: Who was the tornado that just spun out of here?

DAVE (*Grins*): That was the pride of channel six—Edith Hawkins.

BELINDA (*Surprised*): Edith Hawkins? Why, I know that woman.

DAVE: Did she recognize you?

BELINDA: No—

DAVE: Good! Come on, meet Susan. Susan, meet Helen and Jack. They do commercials for channel six. Miss Hawkins doesn't know I've hired them.

SUSAN: Hired them?

DAVE (*Nods*): Helen and Jack are going to help us out.

BELINDA: We've heard about you, Susan.

CARL: *And* your brother.

SUSAN: Dave, what's the meaning of this?

DAVE: You told me you wanted Johnny out of the contest. I agreed—after I'd read his script.

BELINDA: We've read the script, too.

CARL (*To* SUSAN): So we've consented to play the roles of his leading characters.

SUSAN: His *characters?*

CARL (*Nods*): Belinda and Carl.

SUSAN: Belinda and Carl?

BELINDA: We're here to put on a performance, just for your brother's benefit.

SUSAN: You mean you're going to pose as Belinda and Carl?

BELINDA (*To* SUSAN): Dave worked it all out for us.

SUSAN: I never heard of such a thing!

DAVE: Neither has Johnny—we hope.

CARL: Dave has even written our lines. They're terrific.

BELINDA: After your brother sees his characters come to life, I'm guessing he'll abandon his script.

CARL: Johnny'll take one look and think he's going crazy.

DAVE: Miss Hawkins already thinks it. (*To* CARL) Now, you and Helen hide in the sunroom until Johnny shows up. (*He indicates door right.*) As soon as Johnny gets settled down to his script, you can go into your act. (CARL *nods, moves right.*)

BELINDA: Leave it to us. We'll make an entrance at the proper time.

DAVE: You've no objection, Susan?

SUSAN: I suppose not. What am I to do?

CARL (*To* SUSAN): Dave will explain. Just follow his instructions. (CARL *grins at* BELINDA. BELINDA *nods knowingly.* BELINDA *and* CARL *exit right.*)

SUSAN: Dave, do you mean you've honestly hired them to frighten Johnny?

DAVE: He's sure to have a reaction.

SUSAN: I'm already having one. (JOHNNY *dashes into room from left.*)

JOHNNY (*Loudly*): Scram, everybody—scram! Out of my studio, one and all! (*He sits before typewriter.*) Make way for genius!

SUSAN: Johnny, stop it! You didn't even speak to Dave.

JOHNNY (*As he snatches up sheet of paper and rolls it into machine*): Yes, I did. I said "scram."

DAVE: We mustn't bother him, Susan.

JOHNNY: I have to finish this script today. You can see it next week—when it's presented at assembly. After it's awarded first place, I'll give you free tickets to the telecast.

DAVE: Fair enough! Don't you think so, Susan? (MRS. WELLS *enters. She carries a pan of rolls, covered with a napkin.*)

MRS. WELLS: Dave! How are you?

DAVE: Good morning, Mrs. Wells.

JOHNNY: Just what is this place—Grand Central Station?

MRS. WELLS: Johnny, be quiet. I'm taking a pan of rolls to the Browns next door.

JOHNNY: Thank goodness, *somebody's* getting out of here.

MRS. WELLS: That's enough, Johnny. By the way, young man, I've just inspected the back yard. It looks as if a bulldozer had gone berserk over the grass.

JOHNNY: I was in a hurry, Mom. If I don't finish this script today, I can't meet the deadline.

DAVE: We don't want anything to hinder the completion of your masterpiece, Johnny.

JOHNNY (*Proudly*): Mom, did you hear what Dave said? He's read only part of my script, and already he thinks it's a masterpiece. What do you think of that?

MRS. WELLS: If I even dared think, I'd probably have a nervous breakdown. (*She exits.*)

JOHNNY: Will you characters kindly get out of here? How do you expect me to concentrate with all this yap-yap?

DAVE: Come along, Susan. (*He moves to door.*)

SUSAN: But, Dave—

JOHNNY: You heard what your dream prince said. Go on —vanish like an Indian. (SUSAN *and* DAVE *exit. Deep in thought,* JOHNNY *picks up an apple, takes a bite, and replaces apple in dish. He reaches for a pickle, but before he can take a bite,* BELINDA *and* CARL *enter.* JOHNNY *looks up, startled.*)

CARL (*To* JOHNNY): Good morning, sir. (JOHNNY *replaces pickle in dish.*)

JOHNNY: Who are you? What are you doing in here? This is my studio. If you want to see Mom or sis—

CARL: We wish to see you, sir.

BELINDA: He's Johnny Wells, all right. I've heard he sizzles every time anybody walks in.

JOHNNY: Certainly I'm Johnny Wells. I'm writing a script.

CARL: We know, we know.

JOHNNY: Who do you think you are, barging in here?

BELINDA: Look at him—bristling like a porcupine. Just as I expected.

JOHNNY: I don't know either of you.

CARL: You're to blame for our visit.

BELINDA (*Nods*): You've made us what we are today. (EDITH *appears at door. She stops to watch. The others do not see her.*)

JOHNNY: See here, get out before I toss you out!

BELINDA: Listen to the child!

JOHNNY: Child? I'm an author.

BELINDA: You—an author? Pardon me while I go into silent hysterics.

CARL: Don't you recognize me?

JOHNNY: I've never even seen you.

CARL: I'm Carl.

JOHNNY (*Startled*): Carl? (EDITH *watches with increased interest.*)

CARL: The leading male character in that script you're writing.

JOHNNY (*Gasps*): What!

CARL: This is Belinda, the woman you've created as my wife.

JOHNNY: Belinda!

BELINDA: Who did you think we were—Columbus and Queen Isabella?

JOHNNY: You're crazy!

BELINDA: *We're* not the crazy ones.

CARL: Belinda and I are not satisfied with this set-up. That's why we're here.

JOHNNY: This must be a joke.

BELINDA: The only joke is that script of yours.

JOHNNY: You're just trying to kid me into thinking you're my characters.

CARL: We're not kidding, Johnny.

JOHNNY: But things like this don't happen! It's impossible.

BELINDA: It's the script that's impossible.

JOHNNY: I'm asleep. I've gone to sleep. That's my trouble.

BELINDA: You're awake, Junior. So are we. (JOHNNY *is frightened.*)

JOHNNY: I'm dreaming. You're not real—either of you.

CARL: We're certainly not real, the way you've created us.

BELINDA: You've made us as counterfeit as a couple of lead dimes in a pay phone.

JOHNNY (*Places hand over his eyes*): I know I've gone to sleep.

CARL: Belinda and I have fair and just grounds for a suit.

JOHNNY (*Loudly*): Get out of my dreams—both of you. *Get out!*

CARL: You've made my wife an international spy. I don't like it.

BELINDA (*Nods*): I'm a respectable woman!

JOHNNY (*Covers his ears*): Stop it! I won't listen. I'm having a nightmare! (*Jumps up, points to dish*) That's it! I've been eating apples and dill pickles.

CARL: Apples and dill pickles have nothing to do with this.

BELINDA: My poor Carl—he has never been a secret agent in his life until now. You're forcing him to work nights, Saturdays and holidays, chasing around the country, looking for a spy.

CARL: Then you had the crust to select my wife as the guilty party.

JOHNNY: I have to wake up. I have to wake up. I've been eating too much.

BELINDA: The trouble's not in your stomach, Junior. It's

in your head. (*Turns to* CARL) What are you waiting for, Carl? Put the poor sap out of the way.

JOHNNY (*Horrified*): Out of the way?

BELINDA (*To* JOHNNY): Carl has to end this business— which means you're getting bumped off.

JOHNNY: *Me?* Bumped off? (*Wildly*) No, no! You can't! (*Groans*) I'm in the middle of a nightmare! (*Desperately* JOHNNY *pinches himself.*) Wake up, Johnny! For Pete's sake, wake up! (CARL *draws a revolver.*)

CARL: You're awake—but you won't be for long.

JOHNNY (*Jumps up in terror*): Put that gun away!

CARL (*Smiles coldly*): It's really your gun, Junior. You gave it to me—early in the first scene. Remember? You wrote in the script that I pulled out the dresser drawer and—

JOHNNY (*In complete panic*): Put it down! Put it down, I tell you!

BELINDA (*To* CARL): Let him have it, Carl. If he lives to finish this script, I'll never be able to hold up my head again. (CARL *points gun at* JOHNNY.)

JOHNNY (*Screams*): No, no! Help! Help! Help me, help me! (SUSAN *and* DAVE *rush into the room.*)

SUSAN: Johnny, Johnny! What's the matter? (JOHNNY *attempts to hide behind* SUSAN. EDITH *continues to watch.* CARL *and* BELINDA *back toward door right.*)

JOHNNY: Wake me up, sis! Wake me up! I'm asleep!

SUSAN (*Affects surprise*): You're *what?*

JOHNNY: I'm having a nightmare! (*He slaps himself vigorously.*)

DAVE: A nightmare? That's impossible, Johnny. You're as much awake as I am.

JOHNNY: Awake? (*Fearfully.*) I'm awake? (JOHNNY *gazes in amazement at* DAVE. *At last he looks at* CARL *and* BELINDA. *He points at them*) Look over there. (DAVE *and* SUSAN *turn toward* BELINDA *and* CARL.)

DAVE: Look at what, Johnny?

JOHNNY: Those two characters.

DAVE: I don't see any characters.

JOHNNY (*Jumps up*): You have to see them! They're standing right there—Carl and Belinda.

BELINDA: Take it easy, buster.

JOHNNY: There! She talked! You heard her, didn't you, sis? You heard her speak.

SUSAN: Johnny, you're ill.

CARL: He'd *have* to be ill to write such a foul script.

JOHNNY: Now *he's* talking! You heard him, didn't you, Dave?

DAVE: Johnny, I've been afraid of this. You're overworking.

JOHNNY: Do you mean neither of you can see what *I* see? Or hear what *I* hear? (SUSAN *gently pushes* JOHNNY *into chair.*)

SUSAN (*Soothingly*): We'll get you to bed, darling. Then we'll phone the doctor.

DAVE: Once you're settled in a nice, quiet institution—

JOHNNY (*Horrified*): You think I'm *batty?*

DAVE: You'll get over it. (CARL *and* BELINDA *exit.*)

SUSAN (*Pats* JOHNNY'S *shoulder*): Just relax, Johnny. (*To* DAVE) The phone's in the sunroom, Dave. (DAVE *crosses right.*)

JOHNNY: Stop! Stop! (*He discovers that* CARL *and* BELINDA

have vanished.) Look—*they're gone!* (JOHNNY *springs to his feet.*)

DAVE (*Turns to* JOHNNY): Gone? Who?

JOHNNY: Carl and Belinda. They've vanished.

SUSAN: You can explain all this to the doctor.

JOHNNY: I will not! Nothing's wrong with me now. I'm perfect!

DAVE: My dear boy—

JOHNNY: Maybe I *have* been concentrating too much, but I'm all right now. If you think I'm going to finish that script and end up in an institution, *you're* crazy!

SUSAN: Johnny! Do you mean it?

JOHNNY: You don't need to plead with me, either. I have to consider my health! (JOHNNY *tears the script into shreds.* DAVE *and* SUSAN *attempt to hide their elation.*)

SUSAN (*Gasps*): Johnny, look what you're doing!

JOHNNY (*To* SUSAN): You ought to be thankful you have a brother who knows when he's working too much. (JOHNNY *tosses scraps of paper onto table. He starts toward door, left.*)

SUSAN: Where are you going?

JOHNNY: Out to the back yard—to remow that grass! (EDITH *applauds loudly.* JOHNNY, DAVE *and* SUSAN *turn in surprise to* EDITH. EDITH *steps into the room.*)

SUSAN (*Amazed*): Miss Hawkins!

EDITH (*Still applauds*): It was marvelous—simply marvelous!

DAVE (*Startled*): Marvelous?

EDITH: A positive sensation. (*To* DAVE.) Call in the other performers at once! Don't delay! Hurry, hurry! (DAVE *opens door right.* BELINDA *and* CARL *enter.*)

JOHNNY (*Wide-eyed, to* EDITH): *Performers,* did you say?
(MRS. WELLS *enters.*)

MRS. WELLS: My goodness! What on earth is going on in
this house?

EDITH (*Enthusiastically*): Are you Mrs. Wells?

MRS. WELLS: I am. And I demand to know—

EDITH (*Breaks in*): My dear, I've just witnessed the rehearsal of a sensational script—right here in your own
living room. I stood frozen at the doorway—me, Edith
Hawkins. I watched it all.

DAVE (*Startled*): You did?

SUSAN: Watched it all?

EDITH: Such an overwhelming idea—all about a young
man who writes a script. Then the characters come to
life. The young man thinks he's losing his mind.

JOHNNY: You mean it wasn't a nightmare?

MRS. WELLS: What *is* this all about?

EDITH (*Triumphantly*): I shall give this script first prize.
You students might as well cancel the tryouts at your
assembly. *This* is the play we'll telecast. Tell me, who
created this amazing situation?

BELINDA: Why, it was Dave's idea.

EDITH: Who wrote the lines?

CARL: Dave wrote them. (EDITH *dashes to* DAVE. *She grasps
his arm, raises it high in the air.*)

EDITH: The winner—with a knockout!

DAVE: Do you mean *I* get first prize?

JOHNNY: Hey, you can't do this to me!

EDITH: Young man, don't try to tell me *you're* the author
of this hilarious script.

JOHNNY: Not the way you saw it.

EDITH: That's enough! (*To* DAVE) You're the winner.

MRS. WELLS: Will someone—anyone—please explain what's going on in my own house? (MRS. WELLS *is ignored.*)

JOHNNY: I have to make a name for myself—

EDITH: You'll make a name for yourself, all right. If you give as good a performance when this script is telecast, you'll be the talk of the air waves.

JOHNNY: I will? (*He turns to* MRS. WELLS.) Mom, did you hear that? I'm going to act on television. I'll be famous!

MRS. WELLS: And I'll be a raving maniac if somebody doesn't tell me—(JOHNNY *rushes upstage, pushing* EDITH *and* MRS. WELLS *aside.*) Johnny Wells!

JOHNNY (*Hurriedly*): Excuse me.

MRS. WELLS: Johnny, where *are* you going?

JOHNNY (*Turns with a broad grin*): I have to send a telegram to Uncle Ben. I have to warn him to start saving for my free vacation. I'm going to sign that message— "Your nephew—*Johnny Nightmare!*" (JOHNNY *happily dashes through center doorway.* MRS. WELLS *is in utter confusion. The others beam enthusiastically. The curtain quickly falls.*)

THE END

Production Notes

JOHNNY NIGHTMARE

Characters: 3 male; 4 female.

Playing Time: 25 minutes.

Costumes: Modern dress. Belinda wears a long, slinky black dress and jewels. Carl wears a tweed business suit.

Properties: Typing paper, dish with pickles and apples, grocery bag, vacuum cleaner, typewriter, and gun.

Setting: A living room. Entrances at left, right, and rear lead to rear rooms, sunroom, and outdoors, respectively. Near center are a chair and a table. The rest of the room is furnished comfortably.

Lighting: No special effects.

Briefly Speaking

Characters

IRENE, *at the typewriter*
WILSON, *a salesman*
TOM, *Irene's friend*
HANNAH, *the cleaning woman*

TIME: *Early afternoon.*
SETTING: *An office reception room. Doors at right and left lead to the outer hall of the building and to a private office adjoining the reception room. A small sign, neatly lettered "Private," is attached to the left door. Down left are a receptionist's desk with attached typewriter stand and a chair. Near center of room and slightly upstage are three office chairs, placed side by side in a row. On the desk is a sign, "Be Brief!"*
AT RISE: IRENE, *an attractive, smartly-groomed young woman, sits typing. As she types,* WILSON *enters noisily from right, carrying a brief case.* WILSON *is the typical high-pressure salesman, too talkative, too energetic, and too self-assured.*

WILSON (*Loudly and impressively, as he crosses to desk*): Good afternoon! Good afternoon! (IRENE *looks up from the typewriter. She swings around in her chair to face* WILSON. *She is annoyed.*) My name is Wilson—Sam Wilson—*the* Sam Wilson. (*He whips a card from his pocket, thrusts it at* IRENE.) My card. (IRENE *takes card.* WILSON *breezily flips off his hat.*) I'm here to see your boss, my little chick. I don't know his name, but it doesn't matter. He'll be tickled to see me, plenty tickled. This is my first trip in these parts. But it's a great day for the people I've consented to call on.

IRENE (*Ruffled*): Please!

WILSON (*Pays no attention to* IRENE's *protest*): I'm not one to boast, but I'm probably the best salesman in this state —in the nation, probably! And what a line I'm offering —*what* a line! Everybody's absolutely *begging* for an order through good old Sam Wilson. Folks say it's an honor when I call on 'em. (*He flashes a confident smile.*) So I'll just breeze on into the office of your boss. (*He starts for door left.*)

IRENE (*Angrily cuts in, as she jumps up*): Stop!

WILSON (*Hesitates, turns to* IRENE): Me? But I'm Sam Wilson. I have a reputation, and when I start talking—

IRENE (*Emphatically*): Exactly!

WILSON (*Annoyed, as he returns to center*): Hey, are you trying to give me the brush-off?

IRENE (*Sharply*): Yes!

WILSON (*After a puzzled pause*): You know something? You're a funny dame. What's the matter? Can't you answer in more than one word?

IRENE: No!

WILSON: Then let good old Sam Wilson tip you off. If you don't speak up and talk right out in this world, you won't—(*But* IRENE *suddenly snatches the "Be Brief" sign from desk.*)

IRENE (*Grimly points to sign*): Look!

WILSON (*For a moment taken aback*): What's that?

IRENE (*Displays sign for* WILSON'S *benefit*): Read!

WILSON (*Reads*): "Be Brief!" (*Scoffs, as he looks up.*) So that's the reason for this one-word monkey business.

IRENE: Certainly.

WILSON: Well, if you want to know what I think—

IRENE (*Cuts in, as she points to row of chairs*): Sit!

WILSON (*Protests*): Hold on, now! I told you I was Sam Wilson and I—

IRENE (*Commandingly*): Sit! (*Again* WILSON *starts to protest, then gives up with a shrug.*)

WILSON: O.K., sister, O.K. (WILSON *struts toward the third chair, the one nearest door left. But* IRENE *swiftly moves to him. Roughly she grasps* WILSON'S *coat collar, pulls him away from third chair.*)

IRENE (*Loudly, as she does so*): No!

WILSON (*Squirms*): Hey! Cut it out!

IRENE (*Marches* WILSON *to first chair, the one most removed from door left*): There! (*She indicates first chair.*)

WILSON (*Frees himself, turns to* IRENE): But look where I'll be anchored, sister—the last chair from the door. And if anybody else walks in, you might put 'em ahead of me.

IRENE: Exactly!

WILSON: But I'm not in the habit of waiting.

IRENE (*Points to first chair*): Sit. (WILSON *hesitates, then unhappily obeys.* IRENE *returns to desk.*)

WILSON (*After a pause*): Listen, stormy weather, if I were your boss, you wouldn't last five minutes.

IRENE (*Turns warningly*): Enough!

WILSON: See here, can't you stretch a sentence into more than one word? First thing you know, you'll have *me* talkin' like that.

IRENE: Good! (*She sits at desk, picks up papers from file.*)

WILSON: You mean everybody's supposed to tighten up like that around here?

IRENE: Yes.

WILSON (*Sputters*): Crackpot idea, if I ever heard one!

IRENE (*Sharply*): Wilson!

WILSON (*Sighs in disgust*): Yeah. (*There is a pause.* IRENE *works at desk.* WILSON *uncomfortably holds brief case and hat on his knees. He's becoming increasingly nervous and impatient. At last he reaches a point where he can stand the silence no longer.*) Look here, I'm goin' to blow my top if I can't speak up and—

IRENE (*Looks up*): Wilson!

WILSON (*Sighs hopelessly*): O.K. (IRENE *turns again to desk. There is another pause.* WILSON *gazes at the two vacant chairs between him and door left. Then an idea slowly begins to form in* WILSON'S *mind. He grins slyly. At last he quietly and cautiously rises. On tiptoe he moves to third chair. But as he starts to sit,* IRENE, *who has not looked up from desk, speaks sharply and commandingly.*)

IRENE: Wilson! (WILSON *gives a violent start.*)

WILSON (*Angrily*): How could you have seen me when you were—

IRENE (*Looks up, points to first chair*): Back! (WILSON *is defeated. Sighing gloomily, he rises. He retreats to first chair. As he sits,* IRENE *returns to papers on desk.* WILSON *glances at his watch nervously. Then he places his hands quietly in his lap, but he can't remain still. So he smooths his hair, studies the design on his tie, and finally counts the buttons on his coat. Unthinkingly, he then pulls a pen from his breast pocket. At first he gazes idly at the pen. Then, as if struck by a new idea, he rises, smiling broadly. With considerable self-assurance he now strolls to* IRENE'S *desk. He pauses, then deliberately begins to dangle the pen in front of* IRENE. *Suddenly* IRENE *looks up, startled.*)

WILSON (*With a bright smile*): Hello.

IRENE: Return! (*She points to chair.*)

WILSON (*Protests*): Wait.

IRENE (*After a slight pause*): Why?

WILSON (*Continues to dangle pen*): Pen?

IRENE (*Puzzled*): Pen?

WILSON (*Nods*): Yours.

IRENE (*Startled*): Mine?

WILSON (*Nods heartily*): Gift.

IRENE (*Pleased, in spite of her annoyance*): Gift?

WILSON (*Nods*): Yours. (WILSON *thrusts pen into* IRENE'S *hand.*)

IRENE (*With a weak protest*): Goodness!

WILSON (*Indicates pen*): New.

IRENE (*Unable to hide her pleasure*): Really?

WILSON (*Nods*): Expensive.

IRENE (*Questioningly*): Mine?

WILSON (*Emphatically*): Honest.

IRENE (*Suddenly smiles up at* WILSON): Thanks! (IRENE *studies pen. Grinning triumphantly,* WILSON *returns to row of chairs. Before he sits, he turns to* IRENE.)

WILSON (*Significantly*): Wait?

IRENE (*Nods as she looks up*): Continue.

WILSON (*Indicates first chair*): Here?

IRENE (*Hesitantly*): No.

WILSON: Where?

IRENE (*Pauses, then points to middle chair in row*): There. (*Happily* WILSON *sits in center chair.* IRENE *places pen on desk, then picks up a letter. There is a pause, but* WILSON *soon glances impatiently at door left, then looks again at his watch. Now he begins to study the third chair, the one near office door.* WILSON *seems deep in thought. He takes billfold from his pocket, removes two reserved tickets from billfold. For a moment he gazes sadly at the tickets. He replaces billfold in his pocket, then rises and marches to* IRENE'S *desk, pauses. Slowly he begins to wave the pair of tickets in front of her. Almost as though dancing,* WILSON'S *entire body moves in rhythm as he flutters the tickets.* IRENE *suddenly looks up.*)

WILSON (*Smiles, as he waves the tickets*): See?

IRENE (*Vaguely*): Tickets?

WILSON (*Nods*): Two.

IRENE: But—

WILSON: Reserved.

IRENE: Reserved?

WILSON (*Nods*): Baseball.

IRENE (*With an excited catch in her voice*): Oh!

WILSON (*With a flourish*): Yours.

IRENE: *Mine?*

WILSON (*Nods*): Gift.

IRENE (*Draws back slightly*): No.

WILSON (*Thrusts tickets into* IRENE'S *hand*): Yes!

IRENE (*Attempts to protest*): But—

WILSON (*Stops her*): Enough! (IRENE *studies the tickets in silence. She reads date of game printed on tickets.*)

IRENE (*At last looks at* WILSON): Today?

WILSON (*Nods*): Afternoon!

IRENE (*A bit breathlessly*): Goodness!

WILSON: Attending? (*For a moment* IRENE *doesnt' answer. Then she suddenly gazes at him with an excited smile.*)

IRENE (*Beams*): Yes!

WILSON: Alone?

IRENE (*Thoughtfully*): No.

WILSON (*Questioningly*): Inviting?

IRENE (*Makes up her mind*): Friend.

WILSON: Good!

IRENE: Thanks. (*She places tickets on desk.* WILSON *is indeed victorious. Boldly he marches to third chair, the one near door left. He pauses, turns to* IRENE.)

WILSON (*Indicates himself*): Wait?

IRENE (*Smiles*): Briefly.

WILSON (*Fearlessly indicates third chair*): Here?

IRENE (*After a pause*): Yes. (WILSON *sits in third chair. He leans back expansively, proud of his achievement. Immediately* TOM *enters from right.* TOM *is a well-groomed man of thirty. Hatless, he appears to have just stepped across the hall from another office. He pauses at right.*)

TOM (*To* IRENE, *with a friendly smile*): Hello—

IRENE (*Looks up, happily surprised*): Tom!

TOM (*Crosses to* IRENE): Busy?

IRENE (*Hesitates slightly*): No.

TOM (*Glances at* WILSON, *then turns questioningly to* IRENE): Customer? (*He indicates* WILSON.)

IRENE (*Introduces* TOM *to* WILSON): Wilson.

TOM (*Grins at* WILSON): Hello.

WILSON (*Returns* TOM'S *grin*): Hello.

TOM (*To* WILSON): Salesman?

WILSON (*Nods expansively*): Advertising.

IRENE (*Picks up* WILSON'S *pen, speaks to* TOM): Tom—

TOM (*Turns to* IRENE): Yes?

IRENE (*Displays pen*): See?

TOM: Yours?

IRENE (*Nods*): Gift.

TOM (*Surprised*): Gift?

IRENE (*Indicates* WILSON): Wilson. (*She smiles at* WILSON.)

TOM: Nice!

IRENE (*Picks up tickets from desk*): Look—(*Extends tickets toward* TOM.)

TOM: Tickets!

WILSON (*Enthusiastically, as he for a moment forgets himself*): The best pair of pasteboards in the—(*Breaks off meekly.*) I mean—baseball.

TOM (*To* IRENE): When?

IRENE: Today.

TOM (*To* IRENE): Yours? (IRENE *nods, then points to* WILSON. WILSON *grins.*)

WILSON (*Emphatically*): Right!

TOM (*To* WILSON): Gift? (WILSON *nods proudly.*)

IRENE (*To* TOM): Tom.

TOM (*Turns to* IRENE): Yes?

IRENE: Busy? (*Questioningly* TOM *indicates himself.* IRENE *nods.*)

TOM: No!

IRENE: Attend?

TOM: Us? (*He points to* IRENE, *then to himself.*)

IRENE: Yes.

TOM (*Enthusiastically*): Sure!

IRENE (*Turns to* WILSON): Object?

WILSON: No.

TOM: But—(*He breaks off, haltingly.*)

IRENE (*To* TOM): What?

TOM (*To* IRENE): Office? (*He gazes around the room.*)

IRENE (*Shrugs*): Unimportant. (*She opens desk drawer, pulls out purse. She slips pen into her purse.*)

TOM (*Steps to* WILSON, *extends his hand*): Thanks.

WILSON (*Jumps up, shakes* TOM's *hand vigorously*): Pleasure!

IRENE (*Rises, speaks to* TOM): Ready?

TOM (*Moves back to* IRENE): Ready. (IRENE *hands* TOM *the tickets. She moves around desk to* TOM, *places her arm through his. They move toward door right.*)

WILSON (*Calls suddenly to* IRENE): Wait—!

IRENE (*Pauses, turns to* WILSON): Well?

WILSON: Me? (*Then he indicates door left.*)

IRENE (*Smiles*): Enter.

WILSON (*Elated*): Now?

IRENE: Yes.

WILSON (*Joyfully*): Fulfillment! (IRENE *and* TOM *exit right. Happily expectant,* WILSON *straightens his tie. He picks up his brief case, starts toward door left. At that moment* HANNAH *enters from right.* HANNAH, *the* elderly cleaning woman, wears a simple frock. She carries dust mop and a wastepaper basket.)

HANNAH (Sees WILSON, calls out sharply): Hey! (WILSON, startled, turns.)

WILSON: Huh?

HANNAH (Commandingly): Stop!

WILSON (Draws himself up with dignity): Permission! (He points to himself, then indicates door left.)

HANNAH (Distastefully, as she suddenly begins to "talk"): Listen, you get yourself lost. I have to clean up this joint. (She marches to desk, places basket on top of it. Then she prepares to clean floor with dust mop.)

WILSON (Amazed by HANNAH's speech): Talking!

HANNAH (Shrugs): Sure I'm talkin'. (WILSON swiftly steps to desk. He snatches up the "Be Brief!" sign, displays it before HANNAH.)

WILSON: See? (Grimly he thrusts sign in HANNAH's free hand.)

HANNAH (Completely unimpressed, as she glances at sign): Oh, I don't pay any attention to that. Least not when the boss is gone.

WILSON (With a violent start): Boss gone?

HANNAH (Nods): She and her gentleman friend from across the hall just left for the baseball game. (WILSON is horrified.) Seems some stupid salesman gave her a new pen and a couple of free tickets.

WILSON (Dazed): Now—now—wait a minute! (Attempts to understand) You mean—she was the—the boss?

HANNAH: Sure. (WILSON begins to sway dizzily.) Say, what's eating you, buddy?

WILSON: I—I—(Then he suddenly collapses to the floor.

But HANNAH *is not upset. She's merely annoyed. She glances at the sign in her hand. Then she looks down at the now unconscious* WILSON.)

HANNAH (*Sourly*): Around this office you have to condense everything—(*She leans over, props sign against* WILSON's *body. Then she steps back, firmly places her hands on her hips. She scowls at* WILSON.) You know good and well I'm busy, Junior. So you'd better make that *mighty brief!* (*The curtain quickly falls.*)

THE END

Production Notes

Characters: 2 male; 2 female.

Playing Time: 10 minutes.

Costumes: Irene wears an attractive business suit or dress. Wilson and Tom wear business suits. Hannah wears a cotton dress and apron.

Properties: Brief case, pen, and tickets, for Wilson; dust mop and wastepaper basket, for Hannah; papers, for Irene.

Setting: An office reception room. Door at right leads to the outer hall of the office building; door at left leads to a private office adjoining the reception room. A small sign, neatly lettered "Private," is attached to the left door. Down left are a receptionist's desk, with attached typewriter stand, and chair. When typing, the girl at the desk would be facing toward audience. Near the center of the room and slightly upstage are three office chairs, placed side by side in a row. On the desk is a boldly-lettered sign, "Be Brief!"

Lighting: No special effects.

Cicero the Great

Characters

GRACE TONEFEATHER, *a vigorous and animated woman*
WILLIAM TONEFEATHER, *her loyal and hard-working husband*
MR. BLACK, *a salesman*

TIME: *Early evening.*
SETTING: *The living room of the Tonefeather residence.*
AT RISE: WILLIAM TONEFEATHER *is seated on the divan, reading the evening paper. As he reads,* GRACE TONEFEATHER *enters. For a moment she gazes at* WILLIAM— *and the paper—in silence. Then she crosses to* WILLIAM *and snatches the back section of the paper from his grasp.*

WILLIAM (*Sitting up with a startled protest*): Hey, you're shattering my paper!
GRACE: I only want the back section, William. (*She opens her section of the paper as she moves to a chair.*)

WILLIAM (*Highly annoyed*): Grace, you've taken the sports page.

GRACE (*Completely unconcerned*): I have also taken the women's page, darling. (*She sits in chair, thumbs through the paper.*)

WILLIAM (*Fuming*): You've completely upset my after-dinner reading schedule!

GRACE (*Paying no attention, as she finds the page for which she is searching*): Here it is—"Beauty Hints for the Woman Over Forty." (*She begins to read.*)

WILLIAM (*By now a bit desperate*): Grace, I thought your favorite TV program was on about now.

GRACE (*Chirping as she reads*): This is more relaxing.

WILLIAM (*Sourly*): That's what you've been doing all day —relaxing.

GRACE (*Indignantly, as she puts down her paper*): William Tonefeather! For your information I've had a perfectly *dreadful* day.

WILLIAM: Doing *what?*

GRACE: Opening the door for a constant stream of salesmen. (*Sighing*) Some of them were as firm as the Rock of Gibraltar. The first two or three left me positively exhausted, but—(*She smiles significantly.*) After that, I began to apply my technique. (WILLIAM *is startled. He lays aside his paper.*)

WILLIAM: What?

GRACE: My technique. (*She rises enthusiastically, drops paper into chair.*) William, I have the most wonderful method for ridding this house of peddlers. I've decided to call it the Grace Tonefeather Method of Extermination. (*Smiles*) Of course you want the details.

WILLIAM: Frankly, I do not.

GRACE (*Continuing brightly, paying no attention to* WILLIAM's *remark*): I knew you did, darling. (*She moves to center.*) Now, with my method I don't have to say that I'm busy or not interested in the product—or that I can't afford to buy.

WILLIAM (*Somewhat interested, in spite of himself*): Then what *do* you say?

GRACE: First, I invite the salesman in, just as though I am pleased to see him. Then, the minute he begins to tell me what he's selling, I—(*But* GRACE *breaks off at the sound of a loud knock on center door.*) William, someone's at the door.

WILLIAM (*Groaning unhappily*): Not visitors tonight!

GRACE (*Suddenly*): I know. It's probably that salesman.

WILLIAM: But I thought you said—

GRACE (*Cutting in*): The first one I had this morning, darling—before I started using my extermination method. (*Hurriedly*) I finally told him to come back tonight when you were here.

WILLIAM (*Disgusted*): I don't want to see anybody!

GRACE: Shh! (*She steps swiftly to* WILLIAM.) Of course you don't, darling. (*The knock on door is repeated.* GRACE *speaks to* WILLIAM.) Hide in the other room. (*She pulls* WILLIAM *to his feet.*) When he gets a dose of my technique, he'll be out of here in five minutes. (*She pushes* WILLIAM *toward door left.*) Hurry, William. (WILLIAM *exits left.* GRACE *goes upstage, opens center door.* MR. BLACK *stands at doorway. He carries a vacuum cleaner.* MR. BLACK *is persuasive and smooth-talking— the typical salesman.*)

MR. BLACK (*Heartily, as he removes his hat*): My dear Mrs. Tonefeather! Good evening—good evening. (*He steps quickly into the room.*)

GRACE (*Brightly*): Good evening, Mr. Black.

MR. BLACK (*Beaming*): You did remember my name. Yes, indeed, it's *Black!* Black as midnight and pure as snow. (*He laughs loudly as he places vacuum cleaner on floor. He tosses his hat on chair, then turns to* GRACE.) I was here this morning. Remember?

GRACE (*With a significant smile*): Mr. Black, I've been thinking about you all day.

MR. BLACK: You suggested I return tonight, when your noble, honest and stalwart husband was home.

GRACE: How do you know my husband is noble, honest and stalwart?

MR. BLACK (*Chuckling*): All husbands fit that description when you're selling 'em vacuum cleaners. (*He stoops over, begins to unwind cord attached to cleaner.*) Now, if you'll just call Mr. Tonefeather—

GRACE: But Mr. Black, that won't be necessary now.

MR. BLACK (*Straightening up in sudden disappointment*): Not necessary? But you told me you'd have to—

GRACE (*Breaking in*): But you see, things have changed since you were here this morning. I'm using a different method.

MR. BLACK (*Puzzled*): Different method? (*Suddenly beams.*) But of course! You've decided to make up your *own* mind. (*Nodding enthusiastically*) Mrs. Tonefeather, you *are* an intelligent woman.

GRACE (*A bit vaguely*): Well, I really don't make up my own mind, Mr. Black. You see, Cicero helps me.

MR. BLACK (*Surprised*): But I thought you weren't consulting your husband.

GRACE (*Lightly*): Oh, Cicero isn't my husband. Cicero is my dog.

MR. BLACK (*With a violent start*): Your *dog?*

GRACE (*Smiling brightly*): The most scholarly animal you'd ever meet. He advises me on all my problems.

MR. BLACK (*Visibly shaken*): Mrs. Tonefeather, I'm afraid I didn't quite understand you. I thought you said that this canine—

GRACE (*Gently correcting him*): His name is Cicero, Mr. Black. And I'm certain you heard what I just said.

MR. BLACK (*With effort*): Do you mean that—that Cicero is going to help you decide whether or not you'll buy a vacuum cleaner?

GRACE (*Brightly*): That's right. (*Smiles sweetly.*) After you'd left this morning, Cicero came up to me and said, "Grace—" He always calls me by my first name. "Grace," he said—

MR. BLACK (*Aghast*): He came up to you and *talked?*

GRACE (*Nodding*): Cicero does say the cutest things. (MR. BLACK's *rising alarm is evident.*) You'll simply love his witty remarks.

MR. BLACK (*Weakly*): I will?

GRACE (*Nodding*): And he always comes up with sound advice.

MR. BLACK (*Visibly upset*): Mrs. Tonefeather, I'm certain you didn't mention—er—Cicero this morning.

GRACE (*Easily*): I suppose not. When you were here, I think dear Cicero was outside, swinging through the treetops.

MR. BLACK: Swinging through the treetops?

GRACE (*Nodding briskly*): His daily exercise, you know.

MR. BLACK (*Backing away slightly*): I'm afraid I *didn't* know.

GRACE: So before you begin to demonstrate the cleaner, I'll call Cicero. I left him in the kitchen, drying the dishes, but I'm sure he'll want to ask you a few questions—(GRACE *moves toward door left.* MR. BLACK *gazes at* GRACE *in silent horror. Completely unnerved, he backs across stage to divan.* MR. BLACK *drops onto divan.* GRACE *opens door left. She calls brightly through doorway.*) Cicero! Cicero, darling! Mr. Black has arrived. He wants to show you the vacuum cleaner. (MR. BLACK, *on divan, gazes in silent terror at* GRACE. GRACE *steps to one side of doorway, as though awaiting* CICERO'S *entrance. Then, presumably,* CICERO *enters. But to the audience—and to* MR. BLACK—*the canine is invisible.* GRACE, *however, appears to welcome* CICERO *enthusiastically. She gazes down at doorway floor, then turns proudly to* MR. BLACK.) Here he is, Mr. Black.

MR. BLACK (*After a tense pause, as he gazes blankly toward doorway*): Here is *who?*

GRACE: Cicero, of course. (*She turns, pretends to speak to* CICERO.) Cicero, this is Mr. Black, the man I told you about. (MR. BLACK *is now in panic. He rises slowly.* GRACE *continues to talk to* CICERO.) Mr. Black is going to demonstrate the vacuum cleaner. (GRACE *stoops over, fondly pets the imaginary dog. Then she beams at* MR. BLACK.) Isn't he a fine little dog?

MR. BLACK (*At last, he speaks with supreme effort*): You say Cicero is standing there beside you?

GRACE (*Appearing shocked*): Why, Mr. Black! Can't you

see the darling? (*Again she pretends to pat* CICERO's *head.*) Of course he's just joking, Cicero. (*She turns to* MR. BLACK.) Aren't you, Mr. Black?

MR. BLACK: I—I—(*Breaking off*) Oh, dear!

GRACE (*Peering at* MR. BLACK): Mr. Black, you're not ill, are you?

MR. BLACK: Well—no. (*Smiling weakly*) I guess I didn't see Cicero at first because he's so small.

GRACE (*Amazed*): Small? Cicero small? Why, he's almost as big as I am. (*She speaks to* CICERO.) Aren't you, Cicero? (*She listens, as though* CICERO *is speaking. Suddenly* GRACE *laughs loudly. Then she turns again to* MR. BLACK.) Mr. Black, did you hear what Cicero said? Wasn't that the sweetest answer? (MR. BLACK *shudders. Trembling slightly, he pulls out his handkerchief and mops his forehead. Now he backs behind the divan.*)

MR. BLACK (*With a strained smile, as he attempts to hide his fright*): It sure was. I've never heard anything quite like it.

GRACE (*To* CICERO): Cicero, darling, wasn't that a nice compliment Mr. Black paid you? (*Then she reaches out and grasps the imaginary* CICERO.) Oh, no, Cicero—you musn't jump up and applaud. (*She pretends to push* CICERO *back to the floor on "all fours."*) But, Cicero precious, you simply *can't.* (*She then listens as* CICERO *presumably speaks.*) What did you say, darling? You must whisper louder. (GRACE *leans down, closer to* CICERO.)

MR. BLACK (*At last, from behind divan*): What does Cicero want to do now?

GRACE (*Turning brightly to* MR. BLACK): He's determined to shake hands with you, Mr. Black.

MR. BLACK (*With a violent start*): Oh, my goodness!

GRACE (*To* MR. BLACK): But it really isn't necessary, is it, Mr. Black?

MR. BLACK (*Swaying slightly*): It certainly isn't.

GRACE (*To* CICERO): Now, Cicero, you pick up Mr. Black's hat and sit right there in that chair. (*She indicates chair.*) Mr. Black wants to show us what a nice vacuum cleaner he sells, and he'll answer any question you ask. (MR. BLACK *is near collapse.* GRACE *now listens to a comment from* CICERO.) What's that, Cicero? (*Pause.*) You *do?* (*She turns to* MR. BLACK.) I'm terribly embarrassed, Mr. Black, but Cicero insists it's time for the ice cream man to come down our street. So before you start your demonstration, he wants to run out to the gate to buy a cone. (*Now she turns to* CICERO. *She moves upstage with* CICERO *seemingly at her side. She speaks to* CICERO.) Do you have the correct change, darling? (*She looks down, then smiles brightly.*) Why, of course you do—right there in your sweet little paw. (MR. BLACK *stands in frozen horror.* GRACE *opens the center door. She then steps back to permit* CICERO's *exit. Presumably* CICERO *moves through doorway. The door remains open. Smiling,* GRACE *turns to* MR. BLACK.) You don't mind waiting, do you, Mr. Black? As soon as Cicero buys his strawberry ice cream cone, he'll be skipping back. Then you can tell us all about your vacuum cleaner.

MR. BLACK (*Wild-eyed and trembling*): Mrs. Tonefeather—

GRACE: Yes?

MR. BLACK: You don't need a vacuum cleaner! (*Suddenly* MR. BLACK *dashes around the divan. In complete panic he snatches up his vacuum cleaner.*)

GRACE (*In pretended amazement*): Mr. Black! (MR. BLACK, *grasping the vacuum, plunges madly to upstage center. Pale and shaken, he turns to* GRACE.)

MR. BLACK: Madam, what you need is a reservation in a psychopathic ward! (MR. BLACK, *carrying cleaner, dashes wildly through center doorway. He slams the door behind him. For a moment* GRACE *doesn't move. Then she suddenly breaks into hilarious laughter. Still laughing, she crosses to divan where she sits. Then* WILLIAM'S *loud laughter is heard behind door left.* WILLIAM *enters.*)

WILLIAM (*Between bursts of laughter*): Grace, you're a genius!

GRACE: Then you listened?

WILLIAM (*Nodding*): I overheard every word. (*With a loud shout of hilarity*) Cicero!

GRACE (*Shrieking in glee*): Poor Mr. Black!

WILLIAM (*With equal mirth*): He thinks either you're crazy or *he* is!

GRACE: When I told him Cicero wanted an ice cream cone —(*Again she breaks off with uncontrolled laughter.*)

WILLIAM (*Picking up* MR. BLACK'S *hat from chair*): He even left his hat! (*With a howl of glee,* WILLIAM *drops into chair*) I peeped through the doorway. When I saw the expression on that man's face—(*He breaks into loud laughter again.*)

GRACE: I thought he was going to collapse from fright!

WILLIAM: Grace, I've got to hand it to you. (*Quoting*) "The Tonefeather Method of Extermination!" Honestly, I've never seen anything like it. Black is probably halfway across town by now.

GRACE: That's my technique, William. I'll never be bothered with a salesman again.

WILLIAM: Not after you introduce them to Cicero! (*Howling*) Except there isn't any Cicero. (*Beginning to control his mirth slightly*) Well, you can cross Mr. Black off your list. That's *one* salesman who will never come back. (*Once more* GRACE *and* WILLIAM *break into laughter, but at that moment the center door opens.* MR. BLACK *plunges wildly into the room. He still carries the vacuum cleaner.*)

MR. BLACK (*Yells in fright*): Oh! Oh—!

GRACE (*Jumps up*): Mr. Black! (MR. BLACK *is in terror. He moans loudly.*)

WILLIAM (*Amazed, as he rises*): You!

MR. BLACK (*Groans*): Oh! Oh!

GRACE (*Confused and upset*): Mr. Black, what's the matter?

MR. BLACK (*Trembles violently*): It's Cicero!

GRACE: Cicero?

WILLIAM (*Shocked*): Cicero?

MR. BLACK (*Breathlessly, and in terror*): He's at the gate, all right, like he told you, but he won't let me out of the yard with this vacuum cleaner.

WILLIAM (*Stunned*): Won't let you out? (*Sputtering*) Now see here, you don't know what you're talking about!

MR. BLACK (*To* WILLIAM): I'm talking about your wife's dog. He's crouched outside, waiting to tear up my vacuum cleaner. (*He places cleaner on floor.*)

GRACE (*Aghast*): But that's impossible! (MR. BLACK *stands at center, facing audience. He remains in this position during his conversation with* GRACE *and* WILLIAM.)

MR. BLACK (*To* GRACE): Madam, didn't you let that dog out of the house so he could buy an ice cream cone?

GRACE (*In complete confusion*): Well, I said—

MR. BLACK (*Cutting in*): Of course you did!

WILLIAM (*Advancing to* MR. BLACK): Now wait a minute, buddy—you couldn't have seen Cicero.

MR. BLACK (*With dignity*): And why not, may I ask?

WILLIAM (*Loudly and emphatically*): Because Cicero *isn't* a dog!

MR. BLACK: Then what is he?

WILLIAM (*Hotly*): He's *nothing!*

MR. BLACK (*With a violent start*): Nothing? (*Horrified, he backs away from* WILLIAM.) Mr. Tonefeather, please—

WILLIAM (*With increasing indignation*): I've lived in this house twenty years and I've never seen Cicero. There isn't a canine in this block. The only pet who has ever lived in this house is—is Grace.

MR. BLACK (*Amazed*): Sir, do you mean that?

WILLIAM: Certainly, I mean it!

MR. BLACK: But Cicero is your wife's remarkable dog. She consults him about everything. (*To* GRACE.) Isn't that what you told me, madam?

GRACE (*Greatly upset*): Oh, dear!

MR. BLACK (*Turning to* WILLIAM): Your wife called Cicero into this room. Then she let him out the front door. Cicero wanted to buy an ice cream cone. Now he's standing out there at the gate—

WILLIAM (*Yelling*): I tell you there isn't any Cicero!

MR. BLACK (*Turning to* GRACE, *speaks slowly and signifi-cantly*): Madam, did you hear what your poor confused husband said?

WILLIAM (*Loudly*): I'm not confused! I'm simply saying that—

MR. BLACK (*Soothingly*): We know, Mr. Tonefeather—we know. (*Now he turns again to* GRACE.) My dear lady, I didn't realize your husband was a—(*He taps his head knowingly, as he indicates* WILLIAM.)

WILLIAM (*Explosively*): Now see here! If you think I'm a mental case—

MR. BLACK (*Taking a step back from* WILLIAM): Please, Mr. Tonefeather—(*Smiling, as though speaking to an imbecile*) Remember, we mustn't get excited.

GRACE (*Desperately, to* MR. BLACK): Mr. Black, my husband isn't—(*She pauses in confusion.*)

MR. BLACK (*To* GRACE): He must be, otherwise he wouldn't insist there isn't any Cicero. (*Sadly.*) You *do* have my sympathy, madam. What a trial this must have been to you, all through the years.

WILLIAM (*Shouting wildly*): Now you wait a minute!

MR. BLACK (*To* GRACE): Really, Mrs. Tonefeather, your husband should be in a sanatorium.

WILLIAM (*Yelling at* GRACE): He thinks I'm crazy!

MR. BLACK (*To* GRACE, *as he indicates* WILLIAM): Hear him? I declare, he actually believes Cicero doesn't exist. (*Smiling sympathetically.*) But *we* know better, don't we, Mrs. Tonefeather?

GRACE (*Groaning, as she backs away*): Oh, my! Oh, my!

MR. BLACK (*Sighing*): Of course, I don't know what I'm going to do with this vacuum cleaner. Cicero simply won't let me through the gate with it. He's in love with this cleaner, Mrs. Tonefeather. He wants to keep it. He told me so.

WILLIAM (*Desperately—and about to weep*): He couldn't tell you anything, because there isn't any Cicero!

MR. BLACK (*To* GRACE, *with a sad smile*): There he goes again.

WILLIAM (*Bellowing*): I'm a sane man, I tell you!

MR. BLACK (*Turning sorrowfully to* WILLIAM): My good chap, how I wish you could prove it.

WILLIAM: I'll prove it all right. I'll—(*Suddenly*) I'll *buy* your broken-down vacuum cleaner!

MR. BLACK (*Amazed*): Mr. Tonefeather! You don't know what you're saying, unfortunately.

WILLIAM (*Savagely*): I do know what I'm saying! (*He snatches out his billfold.*)

MR. BLACK (*Hesitating*): Of course, it *is* Cicero's wish—

WILLIAM (*Shrieking*): Cicero!

MR. BLACK (*To* WILLIAM): Let's not become violent—

WILLIAM: I'm not violent, I tell you. (*He pulls bills from billfold.*) I just want to get rid of you. (*He steps to* MR. BLACK, *thrusts bills into his hand.*) Here—in payment for that confounded contraption!

MR. BLACK (*Glancing swiftly at bills*): But Mr. Tonefeather, I'm certain you've given me too much money.

WILLIAM: I don't care! *Just get out of my sight.*

MR. BLACK (*Uneasily*): Anything to make you happy, Mr. Tonefeather—you and Cicero.

WILLIAM (*Roaring*): Don't you mention Cicero again! (*He advances menacingly toward* MR. BLACK.)

MR. BLACK (*Nervously backing upstage*): Yes, sir. Now, just calm yourself—

WILLIAM (*Glaring at* MR. BLACK): If you try to tell anybody I'm crazy—

MR. BLACK (*Hastily*): Oh, I won't, Mr. Tonefeather. Cicero asked me to keep quiet about it. But dear me, he *was* angry.

GRACE (*Suddenly, to* MR. BLACK): Mr. Black, if you so much as mention that dog again—

MR. BLACK (*Raising his hand for silence*): Madam, please—! But—under the circumstances you *do* want this vacuum cleaner, of course.

GRACE (*Angrily*): I'll have to take it, since my husband has paid you. (*Grimly*) But I want you to know that William is perfectly sane, and so am I. I simply pretended I owned a dog. It was just a scheme to— (*Explosively*) Oh, get out of here!

MR. BLACK: But first, madam, may I make a slight observation?

GRACE (*Grimly*): You may not! And you listen to me— (*Emphatically*) Cicero can't talk, Cicero can't walk, Cicero can't bite—simply because *there isn't any Cicero!*

WILLIAM (*Approvingly, to* GRACE): That's tellin' him!

MR. BLACK (*To* GRACE, *innocently disturbed*): Madam— no Cicero?

GRACE: No Cicero!

MR. BLACK (*Questioningly*): No angry Cicero guarding the gate?

GRACE (*With grim finality*): No Cicero *any place!*

MR. BLACK: How strange—

GRACE (*Flinging the words*): There's nothing strange about it! And don't you ever come near this house again!

MR. BLACK: I certainly won't. (*Greatly upset*) But I just can't understand it. After what has happened, you still tell me that—

GRACE (*Breaking in, almost screaming*): *There isn't any Cicero!*

MR. BLACK (*Humbly*): Yes, ma'am. No Cicero. (GRACE *and* WILLIAM *glare angrily at* MR. BLACK. MR. BLACK *hesitates, then thrusts his hands into his trouser pockets. This action raises the back of* MR. BLACK'S *suit coat, exposing the rear of his trousers. Slowly,* MR. BLACK *turns. And now—for the first time—the seat of* MR. BLACK'S *trousers is visible. Except, however, the seat is missing. Seemingly, this area of cloth has been torn to shreds, doubtless by a viciously active and determined animal. Without comment,* MR. BLACK *moves upstage toward center door.* GRACE *and* WILLIAM *now gaze in terror at the tattered expanse of trouser seat.* MR. BLACK, *oblivious to the shattering reaction of the* TONEFEATHERS, *continues upstage. Then, in horror—and with mounting suspicion—*WILLIAM *slowly turns to* GRACE. *And* GRACE, *in utterly confused disbelief, looks at* WILLIAM. GRACE, *speechless, sinks onto divan.* MR. BLACK *opens the center door. The curtain falls.*)

THE END

Production Notes

Cicero the Great

Characters: 2 male; 1 female.

Playing Time: 10 minutes.

Costumes: Modern dress. William wears a white dress shirt, open at the collar. Grace wears a street dress with a smart little apron over it. Mr. Black wears a conservative business suit and a hat. The second time he enters, he wears another pair of trousers, with the seat torn to shreds.

Properties: Newspaper and paper money for William; vacuum cleaner for Mr. Black.

Setting: The comfortably furnished living room of the Tonefeather residence. At downstage right is a divan. An armchair is located at downstage left. Other suitable furniture may be placed about the stage if desired. There are two entrances to the room: an outside door at center back and a door at left which leads to the other rooms of the house.

Lighting: No special effects.

Two for the Show

Characters

BESSIE TOLLMAN, *a devotee of amateur theatricals*
SAM, *her visitor*
VOICE OF ANNOUNCER

TIME: *Evening.*
SETTING: *The living room of the Tollman home.*
AT RISE: BESSIE TOLLMAN *is seated in a chair, holding a magazine, but listening to the news over the radio. The* VOICE OF ANNOUNCER *begins speaking before the curtain rises, and continues as it rises.*

VOICE OF ANNOUNCER (*Fading in*): . . . But it is believed that a satisfactory settlement of this dispute will be reached within a few days. (*Pause*) And this, ladies and gentlemen, concludes the early evening edition of the news. To keep up to the minute with the latest events, keep tuned to this station. Our next regularly scheduled newscast is at six o'clock tomorrow morning. (*Pause*) Now we invite you to stay tuned for the latest weather report. (BESSIE *lays aside her magazine. She rises, moves to radio.*) According to our local forecaster, Mr. Howard Shelby, we may expect partly cloudy skies and rising temperatures tonight and tomorrow, followed by scattered evening showers. The official high today, as reported from the office of the local weather bureau . . . (BESSIE *snaps off the radio. Deep in thought, she moves to center. Mechanically she unfastens the necklace from her neck. Holding necklace, she moves to desk, absently picks up jewel case from desk, opens it. She drops necklace into case. Suddenly from offstage left comes a sharp crash, as though a dish had fallen to the floor.* BESSIE *starts violently. She snaps the case shut, drops it onto desk, and swiftly swings around toward door left. The house is quiet.* BESSIE *is obviously frightened, but she slowly crosses stage. She reaches door left, pauses. Then she grimly lifts her shoulders, takes a deep breath, and exits. There is another pause. Then the door at center slowly opens. At open doorway stands* SAM, *his hat pulled down over his eyes. He holds a revolver in his hand.* SAM *is in his twenties—cold, calculating and dangerous. He peers into the room as if to make certain that he is alone, then steps through doorway and closes door behind him. Cautiously he walks to door left. He opens the door slightly, as if listening for any sound from offstage. The house remains in silence.* SAM *closes the door, again glances briefly around the room. He moves to desk, and notices the jewel case. He slips revolver into the outside pocket of his suitcoat, then snatches up the case, opens it, and gives a cry of pleasure as he discovers the necklace. He draws out the necklace and drops it into his coat pocket. He snaps shut the jewel case and places it on top of desk, but somewhat removed from its original location. SAM leans over desk and quietly starts to pull out a drawer. BESSIE enters briskly from left. SAM's back is to BESSIE.)*

BESSIE *(Stops short with a gasp)*: Oh! *(Swiftly SAM shuts desk drawer and swings around, faces BESSIE. His hand clutches gun hidden in his pocket.)* Why—why—*(For a moment SAM stands frozen. SAM and BESSIE gaze at each other in tense silence. Suddenly BESSIE regains her composure. She smiles, speaks with bright enthusiasm.)* But, of course! You're Mr. Sullivan. *(SAM stiffens. BESSIE pays no attention. She trots across room to SAM. Cordially she extends her hand in greeting.)* My, this *is* a surprise. *(SAM is forced to shake hands.)* I'm Bessie Tollman, you know.

SAM *(His voice strained)*: Bessie Tollman?

BESSIE *(Innocently)*: You tried the doorbell, didn't you? *(Before SAM can answer)* It has been out of order for a week. I'm so glad you walked right in, although I'd never have known you were here if I hadn't returned for my magazine. Do make yourself at home. *(SAM remains silent. He's still wary and menacingly alert, but he slowly removes his hat. BESSIE smiles brightly.)* You know, I've just had the most upsetting experience. I'd turned off the radio—then I heard a simply terrifying crash from the kitchen. I was certain someone had broken into the house. *(Smiles with relief)* But I was wrong. It was only our kitten, Snowball. She'd jumped

onto the table and knocked off a saucer. (*Laughs*) Wasn't
I silly to be frightened? (SAM *doesn't laugh, nor does
he move.* BESSIE *apparently is not aware of his tense
attitude.*) Sit down, Mr. Sullivan.

SAM (*Cautiously, after a pause*): Mr. Sullivan?

BESSIE (*Smiles*): Oh, I know who you are, even though
we've never met. (BESSIE *indicates armchair.*) Take this
chair. It's more comfortable. (*For a moment SAM makes
no move. At last he places his hat on desk. Then he
crosses to armchair and sits down.*) You know, I *do* have
a confession to make. When I walked in here and saw
you, I thought for a moment you were a burglar. I suppose I was nervous because of Snowball and the saucer.
(*Laughs lightly*) But it *was* stupid. I should have known,
even though you didn't find me at once, that you'd immediately begin to rehearse.

SAM (*On guard*): Rehearse?

BESSIE (*Gaily, as she moves right*): Oh, you needn't be
embarrassed about it, Mr. Sullivan. I don't blame you
for wanting to run through your part, whether the other
characters are present or not. (BESSIE *drops into chair
before desk. She turns to SAM.*) But really, I didn't expect you tonight.

SAM: You didn't?

BESSIE: Of course I can understand your enthusiasm. This
love for the theatre *does* get into one's veins, doesn't it?
I realize you're not a member of our local Drama Club,
Mr. Sullivan, but I'm sure you have the same devotion
to amateur theatricals that I have.

SAM (*Slowly begins to understand*): Well, maybe.

BESSIE: When I learned that you had consented to take a

lead in our next production, I was delighted, but surprised.

SAM (*Pointedly*): You're not the only one who's surprised.

BESSIE (*Continues brightly*): Of course I'd never met you, but our director, Mr. Dodd, was elated when you accepted the role. He thinks you're the perfect criminal type.

SAM (*Evenly*): Mr. Dodd must be a smart man.

BESSIE (*Gaily*): *You* should know, Mr. Sullivan. I understand you and Mr. Dodd were boyhood friends. (*Suddenly rises*) But I'm sure I'm boring you. (SAM *jumps up. He's alert and suspicious.* BESSIE *appears brightly innocent.*) You'll just have to stop me when I get on a talking spree.

SAM (*Begins to relax*): You haven't bored me.

BESSIE (*Beams*): I'm so glad.

SAM: You have no idea how revealing your conversation has been.

BESSIE: How nice! (*Pauses thoughtfully*) But really, Mr. Sullivan, I *should* tell you something else—something you might not know.

SAM: There are a good many things I don't know—yet.

BESSIE: It's Mr. Dodd. He's a fine director, of course. (*Slowly*) But he doesn't seem to think too much of my acting ability. I realize my role in the play isn't very important, but I honestly believe he'd like to replace me. Mr. Dodd feels that I'm not emotionally mature. That's the way he expressed it. (*She walks to center.*) In fact, he made the statement that my acting—*smells.*

SAM (*Affects surprise*): He did? Why, the dirty lug!

(*Quickly corrects himself*) I mean—my dear old pal—
(*His voice trails off.*)

BESSIE (*Firmly*): I know I can act. With your help, Mr.
Sullivan, I'm going to prove it to our director. (*Pause*)
I do hope this little meeting hasn't disappointed you.

SAM: Quite the contrary. (*With a significant grin*) In fact,
I consider this a most fortunate situation.

BESSIE (*Pleased*): Mr. Sullivan, you *are* a gentleman.
(*Smiles*) But enough of this chit-chat. I'm sure you want
to rehearse our scene. I'll get my script. (*She moves toward door left.*) I'm afraid I haven't memorized quite
all my role.

SAM (*Quickly alert*): Just a minute!

BESSIE (*Pauses, turns to* SAM): Yes?

SAM (*Hesitates*): I was just curious—

BESSIE: About what, Mr. Sullivan?

SAM: Do you live here alone?

BESSIE (*Startled*): Alone? Goodness, no! Didn't anybody
tell you?

SAM (*Vaguely*): Not specifically.

BESSIE: My husband and I reside in this house. I realize
we're here in the suburbs with no close neighbors—
(*She breaks off with a smile.*) But we like it.

SAM: Yes. So do I.

BESSIE (*Nods*): It *is* cozy and quiet.

SAM (*After a slight pause*): Your husband is at home?

BESSIE: Tonight? Oh, no. He's attending a meeting of
some sort. (*She takes a step back toward center.*) I must
tell you a little joke on him. He went off without his
key. That's why I left the front door unlocked. He'll be

late getting in—you know how men are on their nights
out—and I didn't want him to disturb me. (*As an afterthought.*) I'm so sorry he isn't here to meet you.

SAM: I'm sure we can manage beautifully. (*With a slow
smile*) Just you and I.

BESSIE: I'll pick up my script and be with you in a moment,
Mr. Sullivan. (*She moves to door left, exits. Immediately SAM snaps into action. Quietly but quickly he
crosses stage to desk. He glances briefly across room at
door left, then silently pulls open desk drawer. He fumbles through contents of drawer as though searching for
additional loot. He finds nothing of importance and is
obviously disappointed. He closes drawer, turns from
desk toward audience. After another swift glance toward
door left, he carefully draws out the necklace from his
outside pocket and studies it. With a smug smile, he
slips the necklace back into his pocket. As he steps again
toward center, BESSIE enters from left. She carries a copy
of the play script.*)

SAM: You weren't long.

BESSIE (*With animation*): I've had this script in the kitchen.
I try to study it while I'm drying the dishes. I haven't
memorized for years, Mr. Sullivan, and it *does* seem
difficult.

SAM: I suppose so.

BESSIE (*Thumbs through script*): Let's see now—(*Suddenly
looks up*) I suppose we should run through the scene
where you hold me up.

SAM (*Startled*): Hold you up?

BESSIE (*With a little laugh*): Mr. Sullivan! You act as
though you haven't even read the play.

SAM (*Thinks quickly*): I'm afraid I *haven't* given it as much attention as I should have.

BESSIE (*Nods brightly*): I know. You're a busy man, but you remember, of course, that you take the part of an underworld character—cold, ruthless, dangerous. I play the role of Mrs. Saxon, the wealthy old lady who lives alone. (*She gazes at script, finds the scene.*) Now, in this scene you enter my home and threaten to kill me. (SAM, *listening closely, nods.*) You're already in the room when I enter, but the moment you hear the door open, you swing around and point a pistol at me. (*She breaks off, suddenly disturbed.*) Oh, dear! I wish we had a gun.

SAM (*With a start*): A gun?

BESSIE (*Nods*): It *is* awkward to do the scene without a firearm. I'm sure we don't even have a wooden shotgun around here. (*Sighs*) I suppose you'll have to use either my rolling pin or the egg beater, but I'm afraid we simply can't throw ourselves into the scene.

SAM (*Slowly, after a pause*): Mrs. Tollman—

BESSIE: Yes?

SAM: *I* have a gun.

BESSIE: Really? (*Suddenly smiles.*) But of course! Professional actors always carry their properties with them, don't they? And Mr. Dodd said you'd been on the stage for several years. (*She walks to* SAM, *speaks expectantly.*) Where is it?

SAM: Where's what?

BESSIE (*Brightly*): The gun you're going to shoot me with.

SAM: Oh, the gun. (BESSIE *nods brightly.* SAM *hesitates. At last he slowly draws the revolver from his coat pocket.* BESSIE *peers at it with breathless interest.*)

BESSIE: My goodness, Mr. Sullivan, it looks real.

SAM (*Evenly*): It *is* real.

BESSIE: Honestly? (BESSIE *is happily excited.*) Then our scene's going to be the most authentic one in the play. (*Suddenly*) Do you mind if I hold it?

SAM: Hold what?

BESSIE: The firearm.

SAM: Well, I—I—

BESSIE: I won't drop it. (BESSIE *takes gun from* SAM'S *hand.* SAM *is disturbed, but he attempts to hide his concern.* BESSIE *gazes at the gun with considerable awe. Then she looks up.*) Do you know something, Mr. Sullivan? This is the first time I've ever touched a real gun.

SAM: That's what I guessed.

BESSIE (*Continues to inspect gun*): Goodness, it gives me the creeps. (*She shudders.*)

SAM: I'm glad to hear you say that.

BESSIE (*Gingerly examines the gun as she moves left*): It's so cold and deadly looking. Wouldn't it be simply awful to come face-to-face with a thing like this? I'm certain I'd simply collapse.

SAM (*Delighted by the information*): Really?

BESSIE (*Grips gun more firmly, with her finger on trigger*): On Skid Row it's called a "gat," isn't it?

SAM (*Warningly*): Be careful!

BESSIE (*Still studies gun*): Careful?

SAM: Of that gun. It's loaded. (BESSIE *suddenly becomes a changed character. Instead of a chirping lightheaded woman, she is now grim, cold, courageous. Swiftly she swings around. Unflinchingly she points the gun at* SAM.)

BESSIE (*In a hard and menacing tone*): *I know it's loaded!*

SAM (*With a sudden leap toward* BESSIE): Why, you—

BESSIE (*Snaps the command*): *Don't move!* (*The gun covers* SAM. *He stops, frozen, and gazes in horror at* BESSIE. *After a tense pause,* BESSIE *speaks. Her tone is steel-edged.*) You're Sam Conlow—alias "The Rat"—alias "The Killer." You're wanted in half a dozen states. If you take one step, I'll blow your brains out! I have a trigger-happy finger. (*There is another tense pause.* SAM *is trapped, and he's entirely aware of the fact.*)

SAM (*With effort*): How did you know?

BESSIE: About you? I had my radio on. *You* were featured on the newscast tonight. The story of your escape was the first item. Seems you'd been spotted out this way. Listeners were warned to be on the lookout.

SAM (*Desperately*): You can't prove anything!

BESSIE (*Evenly*): You have my necklace. (SAM *gives a start of surprise. Then he attempts to control his emotion.*)

SAM: What makes you think—

BESSIE (*Cuts in*): You took it out of the jewel case on the desk.

SAM (*Suddenly snarls*): You didn't see me!

BESSIE: No. But the jewel case was moved to the *other* side of the desk after I placed my necklace in it. I noticed the change as soon as I walked in here. You'd picked up the case, opened it, and—

SAM (*Savagely*): Shut up! (*After a pause*) So you think you're smart.

BESSIE: Not smart. Just observant—as any good actress is. (*Neither* BESSIE *nor* SAM *has moved. Suddenly the silence is broken by a loud knock on center door.*)

SAM (*After a tense pause, and without taking his eyes from* BESSIE): Who's that?

BESSIE: The police. I phoned them when I went into the other room after my script.

SAM: You—double-crosser! (*The knock on door is repeated, but* BESSIE *doesn't move. At last* SAM *speaks with sarcasm.*) Well, why don't you go to the door and let 'em in?

BESSIE (*Stoutly*): I won't move until the police bring Mr. Dodd out here. I want that director to see for himself that Bessie Tollman is the best actress in this town! (*In grim triumph* BESSIE *takes a step toward* SAM. *She calls over her shoulder.*) Come in, officer! (BESSIE's *hand is firm and steady as she keeps* SAM *covered with gun. The center door begins to open. The curtain quickly falls.*)

THE END

Production Notes

TWO FOR THE SHOW

Characters: 1 male; 1 female; male off-stage voice.

Playing Time: 15 minutes.

Costumes: Bessie wears housedress and necklace. Sam wears a suit and hat.

Properties: Necklace and script, for Bessie; gun, for Sam.

Setting: A comfortably furnished living room. Doors center and left lead to the front porch and the rear portion of the house. Downstage right is a desk with a drawer in it. On the desk is an empty jewel case, and in front of the desk is a chair. There is an armchair downstage left. Against the back wall is a small table with a radio on it. Other furniture may be added as desired.

Lighting: No special effects.

Word of Honor

Characters

MINNIE WEBB
STELLA WEBB
MR. HIGGINS

TIME: *The present.*
SETTING: *The living room of Minnie and Stella Webb.*
AT RISE: STELLA WEBB, *an elderly spinster, is seated in an armchair. She weeps softly, but with considerable emotion. After a few moments,* MINNIE WEBB, *her sister, enters.*

MINNIE: Stella! Stella Webb! (STELLA *glances up. She takes one look at* MINNIE, *then bursts into a loud sob.*) Stop it! Stop it, I say!
STELLA: Oh, Minnie!
MINNIE: Now you just cease that wailing, Stella. I'm ashamed of you—carrying on like a siege of stormy

344

weather. Blow your nose and start talking. (STELLA *wipes her eyes and rises.*)

STELLA: I don't know what made me do it. (*Gloomily*) But this house *is* cluttered, Minnie, and there are just the two of us living here.

MINNIE: Stella, stop beating around the rosebush. I can tell you're entangled again.

STELLA: I was impulsive.

MINNIE: As you've been for sixty years.

STELLA (*With effort*): Minnie, I said you and I would sell the old china tea set.

MINNIE (*Startled*): The china tea set? (*With a gasp*) Stella, you didn't!

STELLA (*Nods in defeat*): It all happened when I dropped into Mr. Higgins' Antique Shoppe.

MINNIE: Stella, did you tell Mr. Higgins we'd part with the china tea set? (STELLA *nods.*) It's been in the family ever since I can remember!

STELLA: I regretted it, Minnie, the moment I'd left his antique shop, but I'd given him my word, and the Webbs haven't gone back on their word of honor for six generations. As you've always said, the word of a Webb is as dependable as the Fourth of July.

MINNIE: Just what did you tell Mr. Higgins?

STELLA: I said he could take the set to his shop. He thinks he can find a buyer. If he does, he's to settle with us after he deducts his commission.

MINNIE (*Shaken*): Stella Webb, you've done some reckless things in your time, but *this* takes the Parker House rolls!

STELLA: Mr. Higgins is coming for the set this afternoon! (*Breaks into a loud sob*)

MINNIE (*Grimly*): That old skinflint of a Mr. Higgins! He's been trying to get his hands on that tea set for ten years. Then you go and give him your word—

STELLA (*Wails*): Minnie, I'm so ashamed! (*Desperately*) I know we mustn't part with that dear china, so you have to come up with an idea.

MINNIE: That's what you always say, after you find yourself in a barrel of piccalilli.

STELLA: Maybe you can make Mr. Higgins change his mind.

MINNIE: Mr. Higgins is not a man who changes his mind. He's about as unyielding as cement, and you've given him the Webb word of honor. (*With a gloomy sigh*) I don't know what I can do. (*She breaks off suddenly.*) Wait a minute. (*She faces* STELLA.) Now let me get this straight—you told Mr. Higgins he could take our tea set to his shop? (STELLA *nods. For a moment* MINNIE *doesn't speak.*) Of course you can't go back on your word, Stella, but after Mr. Higgins arrives, if he should decide he didn't *want* the tea set, that would release you from the obligation.

STELLA: Minnie, you *do* have an idea!

MINNIE: Maybe.

STELLA: Bless your dear little heart! (*Rushes to* MINNIE) Tell your sister all about it.

MINNIE: I will not! If I did, you'd probably spill the lima beans—and right in front of Mr. Higgins. (*Thoughtfully*) But I am going to try something on him, and if it's to work, you have to follow right along with me,

Stella. Don't you dare act surprised or upset or confused. (*A loud off-stage knock is heard.*)

STELLA (*Frightened*): It's Mr. Higgins!

MINNIE: Sit down, Stella! Quickly!

STELLA: I still don't understand.

MINNIE: Stop arguing! Everything is all right. (*She gives* STELLA *a little push toward sofa. The knock on door is repeated.* STELLA *sinks onto sofa.* MINNIE *opens door.* MR. HIGGINS *enters.*)

MR. HIGGINS: Ah, Miss Minnie! (*He removes his hat.*) My dear lady—good afternoon.

MINNIE: Good afternoon, Mr. Higgins.

MR. HIGGINS: And Miss Stella! What a joy to see you again. How are you?

MINNIE: As usual, she's overcome.

MR. HIGGINS (*To* MINNIE): No doubt your delightful sister has told you of our little business deal.

MINNIE: She has.

MR. HIGGINS: Then there's no need for irrelevant explanations.

MINNIE: None at all, Mr. Higgins.

MR. HIGGINS (*Beams with self-assurance*): I did think at first that Miss Stella was going to back down—after she'd given me permission to pick up the tea set, but I had her golden word of honor.

MINNIE: I know.

MR. HIGGINS: Of course we're all aware that a Webb never goes back on his word.

MINNIE: If you still want to carry the tea set back to your shop, Mr. Higgins, we have no objection.

MR. HIGGINS (*Rubs his hands expectantly*): Indeed I do.

I knew I could depend upon the Webb sisters. Now, if you'll just bring in the china, I'll take it out to the car.

MINNIE: Sit down, Mr. Higgins. (*She indicates chair.*)

MR. HIGGINS: Sit down? (*Smiles*) I can think of nothing I'd enjoy more, Miss Minnie, but it just so happens that I'm in a considerable hurry.

MINNIE: I said sit down, Mr. Higgins. You can spare a few extra minutes.

MR. HIGGINS: But I—

MINNIE: Mr. Higgins!

MR. HIGGINS (*Hastily*): Why, yes, of course. (*He sits.*)

MINNIE (*To* MR. HIGGINS): We've been thinking, Mr. Higgins—haven't we, Stella?

STELLA (*Vaguely*): Indeed—yes. (*To* MR. HIGGINS) We've been simply bubbling over with thoughts.

MINNIE: We've been thinking that if we're to part with the family tea set, we should use it once more before you carry it away.

MR. HIGGINS: Use it once more?

MINNIE: As a final ceremony. A farewell tea party, you might call it.

STELLA: Like the Boston Tea Party—

MINNIE: Stella, I'm talking.

MR. HIGGINS (*Annoyed*): But see here—

MINNIE: It won't take long, Mr. Higgins, and of course you're included. (*To* STELLA) Isn't he, Stella?

STELLA: Yes. We wouldn't do anything unless we included Mr. Higgins.

MINNIE: The tea's almost ready.

MR. HIGGINS (*Starts to rise*): I'm sorry, ladies, but I simply can't stay.

MINNIE (*With authority*): Relax, Mr. Higgins. (MR. HIG-
GINS *drops back into chair*.)

STELLA (*As* MINNIE *starts toward door*): Can I help you,
Minnie dear? (*She starts to rise*.)

MINNIE: You stay right here, Stella. Mr. Higgins needs
somebody to entertain him. (MINNIE *exits*. STELLA *sits
on sofa*.)

STELLA (*To* MR. HIGGINS): Minnie just loves her little
ceremonials.

MR. HIGGINS (*Grimly*): Miss Stella, is this foolishness necessary?

STELLA: If Minnie says so, then it must be necessary. And
I for one could certainly use a cup of tea right now.

MR. HIGGINS: I hadn't planned on this delay. You should
have been firm with your sister.

STELLA: When Minnie makes up her mind about something, she's like the Rock of Gibraltar.

MR. HIGGINS: This is something of a surprise to me.

STELLA: Me, too, Mr. Higgins.

MR. HIGGINS: Was your sister upset by your decision to
part with the china?

STELLA: Well, you know Minnie. She gets over things in
a hurry. (*Pause*) Thank goodness.

MR. HIGGINS: Of course my prospective customer may not
offer much for the set. In that case my payment to you
would be small. But I'm sure that would make no difference to you lovely ladies. After all, none of us cares
to hoard useless articles, do we?

STELLA: I suppose not.

MR. HIGGINS: And since I have the Webb word of honor—

MINNIE (*Off-stage*): Stella! Oh, Stella!

STELLA: Yes, Minnie?

MINNIE (*Off-stage*): Open the door, please.

STELLA (*To* MR. HIGGINS): She must have the tea ready. (*To* MINNIE) Coming! (*To* MR. HIGGINS) Isn't she a fast worker?

MR. HIGGINS (*Nods*): You have to be a fast worker in this age. (STELLA *opens the door.* MINNIE *enters. She is carrying nothing, but from the position of her hands and arms, she appears to be holding a tray. Throughout the remaining action of the play,* MINNIE *appears to be handling the tray and china.* STELLA *gasps.* STELLA'S *back is to* MR. HIGGINS, *and* MINNIE *appears to take no notice of* STELLA'S *reaction.* MR. HIGGINS *sees* MINNIE, *and gives a violent start.*)

MINNIE: Here we are, Mr. Higgins—ready for our little tea party. (*She places "tray" on coffee table.*) Isn't it simply lovely?

MR. HIGGINS (*Amazed*): What's lovely?

MINNIE: Why, the tea set, of course. Really, Mr. Higgins, you act as though you'd never laid your eyes on this set before.

MR. HIGGINS (*Gazing at coffee table*): Have—have I?

MINNIE: Mr. Higgins—really!

MR. HIGGINS: What is this? A joke?

MINNIE: Mr. Higgins, are you trying to make fun of this priceless tea set? (*She indicates the coffee table.*)

MR. HIGGINS: I—I—(*He breaks off.* STELLA *has recovered from her initial shock, and seems to realize* MINNIE'S *plan.*)

STELLA: Mr. Higgins, is something wrong?

MR. HIGGINS: Well, I—do you see it, too?

STELLA: See what?

Mr. Higgins: The tea set?

Stella (*Affects surprise*): Why, of course!

Minnie: I didn't know you had eye trouble, Mr. Higgins.

Mr. Higgins: I haven't! That is—Oh, dear—

Minnie: You don't often see such a graceful teapot, do you? And these delicate little cups and saucers! (*Sighs*) Stella and I are going to miss them. Aren't we, Stella dear?

Stella (*Vigorously*): I should say we are! (Stella *steps to coffee table, and points down at it.*) I love that little sugar bowl. Don't you think it's simply out of this world, Mr. Higgins?

Mr. Higgins (*Weakly*): It certainly is.

Minnie: I doubt that your prospective customer has ever seen a china tea set quite like this.

Mr. Higgins (*With effort*): I'm sure of it.

Minnie: Shall I serve the tea, Stella?

Stella: I wish you would. I'm always so afraid I'll break something. (Minnie *moves behind the coffee table.*) I know you'd be terribly upset if I smashed one of these cups, wouldn't you, Mr. Higgins?

Mr. Higgins: Would I? I mean—yes. Yes, indeed. Miss Minnie—

Minnie (*Cheerfully*): Yes, Mr. Higgins?

Mr. Higgins: That tea set—(*He points*)

Minnie: What about it?

Mr. Higgins: Haven't you made a slight mistake?

Minnie: Mistake?

Stella (*To* Mr. Higgins): Of course not, Mr. Higgins. This is the tea set we discussed when I was in your shop.

Mr. Higgins: It is?

and pack the set. I thought we'd wrap the china, place it in a basket—

MR. HIGGINS: Some other time, please.

STELLA: Minnie, perhaps Mr. Higgins would like to take along a single piece—perhaps a cup. He could show it to his prospective customer.

MR. HIGGINS: Never mind.

MINNIE: Oh, but you must, Mr. Higgins. That's a nice idea, Stella. You can wrap one of these cups in a news-paper. There's one on the table.

MR. HIGGINS (*Moans*): Please—please—

STELLA: It won't take a moment, Mr. Higgins. (*She moves to table and tears a page from paper.*)

MR. HIGGINS: But I—

MINNIE (*To* MR. HIGGINS): Not a word of protest, my dear man. I declare, Mr. Higgins, I'm afraid you're not quite up to par today.

MR. HIGGINS: I'm all right—I think.

STELLA: Here you are, Minnie. (MINNIE *takes the paper.*)

MINNIE: Are you sure one cup will be sufficient? (MR. HIGGINS *nods weakly.*) Then one cup it will be. (*She pretends to select a cup and wraps it in paper.*) Here it is, Stella, all ready for Mr. Higgins. (STELLA *takes the paper to* MR. HIGGINS.)

STELLA: Don't drop it, Mr. Higgins. (*Horrified,* MR. HIGGINS *takes the paper.*)

MINNIE: We should give Mr. Higgins the unsliced lemon, too.

STELLA: Of course!

MR. HIGGINS: No, no!

MINNIE (*As* STELLA *tears another sheet from newspaper*):

Come now, you're strong enough to carry a china cup and a lemon.

STELLA: We'll wrap the lemon for you, too. (*She gives* MINNIE *the paper.*) I know how men are—they never like to carry anything unless it's properly wrapped. (MINNIE *pretends to wrap the lemon.*) You're going directly back to your shop?

MR. HIGGINS: I think I'll stop at a doctor's office on my way.

MINNIE: An excellent idea. You really don't look well, Mr. Higgins. Here's the lemon, Stella. (STELLA *takes the ball of paper to* MR. HIGGINS.)

STELLA (*Smiles*): With our compliments, Mr. Higgins. (MR. HIGGINS *holds his hat.* STELLA *takes hat from him and presses the paper into his hand.*) One nice fresh lemon. If you should wish the entire tea set, we'd be glad to—

MR. HIGGINS (*Groans*): No, no! Just let me out of here!

STELLA: Of course, Mr. Higgins. (STELLA *places* MR. HIGGINS' *hat on his head.*)

MINNIE: I'm sorry you must hurry along, Mr. Higgins, but do come back when you're feeling better.

STELLA: I'm glad you're going to see a doctor. I hope he finds nothing serious.

MINNIE: Goodbye, Mr. Higgins. (MR. HIGGINS *doesn't answer. Like a sleepwalker, he exits.* STELLA *closes door and turns to* MINNIE. *For a moment they do not speak, then they burst into laughter.*)

STELLA: Minnie Webb, you're a genius!

MINNIE: Did you see his face!

STELLA: White as the desert!

MINNIE: He was certain he'd lost his mind!

STELLA: We must have looked crazy, picking up china, drinking tea, handing out a lemon—

MINNIE: Well, we're *not* crazy—which is all that matters.

STELLA: And our precious tea set—saved!

MINNIE: But I'm warning you, Stella—if you get into one more entanglement, I will lose my mind.

STELLA: On the word of a Webb, Minnie—I've been carried away for the last time. (*There is a sharp knock on the door.*) Who's that?

MINNIE: If it's another one of your entanglements, Stella, I'm resigning as your sister. (MINNIE *opens the door.* MR. HIGGINS *enters, carrying a wad of paper.* MINNIE *and* STELLA *look surprised.*) Mr. Higgins!

MR. HIGGINS: Miss Minnie, I'm afraid I walked out without thanking you for your hospitality. I fear I was not quite myself, but I'm much better now. (*He smiles.*) I do hope you dear ladies will forgive me, even if I didn't accept a cup of tea. It did look delicious.

MINNIE: What?

MR. HIGGINS. By the way, I won't be needing this. (*He hands* MINNIE *the wad of paper.*) I'm sure you'll have more use for it than I. (*Smiles*) Goodbye, and thank you. (*He exits.* MINNIE *and* STELLA *are stunned.*)

STELLA: Minnie, what did he give you? (*Both stare at the paper.* MINNIE *slowly unwraps it, finally pulling out a lemon.*)

MINNIE: A lemon! A real lemon! (*They stare horrified at the lemon as the curtain falls.*)

THE END

Production Notes

WORD OF HONOR

Characters: 1 male; 2 female.

Playing Time: 15 minutes.

Costumes: Mr. Higgins wears a conservative business suit and hat. Stella and Minnie wear rather old-fashioned dresses.

Properties: Handkerchief, newspaper, and lemon.

Setting: The living room of Stella and Minnie. The room is comfortable, but very old-fashioned. Furnishings include a sofa, a coffee table, an armchair, and another small table.

Lighting: No special effects.

You'd Never Think It!

Characters

WALTER
GRACE, *his wife*

TIME: *Morning.*

SETTING: *The breakfast room. Downstage is a breakfast table, covered with a bright cloth. At each end of table is a chair. Downstage right is a third chair, over the back of which hangs a man's suit coat. On table are place settings for two.*

AT RISE: **WALTER** *is seated in chair at right side of table, reading the paper and eating. From off-stage left through open doorway* **GRACE** *calls.*

GRACE (*Off-stage*): Walter! (**WALTER** *reads.*) Walter, dear.

WALTER (*Without looking up*): Yes, Grace?

GRACE (*Calls*): Will you have more coffee?

WALTER (*Vaguely*): What did you say?

GRACE (*Still off left*): Can't I bring you more coffee?

WALTER (*At last looks up from paper*): If you will, darling.

(*Now* WALTER *turns and speaks directly to audience.*) If she only knew what I'm thinking! (*With a dry grin*) Grace is acting the role of a thoughtful little wife this morning (*Significantly*)—which means she's preparing to ask a favor. It's probably money again. (*Resolutely*) Well, she's headed for disappointment. This is one time I'm not going to be caught off guard. Oh, Grace is clever —I'll admit that. She starts tossing around the most innocent-sounding bit of conversation, and before I know what it's all about, I've given my consent to some horrible financial transaction. (*Grimly*) But not this morning! I'm listening carefully to everything she says before I make a reply. (GRACE *enters from left, carrying a coffee-pot. Her manner is enthusiastic and vivacious.*)

GRACE (*Cheerfully*): Here's your coffee, dear—just the way you like it. (*She smiles at* WALTER.) Maybe you'd like more toast.

WALTER: No thanks, sweetheart. (*He returns to his paper.*)

GRACE (*Holds coffeepot in her hand, as she now speaks to audience*): If he only knew what I'm thinking! It's a good thing he didn't take me up on that toast offer. There isn't another slice of bread in the house, but this is one morning I've got to appear disgustingly thoughtful and attentive. (GRACE *picks up* WALTER'S *cup, pours more coffee.*)

WALTER (*Turns from paper, speaks to audience*): I was right. I was so right! My wife's up to something. She's entirely too thoughtful and attentive, but (*Firmly*) she won't confuse me this time. (*Reads paper*)

GRACE (*As she replaces* WALTER'S *cup in his saucer*): Anything exciting in the paper, Walter precious? (*To audi-

ence) I was right. I was so right! He's going to be difficult this morning. I can tell by that look in his eye. Sure, I know—he plans to listen carefully to everything I say to him. (*Ironically*) He won't be caught off guard—he thinks. Not Walter! (*Sighs deeply*) I've simply got to have money for a new dress. (*Determinedly*) I've put it over before, and I can put it over again.

WALTER (*Looks up from paper, smiles brightly*): What did you ask me, honey?

GRACE: Nothing important, dear. (GRACE *picks up her own cup, pours coffee.*)

WALTER (*To audience*): I'll say it wasn't important. She's working up to something. She thinks I'm paying no attention, but when she finally slips in the fatal question—and she will—I'll throw her off base by coming right back with a flat refusal. (*Grins slyly*) I can hardly wait to see her expression.

GRACE (*Places coffeepot on table*): I merely remarked—was there anything exciting in the paper? (*She smiles sweetly at* WALTER, *then moves to chair at left of table. Now she speaks to audience.*) He heard what I said, the goof! He's listening so carefully that his ears are about to fall off. (*She sits in chair to left of table.*)

WALTER (*Casually, to* GRACE): No, not much in the way of news this morning, Grace. (*To audience*) She wants to know what's in the paper! She wouldn't care if we'd been invaded from outer space. Just that old lull-you-to-sleep technique again. (*He places his paper to one side, picks up his cup, sips.*)

GRACE (*To* WALTER): All one reads in the papers these days is that the cost of living is going up. (*Picks up her coffee cup, speaks to audience.*) If he's really listening, that "cost of living" crack will smoke him out. (*She sips coffee.*)

WALTER (*Looks up, suddenly interested*): Cost of living, did you say? What made you bring up *that* subject? (*As* GRACE *calmly sips coffee,* WALTER *turns to audience.*) As if I didn't know! In a minute she plans to drop in a question like—don't I think she should have an increase in her allowance? (*Grimly*) Well, I'll fix that little plan. (*He turns to* GRACE.) Why discuss the cost of living?

GRACE (*With a shrug of indifference*): I don't know. It's just that everybody talks about it. (*To audience*) Yes, he's listening all right—the old rabbit ears!

WALTER (*Nods in agreement*): You're right, Grace. *We* should discuss it, too. (*He takes a final gulp of coffee, then rises.*) Things are getting more expensive every day. We've got to economize—both of us. (*He turns smugly to audience.*) There! That remark will stop her. Old Mrs. Smooth-Tongue didn't catch me asleep that time.

GRACE (*Humbly*): I'm doing the best I can to watch our budget, dear. (*As* WALTER *moves to chair right,* GRACE *speaks to audience.*) He's really going to put up a fight to save his pocketbook this morning. (WALTER *puts on coat.*) I have to try another approach. If he's determined to listen to every question I ask him, I might as well— (*She breaks off suddenly as an idea strikes her.*) Say, I *do* have an idea! I'm not licked yet. (*Now she speaks to* WALTER.) I realize we mustn't be extravagant or wasteful.

WALTER (*Nods heartily to* GRACE): That's the spirit, Grace.

Pinch every penny. (*He turns to audience with a grin.*) This is amazing! For the first time in my life, I have the upper hand in the conversation.

GRACE (*Rises from table as* WALTER *adjusts his suit coat*): I do pinch every penny, Walter. I'm terribly careful. (*She takes a step down left, speaks to audience.*) If he only knew how careful I am with this conversation! I have to be. He thinks he's a wise guy, does he? All right, just remember—he asked for this! (WALTER *steps back to table, picks up his newspaper.* GRACE *turns to him.*) By the way, Walter, I ran into an old friend of yours last week.

WALTER: An old friend? (*He turns to audience.*) Hear that? She changed the subject! That means she had to give up. After twenty years, Grace has at last come face-to-face with defeat. This is a day to celebrate.

GRACE (*Speaks to* WALTER): Yes, I happened to bump into one of your *special* friends. While I was lunching at Stonebeck's, who should come breezing up to the table but—Susan Winters. (*Maliciously, as she turns to audience*) Watch him drop his newspaper.

WALTER (*With a violent start, as he drops his newspaper*): Susan Winters? (*Considerably upset, as he turns to audience.*) Good grief, I didn't know Susan was in town. I haven't seen her for ten years. (*He picks up paper from floor, speaks to* GRACE *with attempted indifference.*) You know, I'd almost forgotten about Susan. (*As though dismissing the subject, he turns his back on* GRACE. *He moves right.*)

GRACE (*Sweetly*): Really? (*She turns to audience, speaks dryly.*) In a pig's eye, he's forgotten! I'll bet he still dreams about that college romance.

WALTER (*His back still to* GRACE): Actually, I was never really interested in Susan. (*He now turns to audience. He's thoughtful and interested.*) Imagine—dear Susan in town again. I declare, I'm glad to hear it.

GRACE (*Easily, as she moves back to table*): No, I suppose you weren't interested in her, dear. (*She speaks to audience as she begins to stack the dishes.*) Ha! If I hadn't come along and snatched him from her, she'd be standing just where I am this moment. (*She glances at* WALTER, *then turns again to audience.*) Just look at him—trying to put on that indifferent act. Indifferent? He's about to swoon from curiosity.

WALTER (*Turns casually to* GRACE, *attempts to appear only vaguely interested*): As I faintly recall, Susan has some distant relatives in this town. (*Pause*) I suppose she's back here on vacation? (*To audience*) Would I like to see her again—just for old time's sake. Dear, understanding Susan. (*Thoughtfully*) Wonder if I dare suggest that we invite her over for dinner?

GRACE (*As she continues to straighten breakfast table*): Susan told me she was living on the West Coast now. (*Turns to audience*) There the big lug stands, wishing I'd invite her to our house—for dinner, probably, but he's afraid to suggest it himself. (WALTER *moves to table. He picks up the remaining half of a slice of toast.*)

WALTER (*Smiles at* GRACE): This toast is wonderful, Grace. I always did say you were the best cook in the state. Too bad more people don't have the chance to enjoy your meals.

GRACE (*Speaks knowingly to audience*): See how he's working up to the subject of a dinner invitation to Susan?

WALTER (*Nibbles on toast, as he moves to right*): I suppose Susan looks about the same. As I remember, she was never particularly attractive. (*To audience*) After all, a man ought to be able to entertain an old friend. Nothing personal, of course. (*Sighs*) Grace has always been suspicious of Susan.

GRACE (*Finishes stacking the dishes at table*): She certainly looked attractive when I saw her last week. (*Elated, as she speaks to audience*) This is perfect! He's getting interested, confused and uncomfortable. (*She picks up dishes, then speaks to* WALTER.) Walter, wouldn't you like to see her again? (*Carrying several dishes,* GRACE *moves to doorway left. She pauses, speaks to audience.*) The poor chump doesn't realize it, but he's being led to the slaughter. (GRACE *exits through doorway left. Excited,* WALTER *swings around. He moves quickly toward doorway left, then pauses.*)

WALTER (*Calls*): I don't think I'd care to see her, Grace. (*To audience*) That ought to sound indifferent enough.

GRACE (*Off-stage*): Susan told me she had heard about your success in business. I think it would be nice to invite her over for dinner.

WALTER (*Startled*): You do? But I—I thought—(*He attempts to cover his surprised pleasure.*) I mean—I'm afraid that would be too much work for you, dear. (*To audience*) That's it, Walter old boy—take it slow and easy. (*He calls again through doorway to* GRACE.) No, Grace, I think we'd better skip it. (*Turns to audience with a grin*) A protesting attitude always gets the best results.

GRACE (*Enters through doorway left, without dishes*):

But Susan *does* want to see you, and I think we should entertain her in our home. (*She moves behind table, speaks to audience.*) Let him go right on protesting, if it makes him feel more noble.

WALTER (*With an indifferent attitude, as he moves right*): That's sweet of you, Grace, but I'm really not interested. (*Smugly, to audience*) In a minute she'll be on her knees, pleading with me.

GRACE (*Suddenly*): All right, Walter—just as you say. Of course we won't ask her, if you'd rather not. (*To audience*) He thought I'd keep on insisting. Now listen to him change his tune!

WALTER (*Swings around nervously, faces* GRACE): Of course, dear, if you insist on entertaining Susan, I've no real objection. In fact, I believe you're right—right as usual. We really should have her over for a meal. (*To audience*) Whew! Was that a close fumble!

GRACE (*Picks up coffeepot from table*): Very well. If she's available, we'll have her here this evening. (*To audience*) This is it! He's at the unconscious stage now. He wouldn't pay any attention to me if I turned handsprings on the table. (*Carrying coffeepot, she moves to doorway left. Then she pauses, turns to* WALTER.) There's just one thing, Walter—(*Now she speaks to audience.*) This is where lover-boy pays through the nose.

WALTER (*His back to* GRACE): Yes, darling. (*To audience*) Imagine—an evening with Susan again. If I do say so, I've directed this situation in a masterful manner.

GRACE (*Stands near doorway left*): If Susan is going to spend the evening with us, I think you should look your best. Maybe you'd better buy yourself a new necktie. (WALTER *nods absently.* GRACE *turns to audience.*) In his condition, he'd agree if I suggested he wear an onion sandwich.

WALTER (*Continues to nod vaguely*): Yes, I think you're right as always, dear. (*Excited, he speaks to audience*) I'll get a haircut, a shoe shine, a manicure—

GRACE (*Continues, to* WALTER): Of course you'll want your little wife to look nice. (*To audience*) Sonny boy is now walking into the trap.

WALTER (*Not listening*): Yes, dear. (*To audience*) I wonder how I'd look in a bow tie? Red and yellow stripes, maybe—

GRACE (*Quietly and evenly*): So I really should have a new dress. Don't you think so, Walter? (*To audience*) I could add a fur coat and a yacht—and the answer would be the same.

WALTER (*His back to* GRACE): Yes, by all means, dear. (*To audience*) I believe I'll buy one of those new sport jackets from the Varsity Shop.

GRACE (*Smiles, as she moves back to table with coffeepot*): That's so sweet of you, darling. If you'll just leave some little old money with me this morning, I'll dash out and pick up an old rag or something. Just any money you happen to have with you. (*She places coffeepot on table as she speaks to audience.*) That word "money" will bring him out of his silly trance.

WALTER (*Suddenly*): *Money?* (*In panic he swings around to* GRACE.) Money for what? (*To audience*) Great heavens, what was she talking about?

GRACE (*Sweetly, as she moves around table and steps to* WALTER): Money for the dress you just said you wanted me to buy. (*She moves close to* WALTER, *smiles up at him.*) You're always so thoughtful and generous, honey. Now where's your billfold? (WALTER *is stunned. Before he can move or answer,* GRACE *has reached into* WALTER's *inside coat pocket. Quickly she snatches out the billfold.*) Oh, here it is.

WALTER (*In rising horror*): Grace, I—I don't exactly understand—I mean, I—I—(*As* GRACE *removes bills from* WALTER's *billfold,* WALTER *turns in amazement to audience.*) She—she did it again! I said it couldn't happen this time!

GRACE (*After she removes currency from billfold*): Walter, I'll leave you a dollar. That will take care of your new tie, carfare and lunch money. (*Brightly she hands* WALTER *his billfold.*)

WALTER (*Still dazed, as he weakly accepts billfold*): Thank you, Grace. (*Almost weeping, he turns to audience.*) How does she do it? That's all I want to know—how does she do it?

GRACE (*Now steps behind* WALTER, *pushes him gently toward doorway left*): You mustn't be late for work, dear. (*She speaks to audience.*) In other words, Walter, get moving before you realize what hit you.

WALTER (*In a stupor, as* GRACE *escorts him toward doorway*): Yes, Grace. (*He pauses at doorway left, turns to audience.*) There's one thing about it—Grace had to consent to entertain Susan before she could get me tangled up. (*A slow grin breaks over his face.*) Come to think of it, at least I've won a partial victory.

GRACE (*To* WALTER): Now hurry along, pet. (*She pats his shoulder.*) I'll see you tonight.

WALTER (*To* GRACE): You'll telephone Susan? (*To audi-

ence) At least out of all this, I'll have an evening with Susan. (*Smiles*) Yes sir, it's worth the money!

GRACE (*To* WALTER): Just leave everything to me. (*She pushes* WALTER *through doorway*) Good-bye, honey— have a happy day. (GRACE *pauses as* WALTER *stumbles through doorway left. Thoughtfully she moves down center. She gazes at the currency in her hand. She begins to smile slyly. Then she faces the audience.*) Poor Walter, I'm afraid he's going to be a little upset when I tell him that dear Susan left for the West Coast—last night! (*Curtain*)

THE END

Production Notes

You'd Never Think It!

Characters: 1 male; 1 female.

Playing Time: 15 minutes.

Costumes: Walter is dressed in a business suit; Grace wears a housedress.

Properties: Place settings for two, serving dishes and utensils, coffeepot, wallet, paper money, newspaper, toast.

Setting: The breakfast room. At downstage center is a breakfast table, covered with a bright cloth. At each end of the table is a chair. Downstage right is a third chair, over the back of which hangs a man's suit coat. On table are place settings for two—plates, cups, saucers, utensils and miscellaneous serving dishes.

Lighting: No special effects.

Double Talk

Characters

AGNES NEWMAN
CHARLES NEWMAN, *her husband*
MR. WELLS, *who owns the dog*

SETTING: *The Newman living room.*
AT RISE: *The stage is unoccupied. After a pause,* CHARLES
NEWMAN *enters briskly. He carries a newspaper.*

CHARLES (*Calling to left*): Agnes! Oh, Agnes! (*He tosses
paper on divan.*) I'm home, dear! (AGNES NEWMAN
*enters left. She holds a brightly colored scarf or stole in
her hand. One end of the scarf—the end not yet visible—
is in shreds.* AGNES *is highly upset.* CHARLES *holds out
his arms and moves toward her enthusiastically.*) Agnes,
honey.

AGNES (*Breaks in*): Oh, stop it, Charles. This is no time for
silly embraces.

CHARLES: What's the matter?

AGNES (*Highly disturbed*): Charles, you simply won't believe it.

CHARLES: Believe what?

AGNES: Look! (*She holds up the scarf. The tattered end is now in view.*) Just look at it, Charles.

CHARLES: I am—and it's the scarf your Aunt Mary sent you from Europe last month. But I don't see why you should be so upset.

AGNES: Charles Newman, look at this *end!* (*She indicates the ragged edge.*)

CHARLES: Great Scott, honey, it *is* in shreds. What happened?

AGNES: It's ruined—completely ruined! And do you know why? Because of that dog! . . . That vicious, destructive dog—

CHARLES (*Breaks in*): Now—now, wait a minute, Agnes. What dog are you talking about?

AGNES: The one that followed that man, of course.

CHARLES (*Drops onto divan*): Agnes, if you'd just explain—

AGNES: I *am* explaining. I hung this scarf on the line to air in the breeze. Then along came a perfectly strange man, followed by this horrible dog. I saw the whole thing. I was standing at the window.

CHARLES: That's nice, I'm sure.

AGNES: It was *not* nice! Suddenly this dog tore across our lawn, right toward our clothesline. He stopped just below the scarf, suddenly leaped into the air and—(*She again holds up the scarf.*) this—this is what he did!

CHARLES (*Attempting to soothe her*): Of course you were upset, honey—

AGNES: Upset? I was furious! I rushed to the door, but before I could get outside, the man and that four-footed monster had disappeared. But I got a good look at them both. Then I phoned Clara and—

CHARLES: Clara?

AGNES (*Nods*): Clara Sims. She knows everything that goes on in this town, and what she doesn't know, she can find out. And, Charles, within thirty minutes she had all the information for me.

CHARLES: What horrible facts did she uncover?

AGNES: This man is a stranger in town. He's investigating some property which belonged to a late relative, and he brought this scarf-eating canine with him. He's stopping at the hotel. (*With grim determination*) If I don't hear from him by tomorrow morning—

CHARLES (*Rises*): Now Agnes, take it easy—

AGNES: I will *not* take it easy! I'm going to make that man pay for the damage. (*She gazes at scarf.*) I ought to charge him double. Maybe I will. I have an idea or two.

CHARLES: You can't bring suit for a damaged scarf.

AGNES: I don't have to sue. I'm working on another plan.

CHARLES (*A bit slyly*): A written confession from the dog, no doubt?

AGNES (*Coolly*): That isn't amusing—and I can handle matters without your assistance.

CHARLES (*With finality*): Then I shan't utter another word of advice.

AGNES: That's good—I hope you won't interfere with my plans.

CHARLES: Don't worry. I'll be searching for my box of fishing tackle—which I'll probably find in the attic. (*He

exits. Immediately the doorbell rings. AGNES *opens door.*
MR. WELLS *stands in doorway. He is a polite but stubborn little man in his late fifties.*)

MR. WELLS (*Removes his hat, steps into room*): Good evening, madam, I am—

AGNES (*Vigorously*): I should say you are!

MR. WELLS (*Startled*): What's that?

AGNES: You needn't introduce yourself. You're Franklin Wells.

MR. WELLS (*Confused*): Why—why, yes, I am, but how did you know?

AGNES: I am Mrs. Newman, and you, Mr. Wells, are in town on personal business. Your companion is a vicious and destructive dog that has ruined this scarf— (*She holds up the scarf.*) And you have now come to my home to settle for the damage.

MR. WELLS: Madam, you amaze me.

AGNES: Of course you *do* admit that your dog is to blame?

MR. WELLS: Well, I did drop around to discuss the matter—

AGNES (*Indicates divan*): Then sit down, Mr. Wells. There's no reason to spend a lot of valuable time in haggling. Let's come directly to the point.

MR. WELLS (*With dignity*): Madam, I am *not* here to haggle, (*He sits on divan.*) and I would advise you not to stir up my anger.

AGNES (*Extends scarf*): I'm the one who is angry! I want you to examine this priceless scarf. It came from Europe. Until this afternoon it was in perfect shape. Now it is an international wreck!

MR. WELLS (*Reaches out, feels material*): Frankly, madam

DOUBLE TALK

—inferior material.

AGNES (*Bristles*): Inferior? The idea! Why, you don't often see a scarf like this!

MR. WELLS: The variety stores are full of them.

AGNES: This is an import, I tell you! It was one of my prized possessions. I shall be lost without it—utterly lost.

MR. WELLS: You can cut off one end.

AGNES: Indeed I shall not! Unless this scarf is complete, it is worthless. Mr. Wells, I demand full payment—and I demand it now.

MR. WELLS (*After a pause*): Very well. (*He rises and removes billfold from his coat pocket.* AGNES, *realizing that a settlement is near, is in better humor.*)

AGNES (*Smiles*): Mr. Wells, I knew you would be reasonable. I could see at once that you are a man who appreciates the better things of life, and I can't imagine anything better than my European scarf. (*She gushes happily.*) I know that many women would be most unreasonable. Some would even make outrageous demands, but when you consider that I am asking only ten dollars—

MR. WELLS (*Pauses abruptly*): Ten dollars?

AGNES (*Nods*): I feel that is a small amount, Mr. Wells— considering my loss. Of course I couldn't possibly replace it for that price—

MR. WELLS (*Breaks in*): For that price you could buy a circus tent. (*With finality*) Mrs. Newman, I am a busy man. I have neither the time nor the inclination to argue the matter. (*He removes a bill from billfold.*) Here's five dollars—you can take it or leave it. (*He drops bill onto coffee table.*)

AGNES (*Indignantly*): Five dollars? *Five dollars?* (*She

sputters.) Why, I—I never heard of such a thing in my life!

MR. WELLS: I'm being extremely generous, if you want the truth. That scarf isn't worth ninety-eight cents.

AGNES (*With a little shriek*): Mr. Wells, do you mean to stand there and suggest that I accept— (*But at that moment* CHARLES *enters briskly from left. He stops, seemingly surprised.*)

CHARLES: Oh—I didn't know we had company.

AGNES (*Turns, rushes wildly to* CHARLES): Charles, this man is—is Mr. Wells. He's the one who owns the dog— the one with teeth! He had the nerve to offer me five dollars for my ruined scarf. (*Urgently*) Charles, talk to him. You're my husband—you're supposed to take charge. Tell him that I simply will not—

CHARLES (*Breaks in*): Just a minute. As I recall, you requested that I keep out of this. According to you, I was not to utter a word of advice, and I am delighted to abide by that request. (*He turns from* AGNES, *crosses to* MR. WELLS. AGNES *is speechless—and for a moment, defeated. Speaking pleasantly,* CHARLES *extends his hand to* MR. WELLS.) I'm Charles Newman, sir.

MR. WELLS (*Shakes hands*): Glad to know you.

CHARLES: Of course you've met my wife.

MR. WELLS: I—I'm afraid I have. (AGNES *stands in silent fury. Then she grimly and noisily marches to door left. She exits, slamming door behind her.* CHARLES *turns toward door left. When he is certain* AGNES *is out of hearing, he again faces* MR. WELLS.)

CHARLES (*With a sigh of relief*): Mr. Wells, you're a great guy.

MR. WELLS: Great?

CHARLES (*Nods*): And I have a confession to make.

MR. WELLS: You?

CHARLES: I overheard your conversation with my wife.

MR. WELLS: About her scarf?

CHARLES (*Nods*): You can't imagine how she has been carrying on.

MR. WELLS: No doubt. I have paid her five dollars, but she is demanding ten.

CHARLES (*Chuckles*): She knows you won't budge from your offer, Mr. Wells. (*Grins.*) That's what amuses me. For the first time in years, my dear wife has met her match. It's a wonderful lesson for her.

MR. WELLS: I'm not here to teach anybody a lesson.

CHARLES: I know, and you have been more than generous, sir. That scarf isn't worth five dollars.

MR. WELLS: That's what I told your wife, and I won't pay her more.

CHARLES (*Quickly removes billfold from his coat pocket*): You're not paying *anything*, Mr. Wells.

MR. WELLS (*Startled*): Not paying?

CHARLES (*Pulls a bill from his billfold*): I'm taking care of this. (*He places his own five-dollar bill on coffee table, picks up the original bill and hands it back to* MR. WELLS.) Here's your bill, sir.

MR. WELLS: But—but, Mr. Newman—

CHARLES (*In high spirits*): This has been worth five dollars to me. Agnes usually gets her way about things around here, but she didn't today! (*He chuckles again.*) Did you see her walk out of this room? She was defeated—

absolutely defeated! (*He gives* MR. WELLS *a friendly pat on the back.*) Accept my thanks, Mr. Wells.

MR. WELLS (*Pleased, as he returns his bill to his billfold*): My goodness, Mr. Newman, you are kind.

CHARLES (*Briskly*): Now I'm driving you back to your hotel.

MR. WELLS: That isn't necessary.

CHARLES: I insist. I'm going your way. I'll get my brief case. (*He steps to door left, then turns to* MR. WELLS.) You can wait for me in the car. I'm parked in the driveway. (MR. WELLS *nods.* CHARLES *exits at left.* MR. WELLS *moves upstage. Suddenly the center door opens.* AGNES *enters. She is wearing the same dress, but she has now added a short jacket and gay little hat to her outfit. Around her neck is the damaged scarf.*)

AGNES (*Pauses abruptly as she sees* MR. WELLS): Oh! Good —good evening.

MR. WELLS (*Startled*): Why, Mrs. Newman!

AGNES (*With affected surprise*): Mrs. Newman? (*Pause*) Did you call me *Mrs. Newman?*

MR. WELLS: Certainly I called you Mrs. Newman.

AGNES (*Laughs*): Oh, this is delightful—simply delightful! But you aren't the first one who has been confused.

MR. WELLS (*Puzzled*): Confused?

AGNES (*Brightly*): Everyone says we *do* resemble each other.

MR. WELLS (*Aghast*): You—*what?*

AGNES (*Nods pleasantly*): But identical twins are *supposed* to look alike, aren't they?

MR. WELLS (*About to choke*): I—*identical twins?*

AGNES: Oh, I can see you're a stranger in town, but even
our friends have difficulty. Since we both live here, it's
more complex than ever. (*Smiles broadly*) Don't you
think so?

MR. WELLS (*Almost speechless*): Do—do you mean that—
that you and—and—

AGNES (*With a bright little laugh*): Oh, dear! I'm afraid
I've upset you, Mr.—Mr.—

MR. WELLS: Mr. Wells—Franklin Wells.

AGNES (*Affects sudden surprise*): You're Mr. Wells? Then
you're the one with the dog—the vicious dog.

MR. WELLS (*With effort*): That—that's what I've been
telling you. (*He breaks off.*) I—I mean, that's what I've
been telling *somebody!*

AGNES: You're just the person I wanted to see, Mr. Wells.
(*Swiftly she removes scarf from around her neck.*) Look
what your dog did to my scarf! (*She holds up scarf.*) Just
look at that tattered edge! (MR. WELLS *views the scarf in
silent horror.*)

MR. WELLS (*At last*): That is—is *your* scarf?

AGNES: Certainly it's my scarf. It was hanging outside on
the line to air in the sun. Then your dog rushed across
the lawn, leaped into the air—

MR. WELLS (*Breaks in with a wail*): Don't! Don't! (*He
drops weakly onto divan and eyes* AGNES.)

AGNES (*Studies* MR. WELLS *with affected concern*): Mr.
Wells, you act as though you had heard this before.

MR. WELLS (*About to collapse*): You mean you're not the
—the *other one?*

AGNES (*Steps to* MR. WELLS): Mr. Wells, are you ill? (*Suddenly*) Perhaps I should call my sister.

MR. WELLS (*Wildly*): No!

AGNES: I *do* think I should be reimbursed for this scarf, Mr. Wells. I feel we should call in the entire family for a conference.

MR. WELLS (*Jumps up*): No! No! (*Desperately and with trembling hands he pulls billfold from his pocket.*) How —how much do you want?

AGNES (*Thinks deeply*): Well, I feel my loss should be worth at least five dollars.

MR. WELLS (*Yanks bill from his billfold*): Here! (*He tosses bill to top of coffee table. The two bills are now together.*)

AGNES (*Gushes enthusiastically*): Thank you, dear Mr. Wells. (CHARLES *enters from left.*)

CHARLES (*To* AGNES, *as he moves to center*): I'm driving Mr. Wells back to the hotel, Agnes.

AGNES: Agnes? (*Laughs at* CHARLES) My goodness, Charles, I even fooled you, didn't I?

CHARLES (*Amazed*): Fooled me?

AGNES (*Turns in high amusement to* MR. WELLS): See, Mr. Wells? At times I even confuse my own brother-in-law. (CHARLES *studies* AGNES *in amazement. Now she turns to* CHARLES.) I just ran into dear Mr. Wells as I came through the front door, and he paid me five dollars for my tattered scarf—the one his dog ruined. Wasn't that generous of him? I wanted to talk it over with Agnes first, but Mr. Wells insisted it wasn't necessary.

CHARLES (*Desperately*): Now—now, wait a minute—you—you stop that!

AGNES (*Laughs*): Oh, be quiet, Charles. After all this time, you should be able to tell whether I'm Agnes or whether I'm—

MR. WELLS (*Breaks in suddenly to* CHARLES): Mr. Newman, you—you needn't drive me to my hotel.

CHARLES (*Takes a step toward* MR. WELLS): Mr. Wells, I— I'm not certain what's going on.

MR. WELLS (*Nervously*): The—the walk will do me good. I—I need air—oh, I need plenty of air! (MR. WELLS *rushes to door and exits. For a moment neither* AGNES *nor* CHARLES *speaks. Then* AGNES *suddenly breaks into wild laughter.*)

CHARLES (*Sputters angrily*): Agnes! Agnes Newman!

AGNES (*Near hysteria*): Yes, Charles—I'm Agnes.

CHARLES (*Hotly*): Of course you are, and you deliberately made that man think you were someone else.

AGNES: He was confused, wasn't he? But he paid me a total of ten dollars, dear—a five-dollar bill to each of us. Remember, Charles, I was holding out for ten dollars. (*She smiles triumphantly at* CHARLES. CHARLES *drops into chair at left. The doorbell rings.* AGNES *opens center door.* MR. WELLS *enters.*) Mr. Wells!

MR. WELLS (*With the air of a complete stranger*): I'm sorry to disturb you folks— (*He glances swiftly around the room.*) but has he been here?

AGNES: Who? Of course *you* were here.

MR. WELLS (*With dignity*): Me? Don't be ridiculous, madam. (*He steps to coffee table, sees the bills.*) Yes, that boy has been here all right—and as usual left his money lying around.

AGNES (*Horrified*): But Mr. Wells, *you're* the one who—

MR. WELLS (*Pays no attention to her protests*): That

brother of mine—I declare, I must follow him every place.

AGNES: Your—your *brother?*

MR. WELLS: I tell you, madam, it's a real problem—being an identical twin. (*He snatches up the bills from coffee table, thrusts them into his pocket, and turns to* AGNES.) Thanks for leaving his money out here. (*He steps to door, then turns to* AGNES. *He speaks slowly—and knowingly.*) Good night—to *both of you*—from *both of us!* (MR. WELLS *grins suddenly, then he exits.* AGNES *gazes toward the door in horrified silence. Then* CHARLES *bursts into wild and hilarious laughter. He drops back into the chair, and his laughter increases as the curtain quickly falls.*)

THE END

Production Notes

DOUBLE TALK

Characters: 2 male; 1 female.
Playing Time: 15 minutes.
Costumes: Everyday clothes. Agnes adds a short jacket and a hat to her costume as indicated in the text.
Properties: Newspaper, brightly colored scarf with one end in shreds, two billfolds with five-dollar bills.
Setting: A pleasantly and comfortably furnished living room. There are two entrances: the outside door upstage center and a door at left leading to the rest of the house. The divan and coffee table are down right, the armchair, down left.
Lighting: No special effects.